Quantum Mechanics: The Physics of the Microscopic World

Benjamin Schumacher, Ph.D.

THE
GREAT
COURSES®

PUBLISHED BY:

THE GREAT COURSES
Corporate Headquarters
4840 Westfields Boulevard, Suite 500
Chantilly, Virginia 20151-2299
Phone: 1-800-832-2412
Fax: 703-378-3819
www.thegreatcourses.com

Benjamin Schumacher, Ph.D.
Professor of Physics
Kenyon College

Benjamin Schumacher is Professor of Physics at Kenyon College, where he has taught for 20 years. He was an undergraduate at Hendrix College and received his Ph.D. in Theoretical Physics from The University of Texas at Austin in 1990, where he was the last doctoral student of John Archibald Wheeler.

Professor Schumacher is the author of numerous scientific papers and two books, including *Physics in Spacetime: An Introduction to Special Relativity* (Rinton Press, 2005). As one of the founders of quantum information theory, Professor Schumacher introduced the term "qubit," invented quantum data compression (also known as "Schumacher compression"), and established several fundamental results about the information capacity of quantum systems. For his contributions, he won the 2002 Quantum Communication Award, the premier international prize in the field, and was named a Fellow of the American Physical Society. Besides quantum information theory, Professor Schumacher has done physics research on black holes, thermodynamics, and statistical mechanics.

Professor Schumacher has spent sabbaticals working at Los Alamos National Laboratory and as a Moore Distinguished Scholar at the Institute for Quantum Information at California Institute of Technology. He has also done research at the Isaac Newton Institute of Cambridge University, the Santa Fe Institute, the Perimeter Institute, the University of New Mexico, the University of Montreal, the University of Innsbruck, and the University of Queensland. At Kenyon College, Professor Schumacher mostly teaches physics, but he also regularly ventures into astronomy, mathematics, scientific computing, and the humanities. ∎

Table of Contents

Table of Contents

Table of Contents

LECTURE 24

Quantum Mechanics:
The Physics of the Microscopic World

Scope:

Quantum mechanics is the fundamental physics of the microscopic world, the domain of atoms and photons and elementary particles. The theory was developed in the early 20th century by Planck, Einstein, Bohr, Heisenberg, and others. Though physics has advanced quite far in the decades since quantum mechanics was born, it remains the basic framework for our deepest insights into nature.

Yet, although it is a cornerstone of modern physics, quantum mechanics remains a profoundly strange picture of reality. The quantum world confronts us with mind-boggling questions. How can light be both wave and particle? Are all electrons truly identical, and what difference can that possibly make? What does it mean when 2 quantum particles are "entangled"—a relationship so weird that Einstein called it "spooky"? Is there really a vast amount of energy in empty space? Can the laws of quantum physics someday make our computers faster and our messages more private?

This course is an introduction to the fundamentals of quantum mechanics, accessible to students without any previous preparation in math and physics. In 24 lectures, using a small toolkit of simple concepts and examples, we will trace the origins of the theory of quantum mechanics, describe its basic principles, and explore some of the most remarkable features of the quantum world.

After surveying the way ahead, the course begins by describing the theories of physics that prevailed before the quantum revolution. We will see how Max Planck and Albert Einstein introduced quantum ideas to explain certain mysterious properties of light. These ideas soon spread to all of physics, affecting our understanding of all types of matter and energy. A central idea is the notion of "wave-particle duality," in which the entities of nature (electrons and so on) can exhibit the characteristics of both waves and particles. This will lead us to Werner Heisenberg's famous uncertainty

1

relation. The new physics posed many puzzles for its founders. This was nowhere better exemplified than in the great debate between Einstein and Niels Bohr over the validity and meaning of quantum mechanics, which we will also explore.

Next we will turn to the task of presenting quantum theory in its clearest and simplest form. We will do this through a careful analysis—a thought experiment involving a single photon traveling through an apparatus called an "interferometer." As we will discover, even so simple a system has a few surprises in store.

The description of particle spin provides us with another useful illustration of quantum principles. Armed with these principles, we will discuss in detail the concept of identical quantum particles. A simple distinction—the difference, in effect, between +1 and −1 in our quantum rules—leads to particles with very different properties. We will see how this distinction plays a role in phenomena including lasers, superfluids, the structure of atoms, and the properties of solids.

This will lead us to our next topic, the riddle of quantum entanglement. As we will show, the behavior of entangled particles challenges some of our most deeply held intuitions about the physical world. Almost as bizarre is Richard Feynman's startling idea that a quantum particle moves from point A to point B by following *every possible path* from A to B, each path making its own contribution. By applying Feynman's principle and the uncertainty principle to "empty space," we find that even the vacuum is a realm of ceaseless quantum activity.

Quantum information theory is a relatively new branch of quantum physics. In our lectures, we will describe some of its remarkable concepts. Unlike ordinary information, quantum information cannot be perfectly copied. It can, on the other hand, be used to send perfectly secret messages and to perform "quantum teleportation." It may even be possible to use quantum physics to construct a quantum computer, a novel and extremely powerful kind of machine for solving mathematical problems.

Our course concludes with a discussion of some philosophical questions. What is the real meaning of quantum mechanics? What does it tell us about the nature of our world? Do our choices and observations help to bring reality into being? Does the randomness of the quantum realm disguise a deeper, universe-spanning order? Or are the myriad possibilities of quantum physics all part of a complex "multiverse" beyond our imagining? What deep principle links together the many mysteries of the quantum world?

A note about mathematics: Quantum mechanics is often framed in highly abstract mathematical terms. (Open up any advanced textbook on the subject and see for yourself!) Yet the central ideas of quantum mechanics are not at all complicated and can be understood by almost anyone. With a few careful simplifications and a very little math, it is possible to embark on a serious exploration of the quantum world. That journey is ours. ■

The Quantum Enigma
Lecture 1

In this course, we are embarking on a journey to a distant world, a world that is governed by strange and unfamiliar laws. By distant, I mean a world far from our everyday experience. I mean a world that is distant not in space, but in size. It's the world of the microscopic, the microscopic world.

What is quantum mechanics? "Mechanics" is the branch of physics that studies force and motion—the way things in the universe evolve over time. "Classical mechanics" is based on Newton's laws of motion. This was the prevailing view of the world before about 1900. It is a branch of classical physics, which also includes thermodynamics and electromagnetism. "Quantum mechanics" is a new theory developed between 1900 and 1930 to replace Newton's laws, especially to account for the behavior of microscopic pieces of matter. "Quantum theory" is a more encompassing term, including a wider application of quantum ideas. "Quantum physics" is the most general term for the physics of the microscopic realm. In everyday usage, however, these terms are practically synonymous.

Quantum mechanics is the most successful physical theory ever devised. It explains the structure of atoms, their combination into molecules, the interaction of light with matter, the behavior of solids and liquids near absolute zero, and many other phenomena. Quantum theory remains the general framework within which modern theories of physics are formed. For example, superstring theory (an exciting but speculative theory of elementary particles and forces) is a quantum theory.

Quantum physics challenges our imaginations in new and unexpected ways. First, quantum theory has a number of surprising implications for probability, the motion of particles, the properties of energy, the strange connectedness of separated systems, and the behavior of information at the smallest physical scales. The "weirdness" of quantum theory is not an incidental feature. It is at the center of the theory, required to make a consistent, accurate physical theory of the microscopic world.

Second, quantum physics has inspired profound philosophical discussions about the basic nature of the physical world. These will also be part of our story. Albert Einstein and Niels Bohr carried on a famous debate on the new physics in the early years of quantum mechanics. Also, the phenomenon of quantum entanglement has led us further and further away from a "common-sense" view of the microscopic realm. Even today, there are several competing ideas about how to interpret the mathematical theory of quantum mechanics.

The "weirdness" of quantum theory is not an incidental feature. It is at the center of the theory, required to make a consistent, accurate physical theory of the microscopic world.

Before we start off, we need to set some ground rules for our course. First, we will simplify our discussion to highlight the fundamental principles, and we will try to note when this happens. Don't be too worried about this. The course explains the real theory, in simplified form. Also, we will often consider "thought experiments"—highly idealized experiments that might be possible in principle, although they may be impractical. In most cases, a more complicated and realistic version can actually be done in a lab.

How will we use mathematics? We will sometimes express the ideas of quantum mechanics symbolically, and we will learn a few simple rules for manipulating and interpreting the symbols. (These rules are no harder than very elementary algebra, though the details differ.) Venturing a short way into the abstract mathematics of quantum theory will allow us to explore the quantum world in a much deeper way. ■

Questions to Consider

1. In the remarkable short film *Powers of Ten*, Charles and Ray Eames "zoom in" on a scene by a magnification of ×10 every few seconds. Imagine creating such a film of your own. You'll need 8 of these ×10 stages to go from a 1inch aluminum cube down to a single aluminum atom. What sorts of common things (bugs, dust specks, cells, molecules) would you show at each stage from cube to atom?

2. In the lecture, we described several conceptual puzzles posed by quantum theory. Which of these seems most intriguing to you?

The Quantum Enigma
Lecture 1—Transcript

Welcome to our course on "Quantum Mechanics, the Physics of the Microscopic World." I'm Ben Schumacher. I'm a Professor of Physics at Kenyon College in Ohio and I'll be your instructor for this course. In this course, we are embarking on a journey to a distant world, a world that is governed by strange and unfamiliar laws. By distant, I mean a world far from our everyday experience. I mean a world that is distant not in space, but in size. It's the world of the microscopic, the microscopic world.

How small do I mean by microscopic? In fact, I don't mean something you can see in a microscope. I mean something far smaller than you can see in an ordinary microscope. The characters of our drama are entities like atoms and subatomic particles, such as electrons and protons and neutrons. Other characters of our drama include photons, which are the particles of light and these are all exceedingly small.

How small is small? How small is an atom? I have here a 1-inch cube of aluminum. It's 1 inch long, 1 inch high, and 1 inch wide. In 1 cubic inch of aluminum, there are 10^{24} aluminum atoms—10^{24}, a 1 followed by 24 zeros. That's 1 trillion, trillion aluminum atoms. There are 100 million aluminum atoms on this edge, a hundred million aluminum atoms on this edge, and a 100 million aluminum atoms on that edge—about 100 million aluminum atoms to the inch. That's a lot, but what about something you actually can see in a microscope? How about a single celled-organism? A typical single-celled organism contains about 1 trillion atoms, a one followed by 12 zeros—10 to the 12th power.

I've been throwing around the number 1 trillion. How big is a trillion? Imagine how big a grain of fine sand is. Now imagine an entire large truckload of sand. That turns out to be about a trillion grains of sand. Or, here's another way of thinking about a trillion. Imagine how many heartbeats you have in a day, distinct heartbeats. That's not actually a very big number. It's only 100,000. Maybe that is a pretty big number, 100,000 heartbeats in a day. Now imagine the entire population of New York City, about 10 million people. That means that there are about 1 trillion human heartbeats in New

York City in a course of a day. A trillion is a really big number and there are a trillion times a trillion atoms of aluminum in this cube of aluminum.

Atoms are pretty small. What about photons? How big are photons? To do that, let's consider an ordinary light bulb like this one. An ordinary 20-watt light bulb emits about 100 million trillion photons in 1 second—a hundred million trillion, that's 10^{20}, a 1 followed by 20 zeros. That's the number of photons that come out of a 20-watt light bulb in a second. These are huge numbers.

Atoms, electrons, and photons are extremely small compared with our everyday experience. Quantum mechanics is the basic physics of this realm, the realm of atoms, electrons, and photons. The microscopic realm is not just a miniature copy of the world of our experience. If that were true, this wouldn't be that interesting of a subject. But, in fact, in the microscopic realm there are lots of surprises. We'll talk about things that will at first be hard to believe, but are nevertheless true about the microscopic realm. But I want to emphasize one important fact. The quantum world is nevertheless our own world. The quantum world is the world we live in and quantum mechanics will explain not just funny things about atoms, but will explain basic facts about the world we see every day.

What is quantum mechanics? Let's take that apart. First of all, what is mechanics? Mechanics is the branch of physics that studies force and motion—how things move, why they move, the laws governing motion in the world, and the way things in the universe evolve over time. That's all mechanics. There's a kind of mechanics called "classical mechanics." Classical mechanics is the theory of mechanics based on Newton's laws of motion developed by Isaac Newton in the late 17th century. Classical mechanics is a branch of a somewhat larger realm called "classical physics," which also includes other subjects such as thermodynamics, which is about heat and energy transformations, electromagnetism, which is about the physics of electric and magnetic fields, and optics, which is about how light propagates. All of these are branches of classical physics. Classical mechanics is sort of at the center of classical physics.

For more than 200 years, classical mechanics was the best theory of physics—the gold standard of theories, far-reaching and extremely precise. If you wanted to know how to predict where a projectile would land or how to build a strong bridge or how the planets were going to move a 1,000 years from now, classical mechanics was the tool you would use to figure that out. Until about the year 1900, the entire story of physics was largely the story of the success of Newtonian mechanics. However, around 1900, it became clear that classical physics could not explain the behavior of the microscopic world. Classical mechanics wasn't enough. Quantum mechanics was the new theory developed to replace Newton's laws and especially to account for microscopic pieces of matter and how they behaved, but also to account for puzzles about the world that we could see and touch with our ordinary senses. It was called "quantum mechanics" because in this theory energy was found, in many circumstances, to come in distinct lumps, distinct packages or quanta of energy. That's the quantum in quantum mechanics.

The first quantum ideas were proposed around 1900, but the theory itself was not fully developed until the 1920s. Quantum mechanics was not constructed in a day; the process of its discovery was a remarkable process with many steps and we'll talk about that process. There are 2 other terms I want to explain. I'll use the phrase "quantum theory." Sometimes I'll say "quantum physics." Technically speaking quantum mechanics, quantum theory, and quantum physics are not quite the same thing. Each term is a little more encompassing than the last, but for our purposes, you can regard them as near synonyms for quantum mechanics. I'll use one or the other just for variety's sake. Don't worry about the distinction.

Quantum mechanics is now the most successful theory of physics ever devised. Some phenomenon explained by quantum mechanics are—and we'll discuss all of these—the basic internal structure of nuclei, atoms, and molecules. We understand that structure because of quantum mechanics. Quantum mechanics explains how light is absorbed and emitted by matter, a very important subject. Quantum mechanics explains how solids and liquids behave, especially at very low temperatures where their behavior can be quite surprising. Quantum mechanics is also the theory that accounts for how elementary particles interact with each other. Quantum mechanics has a tremendous range of applicability. Even though, the basic quantum ideas are now more than 100 years old and quantum theory or quantum mechanics itself is more than 80 years old, quantum theory remains the basic framework within which modern theories of physics are all framed. It's the basic language of physics. For example, superstring theory, which is an exciting but speculative theory of elementary particles and forces, is a quantum theory. Our course is not going to cover superstring theory, but I just want to point out that all of these modern theories like superstring theory are encompassed in the general framework, the same general framework that has been around for more than 80 years. This course is not going to only be concerned with this revolutionary development of quantum mechanics in the years 1900 through about 1930. This course is going to be also interested in developments in quantum mechanics since that time right up to the present day.

This tremendous success is only one side of quantum mechanics. What really makes quantum mechanics interesting is that it is also without a doubt the strangest and most surprising theory of physics ever devised. The laws of the microscopic realm challenge our imagination. It is a wonderful adventure to try to come to grips with the quantum world. Some of the weird implications of quantum theory that we'll discuss—we'll discuss all of these that I mention—are as follows. The first one, quantum mechanics tells us something very strange about the laws of probability. Quantum mechanics tells us that different possibilities can cancel each other out in a way that you never would've expected. Suppose a particle could go from here to here, this point to this point, along 2 different routes. It could go this way; it could go this way. There are 2 possible routes and each route in itself is possible. In quantum mechanics, it can turn out that if both routes are allowed, it's actually impossible for the particle to go from here to here. Each route is possible, but together the possibilities cancel out and the whole thing is impossible. That's completely strange.

Another really strange idea in quantum mechanics is just the whole way that individual particles move through space. It's not that quantum mechanics is just a new theory of motion. It's not just a refinement of Newton's laws of motion from the 17th century. No, quantum mechanics is a new theory of what motion means. In quantum mechanics, particles don't move along definite paths through space. Particles travel through space in the form of waves that spread out and are many places at once. It's very strange.

Another strange aspect of quantum theory is what it tells us about how groups of particles act together. It turns out that 2 quantum particles can actually be exactly identical to one another—more alike than 2 pennies, more alike than identical twins. They can be exactly identical to each other in all of their properties. That may seem like a kind of minor point, but it turns out that this fact, the fact that particles can be identical to each other—2 electrons can be exactly the same—that fact has gigantic implications for the world that we see every day. We'll explore that very strange aspect of quantum theory.

Another strange aspect of quantum theory is quantum entanglement. For my money, quantum entanglement is the strangest thing in this strange old world. Quantum entanglement is a phenomenon that was first studied seriously by Albert Einstein back in the 1930s. Albert Einstein called it "spooky" and it's a good word because quantum entanglement is a kind of strange interconnectedness that can exist between 2 particles even if the particles are far apart. When the particles are observed or interact, they do so in a way that almost seems as if the particles are conspiring together at a distance to make it work. Quantum entanglement is a very, very strange thing and we will certainly discuss that at some length.

Quantum mechanics also tells us some really strange, new, and remarkable things about the properties of energy. Quantum mechanics tells us, first of all, that energy comes in discreet amounts, the "quantum" in quantum physics. That's very different from the old classical physics in which energy was continuous and you can get any quantity of energy. No, in quantum mechanics very often you can only have this amount or that amount and nothing in between. That's the quantum in quantum physics, but that's not the only surprise that quantum mechanics has to tell us about energy. Quantum mechanics also tells us that there is energy present even in empty space, even when there are no particles, even when there's no light shining through the space. Even in empty space, in the vacuum, there's energy. Quantum mechanics not only changes our view of everything. Quantum mechanics also changes our view of nothing.

Quantum mechanics also tells us some very strange and surprising things about the behavior of information. This is a contemporary topic in quantum theory. This is a subject of research going on right now. In fact, it's my own research specialty. It's a subject that I'm passionate about and so I want to tell you about that during this course. In the quantum realm, information is stored and transmitted in process in really weird ways that run counter to our intuition. What's the significance of this? It may be that the weird quantum information properties could lead to powerful new technologies of communication and computing. We may be able to build quantum computers that solve certain problems in bizarre ways. That might happen, but considering information certainly does lead us to powerful new insights into quantum physics and, of course, that's our business here.

You can see with all these many strange aspects of quantum theory that quantum physics has inspired profound philosophical debate. Quantum mechanics is such a surprising set of assertions about the world. What does it all mean? How can the world be like that? These philosophical questions are also an important part of our story. We're going to talk about how Albert Einstein and Niels Bohr, 2 of the founders of quantum theory, carried on a famous debate for years during the early years of quantum mechanics about what the meaning of quantum mechanics might be. Einstein was the quantum skeptic. He thought that there might be something wrong with quantum mechanics or that quantum mechanics might be only an incomplete description of nature. Bohr was the quantum champion. He defended quantum mechanics against Einstein's criticisms. However we conclude that this argument came out, the argument between Einstein and Bohr forced physicists ever since to sharpen their concepts to deal with the weird nature of quantum physics.

Another subject of philosophical discussion has been quantum entanglement. Quantum entanglement was kind of a leftover issue from the Bohr-Einstein debate. Bohr and Einstein discussed it from the 1930s on, but afterwards, decades later, after Bohr and Einstein had both passed on, it was quantum entanglement that most dramatically showed the deficiency of our common sense views of the world. It was quantum mechanical entanglement that showed us that the ideas about the world that you were born with simply do not apply to the microscopic realm. The quantum world is even stranger than Einstein and Bohr realized.

Even today there are competing ideas about how to interpret quantum mechanics. Every physicist knows how to work the mathematics of quantum mechanics. Every physicist knows how to use quantum mechanics to calculate the expected outcome of an experiment, but what physicists do not agree on is what quantum mechanics is telling us about the nature of the universe at the fundamental level. There are 3 very important schools of thought interpreting quantum mechanics. The first is Bohr's "Copenhagen interpretation" of quantum mechanics, so-called because it was sort of originated at Bohr's Institute for Theoretical Physics at the University of Copenhagen. In the Copenhagen interpretation, quantum theory only tells us probabilities. Quantum theory says nothing about what will actually happen. It only computes the odds. The Copenhagen interpretation says no deeper view is possible.

Since the Copenhagen interpretation, 2 further interpretational frameworks have been constructed. One of these is the so-called "hidden variables interpretation." In the hidden variables interpretation, the results of experiments are really predetermined by some hidden factors that we don't know. The probabilities of quantum mechanics simply reflect our ignorance of these secret variables that are going on in the system. Probabilities, in other words, reflect ignorance, but there's something funny about that. That sounds like a common-sense view, but there's something funny about that because in order to account for quantum mechanics, the hidden factors in this interpretation can't be simply a few hidden pieces of information about this particle and that particle. The hidden factors cannot be localized in space. The hidden factors must be part of a hidden order that spans the whole universe and makes quantum mechanics work. That's what you have to believe in to believe the hidden variables interpretation.

Finally, there's the "many worlds interpretation," which has gained, I think, more adherence lately, but is also very strange. In the many worlds interpretation, in an experiment, no one possibility is ever really chosen. Let's suppose we have an experiment in which the particle might go this direction or that direction. Quantum mechanics predicts that each of those occurs with a 50–50 probability. In the many worlds interpretation, it's not the case that one of these things is actually chosen. The particle doesn't go in one direction. The particle actually goes in both directions. Everything happens in different so-called "branches" of the universe.

We might find this a bit of challenge because actually we see the particle go one way or we see it go the other way, but that's just because we too are part of the universe. We also divide. In one branch of the universe, the particle goes this way. We see it goes this way. I report to you that it goes this way and so on. In the other branch of the universe, the particle goes that way. We see that it goes that way. I report to you that it goes that way and so on. We're all part of the branching of the universe. In each branch, we only see one thing happen, but the entire universe contains all of these possible worlds. That's the many worlds interpretation. It seems inescapable that any way we interpret quantum mechanics we're going to have to come to accept something very strange about the world.

What's the structure of this course? The course is roughly divided into a few sections. In Section One, Lectures 2 through 7, we're going to talk about the development of quantum theory between about 1900 and 1930. We're going to do a historical review of how quantum mechanics was discovered. We're not going to quite do it in chronological order. We'll skip around a little bit, but I think it will be clear how we're putting the pieces together. Then, in Section Two, Lectures 8 through 10, we're going to actually learn some basic quantum theory. We're going to learn the abstract symbolic language that physicists use to describe the microscopic world. That's going to be an ambitious task, but we'll take it on in Lectures 8 through 10. Then, there's Section Three of the course, running from Lecture 11 to about Lecture 18. Section Three of the course is a tour of the quantum world—a sightseeing tour with stops at the theory of identical particles, at quantum entanglement, at the physics of the vacuum, and at the laws of the elementary particles. We'll view how quantum theory that we have learned in Section Two applies to all these different aspects of the physical world.

Then, we'll move on to Section Four in the course. Section Four in the course will be from Lecture 19 through 22. That's the one I'm looking forward to. That's where we're going to talk about quantum mechanics and information.

We'll talk about some of the most recent ideas in understanding the quantum world—how the concept of information, which is a very modern concept, a concept that's really only come along since quantum mechanics has been invented, helps us to clarify and understand the many peculiar properties of the quantum world. Then finally, there's Section Five, Lectures 23 and 24, the last 2 lectures of this course. In Section Five, we'll venture into philosophical issues, implications, and questions and speculations about quantum theory and what it says about the nature of the world.

Before we start off, we need to set some ground rules for our course, some general expectations that we might have for the course. The first issue that I want to mention is the issue of simplification. I'm just going to confess to you now that we will often simplify our discussion to get at the fundamental principles. We'll leave out details or complicating factors and present a simplified version of things. We'll try to be honest. We'll try to note when this happens. You, as the student, shouldn't worry about this. Our project is to come to grips with the real theory of quantum mechanics. In our case, simplification will not be falsification, but we will inevitably simplify some of the details.

The second thing you should be aware of is the idea of the thought experiment. We're often going to consider thought experiments. What's a thought experiment? A thought experiment is a highly idealized experiment. It's a highly idealized experimental arrangement that's possible in principle, but it's maybe impractical actually to do in the laboratory. There are a number of reasons why we're going to think a lot about thought experiments. One is, quite frankly, thought experiments are very inexpensive. They just take a little time and attention. But, more importantly, we're highlighting the fundamental principles of quantum mechanics. In the thought experiments, we can do this in a very clear and distinct way. Once again, we'll try to be clear about what we're doing and you should know that sometimes a thought experiment is actually very closely related to a more complicated real experiment that expresses the same idea. Sometimes the thought experiments can be turned into real experiments, if you have a clever experimentalist.

The third issue I want to talk about is the issue of mathematics. Quantum mechanics is an abstract mathematical theory. There's no getting around it and that mathematics is not gratuitous. Physicists use this abstract mathematics because they're forced to in order to account for the behavior of the microscopic world. We can simplify it, but in order to get where we want to go, we need to do a little math. The math we're going to use is really a symbolic language for describing quantum situations. It involves some simple rules resembling high-school algebra for manipulating and interpreting symbols. It's not very difficult, but it is very unfamiliar. We'll have to take the time to learn it, to become adept with that abstract language for dealing with quantum theory. Venturing a short way into the abstract mathematics of quantum theory will allow us to explore the quantum world in a much deeper way and that will be worth it.

Quantum physics is our deepest insight into nature. It's exciting. It's alluring. It's mysterious. It's profound. That's the journey we're going to embark on. Of course, every journey has to start from somewhere. To begin with, we will first need to know something about classical physics, about the physics existing before 1900, the physics from which quantum mechanics sprang. Classical physics is our business in the next lecture. I'll see you then.

The View from 1900
Lecture 2

Throughout the history of human thought, there have been essentially 2 ideas about the fundamental nature of the physical world. ... In a nutshell, those 2 ideas are either the world is made out of things [discrete, indivisible units] or the world is made out of stuff [smooth continuous substances].

In modern terms, you can think of things as digital and stuff as analog. But if we travel back to a much earlier historical period, we can find a version of this debate among the Greek philosophers. The atomists, led by Democritus, considered the world to be composed of discrete, indivisible units called "atoms." Everything is made of atoms, with empty space between them. All phenomena are due to the motions and combinations of atoms. Other philosophers, including Aristotle, believed on the contrary that the basic substances of the world are continuous and infinitely divisible.

The debate resurfaced in the 17th century as early physicists tried to understand the nature of light. Isaac Newton believed that light is a stream of discrete corpuscles that move in straight lines unless their paths are deflected. Different colors of light correspond to different types of corpuscles. Christiaan Huygens believed that light is a continuous wave phenomenon analogous to sound.

In the 19th century, classical physicists arrived at a very successful synthesis of these ideas to explain the physical world. Matter is discrete, they said, while light is composed of continuous waves.

These waves propagate through space, and different colors correspond to different frequencies of the waves. Waves are characterized by their speed v, their wavelength λ, and their frequency f. These are related by the equation $v = \lambda f$.

Is nature essentially discrete, made of things, or is nature continuous, made of stuff? Sand is composed of individual units, grains of sand, but if you stand back from sand dunes they look smooth and continuous.

In the 19th century, classical physicists arrived at a very successful synthesis of these ideas to explain the physical world. Matter is discrete, they said, while light is composed of continuous waves. It was in the 1800s that John Dalton realized that chemical compounds could be explained by assuming that elements are composed of atoms of differing weights, which can combine into molecules. This became the fundamental idea of chemistry. Also in the 1800s, James Clerk Maxwell and Ludwig Boltzmann showed how the properties of a gas (pressure, temperature, and viscosity) can be explained by viewing the gas as a swarm of huge numbers of tiny molecules, moving according to Newton's laws. Heat energy is just the random motion of these molecules. The theory of heat became unified with the theory of mechanics.

Also in the 19th century, scientists conducted experiments that indicated that light is made of waves. Thomas Young devised his famous 2-slit experiment, in which light shows constructive and destructive interference. This demonstrated that light travels in waves. Young measured the wavelength of visible light, which is less than 1 millionth of a meter. Maxwell showed that light is a traveling disturbance in electric and magnetic fields—in short, an electromagnetic wave. The theory of optics became unified with the theory of electromagnetism.

In 1900, Lord Kelvin gave a lecture at the Royal Institution in which he pointed out "two dark clouds" on the horizon of classical physics. Each dark cloud would turn out to be a hurricane. The first dark cloud was the curious result of an experiment by Michelson and Morley, who tried to detect the presence of the ether (the medium of light waves). This experiment later led to the development of Einstein's theory of relativity, revolutionizing our ideas of space and time. The second dark cloud was the thermal radiation ("blackbody radiation") given off by a warm object. If we try to explain this using classical physics, we get a very wrong result. This problem became the origin of quantum physics. ■

Questions to Consider

1. In 1900, no one had ever "seen" an atom or even knew exactly how large they were. Why, then, was it reasonable for physicists and chemists to believe in the existence of atoms?

2. The speed of sound is about 343 m/s. The human ear can detect sounds with a frequency range of 20 to 20,000 cycles/s. What range of wavelengths can the ear detect?

3. In the 2-slit experiment, imagine that 1 slit is somewhat larger than the other, so that the light waves coming from the 2 slits are not equal in intensity. What would the interference pattern look like?

The View from 1900
Lecture 2—Transcript

Welcome to the second lecture of our course on quantum mechanics. Last time, in the first lecture, we previewed the course. We looked ahead at some of the strange features of quantum physics that we'll be learning from now until to the end of the course. Before we do that we must first describe something about classical physics, which can roughly be defined as the view of the physical world that prevailed before the year 1900. We have to do a little history of physics today. When we do that, I prefer to take the long view. Here's the big picture of the history of physics.

Throughout the history of human thought, there have been essentially 2 ideas about the fundamental nature of the physical world and lots of the history of physics has been a debate between these 2 ideas. In a nutshell, those 2 ideas are either the world is made out of things or the world is made out of stuff. What do I mean? Things describe the idea that the basic constituents of nature are discrete, indivisible units. You could have 1 unit or 2 units or 3 units. You can have 17 units, but you can't have 2.718 units. When we ask a question about the quantity of things, we ask the question, how many? How many things do we have? In modern terminology, the things view is the digital view. You could have 1, you can have 2, but you can't have a whole continuous range of values. Then, there's the stuff idea. The stuff idea says that the basic constituents of nature are smooth continuous substances. You can have any amount of stuff. When you ask a question about the quantity of stuff, you ask how much do you have? In modern terminology, stuff represents an analog picture of the world. You can have any value of it.

Let's bring it down to something real. Think about your dinner plate. On your dinner plate, the English peas are thing-like, but the mashed potatoes are stuff-like. The peas come in discrete units. We can ask, how many peas do you have? I have 34 peas on my plate, but you really can't ask exactly how many mashed potatoes do you have? You have to ask, how much mashed potatoes do you have? I have a half a cup of mashed potatoes. The answer to the question of whether a particular thing is thing-like or stuff-like is not always obvious. If you take the peas and you mash them up with your fork, then you get stuff. You get pea stuff, much like mashed potatoes.

The fact that the peas came packaged in little fundamental units was not essential because inside the units was just some stuff. On the other hand, if you look at the mashed potatoes under a microscope, who's to say that the pile of mashed potatoes is not just an immense heap of tiny mashed potato grains. It's like sand. Up close you see that sand is composed of individual units, grains of sand. Sand is thing-like, but if you stand back and look at some sand dunes, they look smooth and continuous. The question of whether nature is thing-like or stuff-like is going to be a little difficult to resolve, but that's the essential debate. Is nature essentially discrete, made of things, or is nature essentially continuous, made of stuff?

There was an early version of this debate among the Greek philosophers. On the one hand, you had the Atomists led by Democritus, who had an essentially thing-like view of the world. They said that everything in the universe was composed of tiny indivisible units called atoms and in between the atoms there was empty space. Atoms and the void, that's the totality of the universe, and all phenomena are due to the motions and combinations of the atoms. That was the Greek Atomist view of nature. Other philosophers, including the Greek philosopher Aristotle, held the opposite view. They favored the stuff-like view. They thought that the basic substances of the world are continuous and infinitely divisible—that there was no fundamental indivisible unit of matter. You could always divide it further. Why did they think this? Why were they unhappy with the Atomists' view? Interestingly, part of the problem was not the atoms themselves but the void, the idea that there was empty space between the atoms. Aristotle didn't think that the notion of completely empty space made sense. He said that nature abhors a vacuum. Because of that, he thought that they had to be continuous substance to fill up all the space. Interestingly, this question about empty space will come up again later in the course, So watch for it. You had the Atomist view, nature's thing-like, and you had the Aristotelian view, that nature is stuff-like, continuous substance, and both ideas had merit. Both ideas could explain observations about the world. Resolving this question is going to be a little bit tricky. Ordinary, everyday observations are not enough to resolve the question.

Let's jump ahead a few centuries, about 20 centuries, to the 17th century. There, the question we're considering is the basic nature of light. What is the basic nature of light? Once again, there are 2 prevailing ideas. On the one hand, you had Isaac Newton, the greatest physicist of his age, famous for his laws of motion and gravitation. He also studied optics, and Isaac Newton came to believe that light is a stream of discrete corpuscles, he called them. Light is thing-like; they were little units of light. Light came in little units, and so the corpuscles of light traveled through space in straight lines unless something deflected them and different colors of light corresponded to different types of corpuscles. There were red corpuscles, there were green corpuscles, there were blue corpuscles, and so on. The intensity of light, the amount of light that you had, corresponded to the number of corpuscles that you had. The question of the intensity of light basically boiled down to the question of, how many corpuscles, how many thing-like units, do you have in light? That's Newton's view.

On the other hand, you had the view of Chris Huygens, the Dutch physicist, the second-greatest physicist of the 17th century. Huygens had the view that light is a continuous wave and he took the analogy of sound. He thought light was a wave like sound waves. Light wasn't sound waves, but it was analogous to it. Waves are things that propagate through space and spread out throughout space. He thought that that's the way light worked. In his view, different colors of light correspond to different wave frequencies, just like the different musical notes correspond to different sound frequencies. The intensity of light was the strength of the vibration in the wave. That can be any continuous value, so Huygens said that the question of the intensity of the light was a "how much" question. How much wave do you have?

We're going to talk about waves a good deal in this course, so let's take a few minutes to sort out a few facts and ideas about waves. Basically, there are 3 numerical quantities that describe a wave. The first one is the wave's speed, which we would write with the letter v. This quantity answers the question of how fast the oscillations in the wave propagate through space. That's measured in meters per second. It's a speed. How fast is the wave going? Sound waves, for example, travel at about 340 meters per second, which is pretty far. That's the speed of sound.

The second quantity about a wave is the wavelength, which is denoted by the Greek letter λ. That's a lambda. How far is it between successive wave crests, successive disturbances? That's the question we're answering. A sound wave is an oscillation of air pressure. At any instant in time, there's a certain distance between one region of high pressure and the next region of high pressure and that distance in space is the wavelength. It's measured in meters. It's a distance. What's the length of a sound wave? Let's take a typical musical note. We'll take Concert A. That's the A above middle C. It's the A that the violin plays when everybody's tuning up. Concert A has a wavelength of about 3/4 of a meter. That's the distance between successive regions of high pressure.

Finally, the third quantity is frequency, which we denote with the letter f. Frequency answers the question how rapidly the oscillations reach a particular point in space. For example, how rapidly do the oscillations and air pressure reach my ear? That's the frequency and with sound waves that determines the musical note that I would hear. Frequency is measured in the number of waves, the number of cycles, per second. A typical musical note, Concert A, has a frequency of 440 cycles per second. These 3 quantities, wave speed, wavelength, and frequency, are connected by what we might call the wave equation, which says that the wave speed, v, is equal to the wavelength times the frequency—$v = \lambda f$. It's a mathematical relationship between wave characteristics and it's a very convenient relation. It means that if you know any 2 of the quantities, you can figure out the third. It means that for a given wave speed, a higher frequency means a shorter wavelength because the product of frequency and wavelength has to equal the wave speed. A lower frequency means a longer wavelength because the product of frequency and wavelength is the wave speed.

Let's get back to our main story. The question is whether nature is discrete, thing-like, or continuous, stuff-like. The Greeks had 2 views of matter. The Atomists thought that matter was thing-like. The Aristotelians thought it was stuff-like. In the 17th century, Newton thought light was made of discrete things, corpuscles. Huygens thought it was made of waves. It was a wave phenomenon analogous to sound. It would be stuff-like.

Now comes a really remarkable period in the history of science, the 19th century. In the 19th century, physicists arrived at a very successful synthesis of these 2 ideas, a way of putting these 2 ideas together. They said that whether nature is discrete or continuous depends on what part of nature you're asking about. In the 19th century, scientists came to believe that matter is basically discrete. Matter is thing-like, while light is composed of continuous waves. Light is stuff-like. Let's take these 2 ideas one by one.

On the one hand, in the 19th century, they came to believe that matter was made of atoms. They used the old Greek word. Why did they believe that? It started right at the beginning of the 19th century with the English chemist John Dalton. Dalton showed how the rules of chemical composition, the rules about what substances could be combined with what and in what proportions they could be combined, could all be explained by supposing that the substances were made of atoms. The idea is that each element is composed of one type of atom. There is a type of atom for hydrogen, there's a type of atom for carbon, there's a type of atom for oxygen, and so on. Atoms of different elements have different weights. The atoms combine to form clusters of atoms called molecules and, for example, water, as Dalton showed, is composed of 2 hydrogen atoms and 1 oxygen atom. Let's suppose that a hydrogen atom has a mass of 1 unit—whatever the mass unit per atoms is—1 unit and there are 2 of those. Oxygen, it turns out, an oxygen atom has a mass of 16 units. Two hydrogens and one oxygen means that the hydrogen and oxygen must be combined in the ratio of 1:8 in mass. Indeed, that's exactly the recipe for water. Dalton was able to explain all kinds of chemical recipes from this idea.

The idea of atoms became the fundamental idea of chemistry. Throughout the 19th century, they applied atoms to more and more ideas about what nature was made of. For example, they were able to explain the structure of crystals by the fact that atoms could be organized in regular arrangements. If you see the facets of a crystal, the facets of a crystal have the shape they do because the atoms of the sub-microscopic scale are in a regular arrangement in space, and so on. I could go on for some time telling you about all the wonderful things that the atomic idea gave to chemistry.

A few decades later, the physicists began to pick up this idea and to use the idea of atoms, the idea that matter is composed of little discrete pieces, to explain more and more things about the world. I want to mention 2 physicists in particular, James Clerk Maxwell, the great Scottish theoretical physicist, and Ludwig Boltzmann, who was from Austria. Those 2, among others, were able to show that a gas and the properties of a gas can be explained if you assume that the gas is composed of atoms. If you assume that the gas is composed of atoms, you can understand the gas's temperature, its pressure, its density, its viscosity—all the properties of the gas in terms of the properties of the atoms. The gas is a swarm of tiny particles—the particles moving and colliding according to Newton's laws of motion, which, of course, had been known for a couple of hundred years by this time. The gas seems continuous because the atoms are very, very small. They're really, really tiny, and so even a small volume of air contains immense numbers of atoms.

The most important insight, however, is their insight that heat energy is really just the random motion of the atoms, the random motion of the particles composing the gas. That was a tremendous insight because before this time there were 2 ideas. There was motion, which is the purview of the signs of mechanics, and there was the subject of heat, which is the purview of the new science of thermodynamics. The 2 subjects didn't have anything to do with each other, but when they realized that heat was really just the energy of microscopic atomic motion, that meant that they were unifying 2 branches of physics. They unified the study of heat, thermodynamics, with the study of motion, mechanics, 1 subject instead of 2. That unification is a tremendous triumph of 19th-century physics, really a great advance in human thought.

What's the other half of the 19th-century synthesis? It's the idea that light is made of waves. How do we know that light is made of waves? We know because of Thomas Young. Thomas Young was a remarkable English scholar. He was a physicist and many other things. He developed the theory of elasticity. He helped to decipher the Egyptian hieroglyphics of the Rosetta Stone. In 1801, Young did a crucial experiment, one of the most important in the history of science, showing that light is a wave. He also measured the wavelength of light and found that the wavelength of light is actually very short. It's less than 1-millionth of a meter. This is such an important experiment in the history of physics that we've arranged to actually do the experiment right here for you as a demonstration. It's actually not very difficult.

Here's the basic setup for what's called "Young's two slit experiment." First, we have a light source. Here's our light source. We use a laser. There's no reason to use a laser in particular. You need a light source that only produces one color of light. In the Huygens view that would mean one wavelength of light and lasers are just very convenient these days. Young, of course, used some other light source. Here's our laser and we're going to shine the light at a barrier here. This barrier has a pair of very narrow vertical slits. The slits are very close together. They're parallel. They're in the vertical direction and they're very thin. They're actually tiny cuts in a piece of foil. We're going to shine the light through these 2 slits and then the light that passes through those 2 slits will go over here and will be projected on this screen where we can see it. I've tilted the screen a little bit, so that you can see it more easily.

What do we observe? When we shine light through one slit, we see a little smear of light on the screen, but what happens when we shine the light through 2 slits? There it is. When we shine the light through 2 slits, we see a pattern of light and dark bands. It's not just a continuous, smooth smear of light across the middle. It's an alteration between a light spot and dark spot and a light spot and a dark spot. Those light and dark bands that go from side to side—that is to say, the smear of light is shown side to side and the bands alternate along that—those light and dark bands are sometimes called "fringes," interference fringes, because that's what's going on. What's going on is interference.

What's interference? Light waves are emerging from each of the 2 slits, and so the light waves from each of the 2 slits propagate through space and they combine at the screen. What we see at the screen is the total light from both slits. At the bright bands, the places where the pattern is very bright, that's a place where the waves from the 2 slits arrive in unison. They are oscillating together at that point, and so that means that the 2 waves add together and form a bigger wave, a more intense wave. You get a bright light because, of course, the intensity of light has to do with how much the wave is oscillating there. You get what's called "constructive interference," 2 waves that add up together to form a bigger wave, 2 beams of light that add together to form a brighter light. What's happening at the dark bands, however, is kind of funny. You see, at the dark bands, the 2 waves are arriving exactly out of sync. When the waves add up together to form a total wave, they actually cancel each other out. There's no wave at all. There's no light at all there. This is called "destructive interference." It's very strange.

To really prove what I'm telling you, we're actually going to do the experiment one step further. I'm going to very carefully cover up one of the slits. This is actually tricky because the slits are quite close together. They're only a quarter of a millimeter apart. I'm going to take this index card, I'm going to very carefully slide it over, and I'm going to cover one of the slits. We'll see what happens to the light pattern when I do that. I move it over very carefully here, cover one slit, and there you go, one slit. It's dimmer, of course, because I've covered up part of the light, but also you notice there are no light and dark bands. That's 2 slits, and 1 slit. Because there are no light and dark bands when I cover up one slit, that means that when I cover up one of the slits there are places on the screen where the light actually gets brighter. The places where there was destructive interference now are receiving light because I've eliminated one of the contributions. It's possible to cover up part of the light source and actually increase the amount of light reaching certain points. That's destructive interference. If light were a stream of corpuscles, nothing like this could happen. This wouldn't be remotely possible. Newton's theory is right out the door. It can't explain this simple observation that Thomas Young made at the beginning of the 1800s. Light is a wave because it exhibits constructive and destructive interference and the 2-slit experiment proves it. Huygens was right.

Light's a wave, but what sort of wave? What's waving? Once again, later in the 19th century, more light was shed, so to speak. A character returns; James Clerk Maxwell is the one who figures it out. Maxwell shows that light is a traveling oscillation of electric and magnetic fields, an electromagnetic wave. The details are fascinating, but they're unimportant for our purposes. I'll just give you the key point. The theory of optics, the theory of light, now became unified with another branch of physics, the theory of electromagnetism. They were recognized to be 2 branches of exactly one theory. Optics and electromagnetism were the same thing. That's another triumph for 19th-century physics, a triumph of the unification of ideas.

This is the view from 1900. On the one hand, we found that matter is made of tiny atoms. In 1900, nobody has seen an atom yet, but very few physicists have doubts that atoms exist. A few have doubts, but most people are pretty sure that atoms exist—even though they're not exactly sure exactly how big they are, but they know they're really small. They can explain so many things by assuming that matter is made of atoms—chemical properties, physical properties, and so on. By 1900, it was clear that the atoms were themselves made of smaller particles. By 1900, they had discovered the electron, which is a little negatively charged piece of matter that's a constituent of atoms, but that doesn't change the basic idea that matter is made of tiny particles. The second part of the 19th-century synthesis, the second part of the view of physics from 1900, is that light is a continuous electromagnetic wave. Matter is thing-like. Light is stuff-like—baby stuff, but stuff-like, continuous.

That's 1900. In the year 1900, the eminent English physicist William Thompson, Lord Kelvin as he's remembered, gave a lecture at the Royal Institution in London, a public lecture about sort of the state of physics. He said the 19th-century synthesis explains a lot about the world. It's a tremendously powerful set of ideas about the world. It unifies some apparently different fields of science. This is a great triumph. It unifies thermodynamics, the science of heat, with mechanics, the science of motion. It unifies optics, the science of light, with electromagnetism. Kelvin and others are at this time interested in going a little bit further trying to understand the relation of light, optics, with heat, thermodynamics. We all know that there is some relation. Very hot objects emit light, so there's got to be some relationship. If we could understand that relationship, that would be the capstone of the whole edifice of classical physics. That's Kelvin's ambition, but Kelvin says there are "two dark clouds" on the horizon of physics. There are 2 dark clouds that seem to show that maybe this is not going to be very easy. In fact, Kelvin is brilliant. He's brilliant because these 2 dark clouds each turn out to be a hurricane. Each of them is going to blow through and knock down the edifice of classical physics. Let's talk about them one by one.

The first one is the curious experiment by 2 American physicists, Michelson and Morley. This experiment basically is asking the question, what is light? What are electric and magnetic fields? The conventional view in the 19th century was that electromagnetism and light were all about disturbances or displacements of something called "the ether." The ether is the medium of electromagnetism. It is to light as air is to sound. It's the thing that conveys light from place to place, and it pervades all of the universe. The universe is full of ether and we know it's there because light propagates through space. The earth in its orbit passes through the ether. That means that right here in this room there should be a pretty stiff ether wind, several kilometers per second, blowing through the room. Michelson and Morley did an extremely precise optical experiment to try to detect this, and they very convincingly and spectacularly failed to do so. They failed to detect the ether. Kelvin said this is a dark cloud because maybe it means that our ideas about light are wrong. Indeed, it's the Michelson-Morley experiment that leads to the development by Albert Einstein of the Special Theory of Relativity, but we're not talking about the Special Theory of Relativity.

We need to talk about the other dark cloud. The other dark cloud is the problem of thermal radiation. As I just mentioned, all warm objects give off electromagnetic radiation. They give off light of one wavelength or another, not necessarily light that we see with our eyes. For example, the light bulb—if I run an electric current through my filament, then it gets hot and radiates electromagnetic radiation. If we use classical physics to try to account for this, how bright the light is, what color it is, we get badly wrong answers. Kelvin said this is a problem. We need to understand what's going on. This dark cloud is the puzzle that becomes the origin of quantum physics, the question of light emitted by a warm object, the light bulb.

Next time, we're going to talk about how 2 revolutionary thinkers, Max Planck and Albert Einstein, turned classical physics on its head, and introduced quantum ideas to explain, in part, the problem of the light bulb. That's the birth of quantum physics. That's next time and I'll see you then.

Two Revolutionaries—Planck and Einstein
Lecture 3

At the beginning of the 20th century, 2 revolutionary thinkers, Max Planck and Albert Einstein, began to question the 19th-century synthesis, and to introduce quantum ideas into physics. ... There were just a few leftover experimental puzzles about light and matter, and to solve them, they needed to change the entire structure of physics.

The first puzzle was the problem of thermal radiation. When a solid object is heated, like the filament of an incandescent light bulb, it gives off radiation. The details are hard to reconcile with classical physics. This is sometimes called "blackbody radiation," since the simplest case occurs when the object is black in color. At a given temperature, all black bodies radiate in the same way. When the classical theory of heat is applied to the radiation, it predicts the lower-frequency radiation (infrared) pretty well. But it predicts a lot more high-frequency radiation (ultraviolet) than is actually observed, or even possible. This is called the "ultraviolet catastrophe."

In 1900, Planck made a strange hypothesis. He supposed that light energy can only be emitted or absorbed by a black body in discrete amounts, called "light quanta." The energy of a light quantum is related to the light frequency by $E = hf$, where h is called "Planck's constant." Because the value of h is so tiny (6.6×10^{-34} J·s), the individual quanta are extremely small. An ordinary light bulb emits around a billion trillion (10^{20}) quanta each second. Since higher frequencies mean higher-energy quanta, groups of atoms cannot emit high-frequency light as readily. Therefore the ultraviolet catastrophe is avoided. A wave can have any intensity and therefore can carry any amount of energy. Planck's quantum hypothesis is a radical change in the way we look at light.

Einstein examined the problem of the "photoelectric effect." This problem arises from the fact that, when light falls on a polished metal surface in a vacuum, electrons can be emitted from the metal, and this process has several features that are hard to explain if light is a wave. The energy of the electrons does not depend on the intensity of the light. If we use a brighter light, we get more electrons, but each one has the same energy as before. Instead, the electrons' energy depends on the frequency of the light. If the frequency is too low, no electrons are produced. The higher the frequency, the higher the electron energy.

In 1905, Einstein realized that Planck's quantum hypothesis amounts to assuming that light comes in the form of discrete particles, later called "photons." This is the key to understanding the photoelectric effect. Each photoelectron gets its energy from a single photon. Some of this energy goes into "prying it loose" from the metal; the electron flies away with the rest. Photons in bright light or dim light have the same energy, so the electron energies are the same in each case. Since $E = hf$, high-frequency light has photons of higher energy, and therefore electrons of higher energy are produced.

In 1905, Einstein realized that Planck's quantum hypothesis amounts to assuming that light comes in the form of discrete particles, later called "photons." This is the key to understanding the photoelectric effect.

The third puzzle is the problem of heat capacities. There was a long-standing puzzle about the heat capacities of pure solids—that is, solids made from 1 type of atom. We will consider the examples of platinum and diamond (carbon). The "heat capacity" is the heat energy needed to raise the temperature of the solid by 1°C. Classical heat theory predicts that all pure solids should have the same heat capacity for the same number of atoms. This is because at a given temperature T all vibrating atoms should have the same energy on average. Carbon atoms, being less massive, would vibrate more times per second than platinum atoms, but they would have the same average energy. Experimental results, however, are quite different. At 1000°C, both platinum and diamond have about the expected heat capacity. At room temperature, around 20°C, platinum behaves as expected but diamond's heat capacity is too small. At −200°C, both platinum and diamond have unexpectedly low heat capacities.

In 1908, Einstein applied quantum ideas to the vibration of atoms. He proposed that atomic vibration energy only comes in discrete quanta of size $E = hf$. This is the first application of quantum physics to matter rather than light. It directly challenges Newton's mechanics in which a vibrating atom can have any amount of energy. For any pure solid, at high T there is enough heat energy for all the atoms to vibrate as expected. But at low T there is not enough heat energy for all of the atoms to vibrate, so the heat capacity is lower than expected. For diamond (carbon atoms), higher vibration f means that the energy quanta are larger. Both $-200°C$ and $20°C$ count as "low" T. For platinum, only $-200°C$ is a "low" T. Einstein's idea, with a few refinements of detail, precisely explains the heat capacities of pure solids at all temperatures. ∎

Questions to Consider

1. In the phenomenon of photoluminescence, atoms absorb light of one frequency, then reemit light of a different frequency. According to Stokes's rule, the emitted light has a lower frequency than the absorbed light. Explain why this fact makes sense given the photon theory. (Einstein discussed Stokes's rule in his photoelectric effect paper.)

2. "The quantum discoveries of Planck and Einstein tell us that what we once supposed to be continuous is actually discrete." Discuss how this statement applies (if it does) to each of the 3 problems we have described.

Two Revolutionaries—Planck and Einstein
Lecture 3—Transcript

Welcome to the third lecture in our course on quantum mechanics. Last time we took a look at classical physics, the basic view of the physical world that prevailed at the end of the 19th century. Classical physics was a tremendous achievement. It was a powerful synthesis of ideas, and it was very successful at explaining all kinds of phenomena. Now, in classical physics, matter is composed of tiny particles called "atoms," and if you assume that matter is made out of atoms, that explains a lot of chemical and physical properties of matter. It explains the laws of chemical combinations, it explains the behavior of gases, and so on. On the other hand, light, in classical physics, is a phenomenon of continuous electromagnetic waves. How do we know that light is a wave phenomenon? We know because we can observe constructive and destructive interference of light waves in Thomas Young's 2-slit experiment. An experiment we actually performed to see for ourselves that light travels as waves.

So now, we're going to continue the story. We're going to continue the story into the 20th century. At the beginning of the 20th century, 2 revolutionary thinkers, Max Planck and Albert Einstein, began to question the 19th-century synthesis, and to introduce quantum ideas into physics. Why would they do that? What was wrong with classical physics? The problem was that there were just a few leftover experimental puzzles about light and matter, and to solve them, they needed to change the entire structure of physics.

So, let's begin. The first puzzle is the problem of thermal radiation. When we heat up a solid object, it gives off radiation. It gives off light, long-wavelength light. An everyday example of that is the light bulb. When we run an electric current through the tungsten filament of a light bulb, that filament gets very, very hot, and it emits light. Now, when we do this, we can ask how much radiation is emitted, and we can ask at what frequencies do the light waves come out? They might be in the visible range—there's a fairly narrow range of frequencies that we can perceive with our eye. Or it could be lower frequency light than that, infrared light. Or it could be higher frequency light than that, ultraviolet light.

Now, when we analyze the thermal radiation from an object, the simplest case actually turns out to be when the object itself is black in color, what's called a "blackbody." The reason for that is kind of paradoxical and surprising. It turns out that the more efficient an object is at absorbing light, the more efficient it is at emitting thermal radiation when you heat it up, and so, a blackbody would be a perfect radiator of thermal radiation. And it turns out that this thermal radiation called "blackbody radiation" is quite interesting. At a given temperature, all blackbodies, no matter what they are made of, radiate in exactly the same way. And so at the end of the 19th century, many scientists tried to apply the classical theory of heat to explain blackbody radiation. And it turns out that this works pretty well for explaining the low-frequency light, the infrared radiation that comes out of a blackbody. But the classical theory predicts way too much high-frequency radiation, way too much ultraviolet radiation.

So, back to the light bulb. We run the electric current through the tungsten filament, it gets very hot—in fact, it gets to more than 2000°C—and what kind of light comes out? Well, mostly it's infrared light. Mostly it's light that's at too low a frequency for us to see, but there's also a good deal of visible light, and there's almost no ultraviolet light from an incandescent light bulb, which is why you don't need to wear sunscreen around an incandescent bulb. It doesn't emit enough ultraviolet light to give you a sunburn.

Okay, so let's try to apply the classical theory of heat to this. And when we do this we find out that ultraviolet light coming from the light bulb should be much more intense than the visible light, and that should be much more intense than the infrared light. We get it exactly wrong. There should be immense amounts of ultraviolet light coming out of the light bulb. This prediction is so badly wrong, so radically wrong, that it came to be called "the ultraviolet catastrophe." And if your theory cannot explain how a light bulb works, well, you need a better theory.

That's where Max Planck came in. At the time of our story, Planck is a German physicist. At age 42, which is quite old for a revolutionary in fact, he's been working on the blackbody problem for some time. Planck realizes that this is a really important problem, a problem that's going to teach him something fundamental. Why does he think this? It's because all blackbodies, whatever they are made of, radiate in exactly the same way. So if he can figure out why that is, he'll learn something fundamental about the relation of heat and light. So he's been working on it for a long time, and finally, in desperation, in the year 1900, he proposes a strange hypothesis. Planck says, suppose that light is not emitted and absorbed continuously, but only in discrete amounts. These discrete amounts he called "light quanta." This is the quantum hypothesis, the quantum in quantum mechanics. The energy in 1 light quantum is related to the frequency of the light. The equation is E, energy, is equal to $h \times f$. Well, where h is a fundamental constant of nature, a new fundamental constant which was later called "Planck's constant," and Planck's constant has a tiny value. It's 6.6×10^{-34} joule seconds. That's really small. If we wrote that in decimals, if we put the decimal point, we'd have to write 33 0s before we got to the first 6. That's an incredibly small number. And so we multiply Planck's constant times the frequency of the light, and that tells us the size of the quantum of light energy.

Now, because Planck's constant is so very, very small—light quanta are very, very small as well, they're very tiny—and that's why energy appears continuous, because it comes in discrete units, but the discrete units are very small. And the light bulb, under Planck's hypothesis, the light bulb would emit something like on the order of 10^{20}—a hundred million trillion light quanta every second.

Okay, how does the light quantum hypothesis explain blackbody radiation? Well, higher frequency light has quanta that have higher energy, and if an object is going to emit a quantum of light, it has to get together in one place enough energy to do so, so it's just harder for an object to emit an ultraviolet photon. The ultraviolet photons have high frequency, they have higher energy; it's just harder to emit them. And so, Planck's hypothesis predicts no ultraviolet catastrophe. The quantum hypothesis, in fact, exactly accounts for all the details of blackbody radiation.

Now, Planck's idea is pretty radical. A continuous wave should carry any amount of energy. The amount of energy carried by the wave is just related to how strong the wave is, and you can make a continuous wave of any strength. Planck himself recognizes how radical his quantum hypothesis is on the very day when he worked out that the quantum hypothesis solved the blackbody radiation problem. He said to his son, "today I have made a discovery as important as Newton's discovery." That's quite a statement to make, and as we'll see, entirely justified.

Okay. That brings us to the second puzzle. The second puzzle is the problem of the photoelectric effect. So, consider the following experiment. Suppose we take a metal surface and we polish it to remove any layer of oxides off the surface, and we put it in a vacuum. And now we shine light on the polished metal surface. What happens? Well, it turns out that electrons, which are tiny electrically charged particles—they are constituents of atoms—electrons are emitted from the surface. So this is why it's called "the photoelectric effect:" photo for the light, electric because you emit electrons.

The photoelectric effect was discovered in the late 1800s, and very soon, scientists had done experiments on it, and they'd made some curious observations about the nature of the photoelectric effect. They could measure both the number of electrons that were emitted by the surface, and the energy of the electrons, how fast they were going. And what they discovered is the energy of the electrons, how fast they were going, does not depend at all on the intensity of the light that you shine. If you shine a brighter light, you get more electrons coming out of the surface, but every electron is moving at the same speed as previously. This is quite amazing. If you imagine that the electrons are being sort of shaken out of the metal by the oscillations of the light, then if the oscillations are stronger, surely the electrons should be more shaken by the light. But even if you do a thousand times brighter light, even if you shine a light of a thousand times greater intensity on the metal surface, you won't have more energy in the electrons, you'll just have more electrons. That's very strange.

Well, what does determine the energy of the electrons? It turns out, that's dependent on the frequency of the light. If the frequency is too low, in fact, you get no photoelectrons at all. Infrared light may not produce any photoelectrons from your metal surface. At higher frequency, you get electrons out, and at even higher frequency, you get faster, higher energy electrons out. So the observation is that the energy of the electrons does not depend on light intensity, the energy of the electrons depends only on the frequency of the light, and that seemed very puzzling.

So, along comes Albert Einstein. Now, Albert Einstein, he's a very romantic figure in the history of science. He's justly famous for all kinds of discoveries. This is the year 1905, which is Einstein's year of miracles. He, in this year, discovers the theory of relativity, demonstrates the equation $E = mc^2$, he explains all kinds of other things, and he also provides a new theory to explain the photoelectric effect. By day, he's a technical expert, third class, in the Swiss Patent Office in 1905; by night, he's a physics revolutionary. Einstein is aware of Planck's work, and so he realizes that Planck's quantum hypothesis amounts to thinking of light as a stream of discrete particles. These particles were later called "photons." So, Einstein realized that Planck's hypothesis was saying that somehow, light is made of photons, and the energy of 1 photon is determined by Planck's formula. Energy is Planck's constant times the frequency of the light.

Okay, that's kind of a strange picture. How does that explain the photoelectric effect? Well, here's what Einstein says. Einstein says that every photoelectron, each and every photoelectron that comes out of the metal, gets its energy from a single photon, a single photon striking the metal. Now, some of the energy of the photon is used up in prying the electron loose from the metal—the electrons are bound to the metal, and so it takes a little energy to pry them loose—but whatever energy is left over after that, the electron gets. And so, photons in bright or dim light of a given color have the same energy, so the electron energies are the same whether you have a bright light or a dim light. But if you change the color, if you change the frequency of the light, then the photons have different energies. The same light with higher frequencies, same intensity of light with a higher frequency, should have photons with higher energy, and so the photoelectrons that are produced will have a higher energy. And Einstein is able to give a detailed account of the photoelectric effect in terms of photons.

Now, this was a very radical idea, and in fact, several experimental physicists were very skeptical, so they went off and they did the experiments very carefully. They measured all kinds of things about the photoelectric effect, and they found that the experiments, the experimental results, agreed exactly with Einstein's theory in every detail. And so in fact Einstein won the Nobel Prize in 1921 for the photoelectric effect, not for relativity theory or any of the many other things that he did, but for the photoelectric effect.

It was that important. So with Planck's explanation of blackbody radiation, and Einstein's explanation of the photoelectric effect, we've sort of gotten ourselves in a weird situation for the theory of light. I mean, the 2-slit experiment, we did the 2-slit experiment; it seems to prove that light is a continuous wave. It's a conclusive experiment. On the other hand, when we do the photoelectric effect, that seems to prove that light is a stream of discrete photons. So there's something really, really funny going on. But it isn't just about light. It's not just something funny about light. Which brings us to the third puzzle.

The third puzzle is the problem of heat capacities. So, what is heat capacity? The heat capacity of an object is the heat energy needed to raise an object's temperature by 1°C. How much energy do I have to add to the object so that its temperature will go up by 1°C? Now, if I have an object with a very high heat capacity, then that object is hard to heat or cool. It takes a lot of energy putting in to make it hotter, it takes a lot of energy taken out to make it cooler. On the other hand, if the object has very low heat capacity, it's relatively easy to heat it or cool it. You don't have to add much energy to heat it up, you don't have to extract much energy to cool it down.

So heat capacity is a very significant quantity in the theory of heat, which was one of the aspects of classical 19th-century physics. And, in the 19th century, there was actually a longstanding puzzle about pure solids. A pure solid is a solid made of one type of atom, a solid of one particular element. So to explain this puzzle, I'm going to introduce a couple of examples. We'll consider platinum metal and diamond, which is made of carbon. I figure as long as we're doing thought-experiments, we might as well use very expensive materials in our experiment.

All right, so classical heat theory, the heat theory of the 19th century, predicts that all pure solids should have about the same heat capacity for the same number of atoms. How does this work? Well, it works that at a given temperature, all atoms should vibrate with the same energy on average, and heat energy is the energy of microscopic random vibrations of the atoms, and at a given temperature they should all have about the same energy. Platinum, the atoms are very heavy, and so they vibrate slower at a given temperature. Carbon atoms are much lighter atoms, and also in diamond they're held together by very stiff covalent bonds, so they vibrate much faster at a given temperature. But the amount of energy in a platinum atom or a carbon atom should be about the same at a given temperature, and that means that all substances, the prediction is, all substances made of one kind of atom, all pure substances, should have about the same heat capacity for a given number of atoms.

So what does the experiment say? The experiment says no, that's not quite true. So, let's consider doing this experiment, and we can imagine doing this experiment at 3 different temperatures. We can imagine doing it at a very high temperature, say 1000°C; or at an intermediate temperature, room temperature is good, 20°C; or very, very cold temperature, like −200°C, about the temperature of liquid nitrogen. And so we can measure the heat capacities of materials at different temperatures.

And if we do the experiment at a very high temperature, 1000°C, hotter than any oven, then we find that both platinum and diamond behave about as expected. You see, the classical theory actually predicts that all solid objects should have a heat capacity of about 25 in particular units—the units are joules per degrees Celsius per mole, but 25 is the number to remember—and both platinum and diamond have heat capacities of about that amount. Maybe they're not exactly right, but it's pretty close to that number. At 1000°C, both of them behave as expected. But now we can imagine doing the experiment at 20°C, room temperature, and then we find that platinum behaves roughly as expected, but diamond's heat capacity is much too low. It takes much too little energy to change the temperature of diamond. And again, we find if we do the experiment at liquid nitrogen temperatures, −200°C, that both platinum and diamond have unexpectedly low heat capacities, and the heat capacity of diamond is very, very tiny. So this doesn't agree at all with classical physics.

Along comes Einstein again, and what Einstein is going to do is he's going to do something really radical, strange, and amazing. Einstein is going to apply quantum ideas not to light, but to the vibrations of atoms. Einstein says suppose atomic vibration energy comes in discrete quanta of size energy equals Planck's constant times the frequency of vibration. In other words, the Planck formula applies not just to energy and light waves, but also the energy in atomic vibrations.

This is the first application of quantum physics to matter. There's no light anywhere in the problem. Light is irrelevant to measuring the heat capacity of these materials. And this is a direct challenge to Newton's mechanics, the most successful theory of physics that had stood for more than 200 years as the gold standard for accurate and far-reaching theories. It's a direct challenge to Newton's mechanics because a vibrating atom in Newton's mechanics can have any energy whatsoever.

So what does Einstein say? Well, consider these pure solids. Consider just some pure solid. At very high temperatures, there is a lot of heat energy for all the atoms to vibrate, just as expected. But suppose we consider the same solid at low temperatures. Then there's not enough heat energy for all the atoms to have at least 1 quantum of energy, because the atom can have 0 quanta or 1 quantum or 2 quanta and so on, but if there's not enough for everybody to have 1 quantum, that means that a lot of the atoms will not be vibrating at all. And so, Einstein will say that since a lot of the atoms aren't even vibrating, the heat capacity of that material will be lower than expected. So, at high temperatures they should behave about as expected because there's plenty of heat energy. At low temperatures, a lot of the atoms are fixed in place without any quanta of vibration energy, and only a few of them are vibrating: the heat capacity is lower.

So what's the difference between high temperatures and low temperatures? What counts as a low temperature for a given substance? And it depends on the substance. It depends on the speed of vibration of the substance, because it depends on how big the quantum of energy is, therefore the frequency of vibration.

So for diamond, you have very high frequency vibrations, and that means that the quantum of vibration energy is relatively high, and that means that both −200°C and 20°C count as low temperatures for diamond. Even at room temperature, most of the atoms in a diamond are not vibrating, they do not have 1 quantum of vibration.

For platinum, on the other hand, those atoms are much more massive, the vibrations of the atoms much slower, and so room temperature, 20°C, counts as high temperature for the platinum vibrations. There's plenty of energy to have plenty of energy quanta for all the atoms. But −200°C, that's low temperature even for platinum. Einstein's idea, with a few refinements, actually precisely explains the observed heat capacities of pure solids of all kinds at all temperatures. It's a remarkable agreement with experiment.

Okay. What's happened in the first decade of the 20th century? Max Planck and Albert Einstein have introduced quantum ideas to explain a series of otherwise baffling observations: blackbody radiation in the case of Planck; the photoelectric effect, and then later the heat capacity of pure solids, explained by Einstein. Both of these were puzzles—or all 3 of these were puzzles—of classical physics, and in each case, Planck and Einstein find that energy comes in discrete units, discrete quanta: the quantum in quantum physics. And the size of the quantum is $E = hf$, energy is Planck's constant times frequency, frequency of light or frequency of vibration. And it's the same Planck's constant for everything: the same Planck's constant for blackbody radiation, the same Planck's constant for the photoelectric effect, the same Planck's constant for the heat capacities of pure solids.

This is one of those really interesting moments in the history of science where we're on the verge of a new point of view. You can tell that there's a great new principle of physics in the offing, a principle that is universal, because the quantum hypothesis appears to apply both to light and to matter; but we don't quite see the details yet. We don't quite have the whole idea. We just see a little bit.

Now, the universal principle, the universal quantum principle that applies to both light and to matter, is a direct challenge to the classical physics that prevailed at the end of the 19th century, because in classical physics, energy can come in any amount. Energy is a continuous quantity. So this means that Planck's and Einstein's discoveries tell us that the universe is discrete, in ways that we never expected, that the old resolution of the universe into matter made of discrete things and light made of continuous wavy stuff, that old distinction must not be quite right.

Well, next time, of course, we're going to probe the other half of the mystery. Not only is nature discrete in ways that we never expected, but it will turn out that nature is also continuous in ways that we never expected. So far we've seen that light, electromagnetic waves, can also act as a stream of particles, a stream of photons. But next time, we're going to find out that particles of matter that we thought were completely discrete can also act as waves. So, every sort of stuff has a little bit of things, every sort of thing is a little stuff like. That's next time. I'll see you then.

Particles of Light, Waves of Matter
Lecture 4

Young's 2-slit experiment demonstrates that light is a wave. ... On the other hand, Einstein's analysis of the photoelectric effect demonstrates that light is composed of discrete particles. ... Our understanding of light must somehow encompass both the wave and the particle ideas.

The quantum view can be summed up as wave-particle duality. The true nature of light cannot be described in simple terms. Both particle and wave pictures are required to explain the behavior of light. The rule of thumb is this: Light travels in the form of waves, with frequency and wavelength, interference effects, etc. But light interacts, is emitted or absorbed, in the form of particles, with discrete energies, etc.

In 1924, Louis de Broglie, following up the suggestion of Einstein, proposed that quantum wave-particle duality must also apply to matter. Particles such as electrons must also have wave properties of frequency, wavelength, interference effects, etc. De Broglie's idea was rapidly confirmed for electrons, which exhibit interference effects when they pass through the regularly spaced atoms in a crystal. Electron waves constructively interfere in some directions and destructively interfere in others. Modern experiments have demonstrated the wave properties of even larger pieces of matter, including neutrons

A particle has a definite position, but a wave is spread out. How can we reconcile this? The Born rule states that the intensity of a wave ... tells us the probability of finding the particle at any given location.

and entire atoms. In one recent experiment, a 2-slit experiment was done with C_{60} molecules, which are more than a million times more massive than electrons.

There is a connection between wave and particle properties. The Planck-de Broglie relations connect the mechanical properties of waves and particles. A particle of mass m moving with a speed v has a momentum $p = mv$ and an energy $E = \frac{1}{2}mv^2$. Waves on the other hand are characterized by their wavelength λ and frequency f. Particle properties are connected to wave properties by Planck's constant (h): $E = hf$ and $p = \frac{h}{\lambda}$. The typical wavelength of electrons in atoms is extremely small, <1 nm (10^{-9} m).

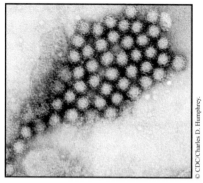

© CDC/Charles D. Humphrey.

This transmission electron micrograph (TEM) revealed some of the ultrastructural morphology displayed by norovirus virions, or virus particles.

The Born rule, named after physicist Max Born, provides another connection between wave and particle properties. A particle has a definite position, but a wave is spread out all over the place. How can we reconcile this? The Born rule states that the intensity of a wave, given by the square of its amplitude, tells us the probability of finding the particle at any given location. We illustrate the Born rule by examining an electron 2-slit experiment, 1 particle at a time. Each particle lands randomly, but after billions of particles arrive a statistical pattern emerges. Constructive interference enhances the probability of a particle being found in a given location, while destructive interference suppresses it. ∎

Questions to Consider

1. Let's put some numbers to wave-particle duality. The value of Planck's constant is about 6.6×10^{-34} kg·m²/s. An electron has a mass of 9.1×10^{-31} kg. Suppose an electron is moving at a speed of 2.0×10^6 m/s. (This might seem fast, but it is actually a typical speed for an electron in an atom.) First find the electron's energy and momentum; then calculate its quantum frequency and wavelength.

2. In a 2-slit experiment, if we open only 1 slit or the other, suppose the probability that a photon reaches a given point is P (the same in either case). Now we open both slits and repeat the experiment. Explain why the probability that a photon reaches the given point might be anything between 0 and $4P$.

3. In "classical" wave physics, the intensity of a light wave gives the amount of energy it carries. The Born rule tells us that in quantum physics, the intensity gives the probability of finding a photon in that region. How are these 2 ideas related?

Particles of Light, Waves of Matter
Lecture 4—Transcript

Welcome to the fourth lecture in our course on quantum mechanics. In the previous lecture, we saw how, in the early years of the 20th century, 2 revolutionaries, Max Planck and Albert Einstein, challenged the ideas of classical physics especially, but not exclusively, about the nature of light. The experiments seemed to present us with paradoxical results that are very hard to understand together.

On the one hand, Young's 2-slit experiment demonstrates that light is a wave. We see the constructive and destructive interference of these waves. We can measure the wavelength of light, which is less than a millionth of a meter. On the other hand, Einstein's analysis of the photoelectric effect demonstrates that light is composed of discrete particles, discrete photons. The number of photons, the light intensity, determines the number of the electrons produced in the experiment. The energy of the photons, the light frequency, determines the energy of the electrons that are produced. We can use this to measure the energy of the photons.

We can't just dismiss either of these experimental results. Our understanding of light must somehow encompass both the wave and the particle ideas. What's our goal in this lecture? Our goal in this lecture is to try to sort out the mess, to try to resolve the paradox a little bit, and to show how this paradox applies not just to light but also to matter. The quantum view can be summed up in a single phrase: Wave-particle duality. What does that mean?

It's something like this. The true nature of light cannot be described in simple terms. Our language just isn't equipped to describe the way light really is. We need both wave and particle pictures to explain the behavior of light, but that might make us uneasy. How can we use both wave pictures and particle pictures? Isn't that a logical contradiction? Won't we get in trouble trying to use 2 contradictory pictures to describe light? That's an immensely tricky question. It's maybe the trickiest question in all of science and we'll spend the next few lectures trying to understand that question and trying to see how the scientists in the early 20th century wrestled with it. But, for now, let me give you a rough rule of thumb, a rule for wave-particle duality.

The first rule of thumb is that light travels in the form of waves with frequency and wavelength exhibiting constructive and destructive interference and so on. Light travels as a wave. The other rule of thumb is that light interacts; it's emitted or absorbed in the form of discrete particles, discrete photons, lumps of discrete energy. Young's 2-slit experiment is an experiment about how light travels. How does light travel through a barrier that contains 2 slits? Since it's an experiment about how light travels, we get a wave result. But the photoelectric effect is an experiment about how light interacts with matter, how light delivers its energy to a polished metal surface. We get particle results. We get discrete photons. Recall our story in Lecture 2, how the history of physics is sort of the history of asking whether nature is fundamentally discrete, thing-like, or fundamentally continuous, stuff-like. The answer for light appears to be that light is both discrete, thing-like, and continuous, stuff-like. It has properties of both kinds, which is a very strange new answer to an old question. That picture of wave-particle duality is a bit oversimplified, but it's not too bad for a start. Light travels as a wave, interacts like a particle.

Even in the early days of quantum theory, it was clear that quantum theory was not just about the nature of light. Remember Einstein's analysis of the heat capacities of solids. At low temperatures, the heat capacities of a pure solid, a solid containing only one kind of atom, was much less than we expected. Einstein explained this by applying quantum ideas to matter, to the vibrations of the atomic constituents of the solid. The energy of atomic vibrations comes in discrete amounts. A physicist would say that this energy is quantized. This energy follows the quantum rule. We already know that this terrible quantum business is not just a problem with light. It also has infected matter. It's something that applies to everything. Where does all this lead? I want to skip ahead a little bit in our story. I want to skip from 1908 when Einstein does his work on the heat capacities of solids all the way up to 1924. I will come back and talk about what happens in between, but let's jump ahead to 1924.

What's happened in the meantime? Quite a lot of things have happened in the meantime. The First World War has happened in the meantime, but also in the story of quantum physics, there have been many discoveries about quantum physics. Lots of hard thinking about quantum physics, indeed, a perplexity about quantum physics. It's pretty clear that quantum physics is the most important new thing in physics. But for a whole generation, physicists are unable to make a coherent theory out of quantum ideas. In 1924, along comes Louis de Broglie. Louis de Broglie is a French aristocrat, a bon vivant. In fact he's a Prince of the blood and he's also a physics doctoral student. In his doctoral thesis, he proposes a radical new idea. He proposes that quantum wave-particle duality applies not only to light, but also to matter. He says that particles like electrons must also have wave characteristics. Electrons have frequency. They have wavelength. They exhibit constructive and destructive interference effects and so on. This sounds very strange. We think of electrons as particles. We think of electrons as little baseballs. How can a baseball have a wavelength?

Even though the idea is very strange, de Broglie's idea is very soon spectacularly confirmed in the laboratory. In an experiment that was done in several different places, they shot electrons at a crystal. In a crystal, the atoms are arranged in very orderly ranks and rows. It's a regular arrangement of atoms and the electrons go through the crystal and they come out the other side, but they only come out in certain directions. The electrons go this way or this way or this way, but not in between. Why is that? The spaces between the atoms act like the slits in Young's 2-slit experiment. The waves of the electron—whatever those are—the electron waves constructively interfere in some directions and destructively interfere in others. The electrons only come out in certain directions and, in fact, you can measure the wavelength of an electron. de Broglie is right.

How does it work? How are the wave and particle pictures connected to each other? Let's suppose we have a particle of mass, m, moving at a speed, v. For example, take a pitched baseball. The baseball has 2 important characteristics. First of all, it has energy. The energy of the baseball is $E = 1/2mv^2$; this is sometimes called "kinetic energy," energy due to its motion. What does the energy tell us? The energy basically tells us how much work the pitcher has to do to throw it. And a closely related characteristic of the baseball is the momentum of the baseball, which is just the mass times the velocity, the mass times how fast it's going, answers the question, if a baseball hit you, how hard would it hit? Energy and momentum are characteristics of a particle.

Waves, as we saw, are characterized by their frequency, f, and their wavelength, which is denoted by the Greek λ, as you'll remember. Recall we talked about the frequency and wavelength of sound waves. The frequency of a musical note is a few hundred waves per second. That's the number of waves that pass by a fixed point in space, like your ear, each second. The wavelength of a musical note is something like a meter. Maybe it's a bit smaller than a meter, maybe a bit bigger than a meter, but it's a pretty good sized wave and that's the spatial separation between successive disturbances in the periodic wave.

de Broglie's idea is to somehow connect the particle properties, energy and momentum, to the wave properties of frequency and wavelength. The connection between them is going to involve Planck's constant, the constant that Planck found that relates energy and frequency. We already know one of the relations. It's Planck's old formula that the energy of the particle is equal to Planck's constant times the frequency of the wave. What de Broglie does, is he adds another relation. He says that momentum and the wavelength are related. That the momentum of the particle, p, is equal to Planck's constant divided by the wavelength of the wave λ: $p = h/\lambda$. That's the relation between momentum and wavelength.

Remember that Planck's constant is really small. It's a very, very tiny number and so that means that the typical wavelength that we're talking about for electrons and atoms is going to be really, really tiny. The wavelength for an electron and an atom is very small, less than 1 nanometer, 1 billionth of a meter in size. These are very short wavelengths and already you can see that the more massive the particle is, the more its momentum will be at a given speed. If its momentum is larger, then de Broglie's formula tells us that its wavelength will be shorter. Its wavelength will be even shorter. The electron wavelengths are already really tiny. The wavelengths for more massive particles are even smaller and, because the wavelengths are so small, it's extremely difficult to do interference experiments and see the interference effects for large particles. It's essentially impossible to do an interference experiment with a baseball. The wavelength of the baseball is just too short.

We can do interference experiments with electrons. We really can't, as a practical matter, do it with a baseball. How far can we go? How large a particle can we do an interference experiment with and see its de Broglie waves, to measure its de Broglie wavelength? We can do interference experiments with neutrons, for example, which are nuclear particles that are a couple of thousand times more massive than electrons. We can do interference experiments now with entire atoms, which are even larger, but recently, in 1999 in Vienna, a group of physicists led by Anton Zeilinger did the greatest demonstration yet. They did what essentially amounts to a two slit experiment using entire molecules of 60 carbon atoms. How could we visualize a molecule of 60 carbon atoms? It turns out it's very similar to a familiar sort of structure, a structure of a soccer ball. Imagine that the lines on the soccer ball, every place where the lines intersect there's a carbon atom, and the lines between the carbon atoms are the chemical bonds between them. Then, the soccer ball has a certain structure of vertices, a structure of intersections. If you count them, there turns out to be exactly 60 vertices on a soccer ball and in the C-60 molecule, the 60 carbon atoms are arranged in exactly this way. They form a kind of spherical cage. It's, of course, much smaller than a soccer ball. It's about 200 million times smaller than this soccer ball. It's pretty small. It's a molecule though containing 60 carbon atoms, and they were able to show that such molecules exhibit constructive and destructive interference as predicted by Louis de Broglie.

A C-60 molecule is 100 million times more massive than an electron. That's quite a remarkable experimental result. Anton Zeilinger, the leader of this group, is famous for taking thought experiments, things that seem very idealized and impossible to do, and turning them into real experiments. Anton tells me that his ambition is to do a 2-slit interference experiment with something even bigger than a C-60 molecule. He wants to do it with a virus. A virus that's thousands or even hundreds of thousands of times bigger than a C-60 molecule to exhibit interference in something that, by some definitions, is actually a living thing. It sounds pretty extreme, but I wouldn't bet against Anton Zeilinger.

The Planck-de Broglie relations connect particle properties, energy and momentum, to wave properties, wavelength and frequency. The link between the particle properties and the wave properties is Planck's constant, h, but that still leaves things very mysterious. When we talk about electron waves, what do we mean? What are we talking about? When we talk about a sound wave, you know what a sound wave is. It's a periodic disturbance in air pressure that travels through the room. When I talk about light waves, I have an idea of what I mean. It's a periodic disturbance in the electromagnetic field that travels through a room, but if I talk about electron waves, that's a periodic disturbance in what? When I talk about electron waves, what's waving?

That brings us to the second connection between particles and waves. That's called the "Born Rule." The Born Rule may sound like a spy novel by Robert Ludlum, but actually what it is, is it's a brilliant insight, one of many, by Max Born, the great German physicist and one of the inventors of quantum mechanics. He's also, people my age are interested to find out, the grandfather of the Australian pop singer Olivia Newton-John. It's a talented family. Here's the basic problem that Born was considering. A particle is something that has a definite position in space. It's here and not here. A wave, on the other hand, is spread out all over space. How do we reconcile these 2 facts? How do we reconcile these 2 pictures in quantum theory? Particles which are located in just one place, and when you go look for a particle you find it in one place, and a wave which is spread out all over the place. Here's the Born Rule. Here's Born's great discovery: the intensity of the quantum wave at a point tells us the probability of finding the particle at that point. The intensity of the wave determines the probability of finding the particle there.

Let's take that apart. What's the first issue? The first issue is to say something about what we mean by wave intensity. Wave intensity turns out to be proportional to the square of the wave amplitude. Imagine waves; the wave amplitude is the height of the waves. How high the waves are and the intensity of those waves is how much energy those waves carry. It turns out that the intensity is given by the square of the amplitude. Waves that are twice as high actually carry 4 times as much energy, which is something to remember when you go surfing. A wave that's twice as high is really 4 times as powerful. That's wave intensity. It's the square of the amplitude and it measures, in ordinary waves, the amount of energy carried by the wave. Wave intensity gives particle probability. Here's Born's insight. Quantum theory does not tell us where a particle is. Quantum theory can't tell us where a particle is. It could be here; it could be there. Quantum mechanics tells us the probability that the particle may be found here or found there. Quantum mechanics only tells us the probabilities. Where does the particle wind up? That's random. It's a gamble. Quantum mechanics fixes the odds.

Let's illustrate the Born Rule by doing a 2-slit experiment on electrons. We set a pair of slits. We send electrons through the apparatus, one electron at a time, and we record where the electron hits the screen each time. Each time we do it, each particle lands randomly. If you send through 10 particles, you have just a few scattered spots on our screen where electrons have landed, but as you send more and more particles, send a 100 particles or a 1,000 particles or 10,000 particles, a statistical pattern begins to emerge because probabilities tells us what happens statistically. If an event has a probability of 1/2 that means that if you do the same experiment many, many times about 50% of the time, one half of the time, that event takes place. If you send many, many particles, a statistical pattern begins to emerge. If you send through billions of particles, so many particles that you can't really distinguish the individual particles, then what you get is a continuous interference pattern for the electrons in the experiment. In the places where you have constructive interference, the electron is more likely to land there. The probability is high. In the places where you have destructive interference, the electron is much less likely to land there. Maybe the probability is 0 and the electron can never land there. That's destructive interference.

Of course, we can do the same with light. We could use Young's 2-slit experiment, one photon at a time, and as it happens I actually just did that exact experiment in the lab last week. Instead of using a laser, we used an extremely dim light source, an extremely dim light bulb essentially and a dark green filter in front of it. You only got one green photon at a time in the experiment. Each photon passed through the slits and hit the screen in a random place. We found out where it hit by using a very sensitive photon detector, which, in fact, is the only expensive thing about the experiment. It costs several thousand dollars. One photon at a time and, in fact, we arranged it so whenever a photon hit the detector, an electrical signal would trigger an audible click. We could hear the photons, one by one, hitting the detector—click, click, click, click, click. Only a few photons per second reached the detector and since the photons traveled from one end of the experiment to the other in a few billionths of a second, that means that only one photon at a time was going through the detector. Nevertheless, we got an interference pattern. There were bright spots and, by bright spots, I mean places where the photon is more likely to land. The photon would land with fair frequency. There were dark spots, which were places where a photon seldom or never would land. After a long time, the random clicks in the detector resolved themselves into a beautiful interference pattern. This is really a beautiful demonstration of the Born Rule. The wave intensity corresponds to the particle probability.

Let's go back and sum things up a little bit. The microscopic world in quantum theory is governed by the principle of wave-particle duality. Everything, light, matter, absolutely everything has both wave properties and particle properties. This is true for light. It's true for electrons. It's true for atoms. It's true for molecules of carbon-60. It's true for everything.

These wave and particle probabilities are related in a couple of subtle ways. First of all, there's the Planck-de Broglie relations. The energy and momentum of a particle are related to the frequency and wavelength of the wave. If the particle has high energy and momentum, the frequency will be very high, the wavelength will be very short. If the particle has very low energy and momentum, the frequency will be very low for the wave, the wavelength will be very long. Wave and particle properties are related.

Then, there's the other connection, which is the Born Rule. The wave intensity, which is given by the square of the amplitude of the wave, determines the particle probability, the probability that an experiment will find the particle in a particular place. In quantum mechanics, individual events are random. Quantum mechanics predicts only probabilities. It doesn't predict what will happen in detail. It only predicts the odds of this happening or that happening and, because of this, everything in nature is both thing-like and stuff-like. It's thing-like because everything in nature is discrete. Energy comes in discrete quanta. Particles come in 1 particle or 2 particles or 3 particles, but not 1.75 particles. Everything is thing-like, but everything's also stuff-like. Everything's described by continuous waves in space. These waves are waves of probability. The waves' intensity gives the probability of finding a particle. Even though the particle is discrete, the probability waves can be continuous.

In the next lecture, we're going to go a step further. We're going to describe how de Broglie's waves tell us about the inner structure of the atom. In so doing, we're going to solve a gigantic puzzle. What puzzle is that? It turns out that if classical physics were true, all atoms everywhere should implode in on themselves, collapse in on themselves, in a very short period of time—a period of time less than 1 microsecond, less than a millionth of a second. All atoms everywhere should implode in less than a microsecond. If this happened, it would be very unfortunate. Luckily for us, it doesn't happen. Luckily for us, somehow the matter, the atoms making up matter, somehow there's a stability that classical physics doesn't predict. Atoms are stable and that's a mystery. Why are atoms stable? The answer comes next time. See you then.

Standing Waves and Stable Atoms
Lecture 5

In the last lecture, we saw and explored the strange quantum idea of wave-particle duality, an idea that applies both to light and to matter. Everything has both wave properties and particle properties. ... This time we're going to see how the wave characteristics of matter explain the structure of atoms.

In 1909, Ernest Rutherford supervised experiments to scatter fast-moving particles from gold foil. These experiments led him to propose a "solar system" model of atomic structure. In this model, most of the atom's mass lies in the heavy, positively charged nucleus at its center. Electrons, with a negative charge and relatively low mass, orbit the nucleus, held in place by the attractive electric force between positive and negative charges. This leads to a puzzle: In classical mechanics, an orbiting electron should emit electromagnetic radiation. It should therefore lose energy and spiral inward toward the nucleus. Rutherford's atom should implode in less than 1 microsecond!

In 1913, Niels Bohr, a postdoctoral student in Rutherford's lab, used the new quantum ideas to explain atomic structure. Bohr proposed that only certain discrete orbits are possible for the electron in the atom. If the electron is in the innermost possible orbit, it can no longer spiral inward. Thus atoms can be stable. When an electron "jumps" from one orbit to another, it absorbs or emits a photon. We can also imagine more abstractly: Different Bohr orbits are "rungs" on an "energy ladder" for the electron.

Nobel Prize winner Ernest Rutherford (1871–1937) was the first researcher to produce an artificial transmutation of elements, using alpha particles to transform nitrogen into oxygen.

To climb up to a higher rung, the electron must absorb a photon; to descend, it must emit a photon. The photon energies are determined by the spacing of these energy levels. Bohr was able to predict the pattern of energy levels in hydrogen atoms, which only have a single electron. This pattern accounts for the discrete colors of light (photon energies) produced by hot hydrogen gas. This is called the "emission spectrum" of the element.

Bohr's orbits correspond to "standing wave patterns" of electrons moving around the nucleus. They can be nicely explained by de Broglie's electron waves, although this was not Bohr's original explanation. In de Broglie's version of Bohr's model, in any wave system enclosed in space, only certain wave patterns are possible. An easy example of this is a stretched piano wire. The wave must "fit" between the fixed ends of the wire. Only certain wavelengths and frequencies (or combinations of these) can occur, which is why the piano wire vibrates with a definite note when struck. As an electron orbits an atom, only certain wave patterns "fit" around the atom. Thus only certain wavelengths and frequencies are possible. These standing wave patterns determine the possible Bohr orbits.

In de Broglie's version of Bohr's model, in any wave system enclosed in space, only certain wave patterns are possible.

In 1926, Erwin Schrödinger provided a detailed mathematical description of de Broglie's waves. His description is embodied in the famous Schrödinger equation, which is one of the fundamental equations in all of physics. Here is one form of the equation:

$$-\frac{\hbar^2}{2m}\nabla^2\Psi + U(x, y, z)\Psi = i\hbar\frac{\partial\Psi}{\partial t}.$$

The Ψ in this equation is the "wave function" of the electron. The wave intensity $|\Psi|^2$ gives the probability of finding the electron at any given point in space. Solving the Schrödinger equation gives 3-dimensional standing wave patterns for an electron in an atom. Each wave pattern corresponds to a different energy level. The wave patterns are changed by the emission or absorption of photons. In an ordinary advanced quantum mechanics course, students spend at least 90% of their time learning methods for solving the Schrödinger equation. This can be a very hard task, especially when the situation is complicated.

The Schrödinger equation and quantum mechanics do a good job of explaining energy levels for atoms and molecules, the emission and absorption of light by atoms, and the way atoms are affected by outside forces (e.g., stretched by electric fields or twisted by magnetic fields). All of these can be calculated from the standing wave patterns of de Broglie waves, determined by the Schrödinger equation. ■

Questions to Consider

1. Before Rutherford's scattering experiment, a leading idea of atomic structure was J. J. Thomson's "plum-pudding" theory. In this model, negatively charged electrons were embedded in a diffuse, positively charged "pudding." If Thomson's model had been correct, how would the scattering experiment have turned out differently?

2. A piano wire can vibrate at a certain fundamental frequency f and also at higher "overtone" frequencies $2f$, $3f$, and so on. If you have access to a piano, try the following experiment. Hold down the key for middle C (262 cycles/s) without playing the note. Now briefly play each of the following notes and listen to how the open C string responds: C (1 octave up, or 524 cycles/s), G (1.5 octaves up, or 784 cycles/s), and C (2 octaves up, or 1048 cycles/s). Also try this with other notes. What do you observe?

3. Excited hydrogen atoms emit violet, blue-green, and red light. These correspond to electrons dropping to the second energy level from the ones above it: $3 \Rightarrow 2$, $4 \Rightarrow 2$ and $5 \Rightarrow 2$. Which jumps correspond to which emitted colors and why? (Recall that violet light has a higher frequency than red light.)

Standing Waves and Stable Atoms
Lecture 5—Transcript

Welcome to the fifth lecture in our course on quantum mechanics. In the last lecture, we saw and explored the strange quantum idea of wave-particle duality, an idea that applies both to light and to matter. Everything has both wave properties and particle properties. Light has light waves. Also, light is made of photons. Electrons are particles, but they also have wave properties, frequency, wavelength, and constructive and destructive interference. There are 2 connections between wave and particle ideas. The first connection is encompassed in the Planck-de Broglie relations, formulas that connect the particle energy and momentum with the wave frequency and wavelength. The second connection is the Born Rule that the wave intensity determines the particle probability, that the waves in quantum mechanics are waves of probability.

This time we're going to see how the wave characteristics of matter explain the structure of atoms. What do we mean by the structure of atoms? Of course, to the Greeks, there was no real question about the structure of atoms. The very word atom comes from a Greek word meaning "not divisible." Atoms are not made of parts. Plato believed that atoms of different kinds had different shapes, but basically Greeks believed that atoms had no parts, no internal structure. But, by the end of the 19th century, it became clear that the true atoms of nature did have an internal structure. Atomic structure, how those parts are arranged, was a serious problem in the early 1900s. By 1900, it was clear that atoms were made of smaller pieces like electrons. The question is, what's the internal arrangement of the atom? Of course, atoms are thousands of times too small for an ordinary microscope to see them, so it's kind of hard to figure out what their internal arrangement is.

There were lots of theories. There was one theory, in which basically an atom was like a blueberry muffin and the electrons were like the blueberries stuck in the muffin. That was one theory, but then along came Ernest Rutherford. Ernest Rutherford was a New Zealander. He was a physicist at this time working at the University of Manchester. Rutherford was one of the greatest experimental physicists of all time. At least half a dozen Nobel prizes were won by Rutherford or by his students and collaborators at his lab in Manchester. By 1909, the time when we join Rutherford in the story, he's already won his Nobel Prize in 1908 for his work on radioactivity. What Rutherford does is he directs Hans Geiger, his assistant, the Geiger of Geiger counters, and Ernest Marsden who was a graduate student to do a particular experiment. He said, I want you to take fast moving particles from radioactive materials, the particles emitted by radioactive material, and I want you to shoot those particles at a thin, gold foil. I want you to see how those particles scatter. Some of the particles will go barging on through the gold foil, but some of them may be deflected a little bit. We want to see how many are deflected at what angles, how many go out at what angles.

Geiger and Marsden go into the lab. They very carefully do this experiment and they come back to Rutherford. They said, we see some of the particles being scattered at very large angles. In fact, some of the particles bounce off of the gold foil and come back. This is a very surprising result. In fact, Rutherford later said it was the most astonishing thing that had ever happened to him in his life. He said it was as if you'd taken a 16-inch artillery shell, fired it at some tissue paper, and had it bounce back at you. That's maybe an exaggeration, but it is something like shooting a bullet at a muffin and having the bullet bounce off.

Rutherford realizes that his experiment has revealed something about the inner structure of the atom. Rutherford is able to use his experimental data to create a model of the inside of an atom. This is the solar system model of the atom. In the solar system model, most of the mass of the atom lies in a heavy central nucleus, which is positively charged, which acts as the sun of our tiny solar system. This heavy central nucleus, this very dense concentration of mass, that's the thing that Rutherford's particles are bouncing off of. In fact, Rutherford's experimental data allow him to determine the size of this nucleus and it's about 100 thousand times smaller than an atom. Almost all of the mass is in a very tiny part of the center of the atom. Around the nucleus you have the electrons, which have very low mass and are negatively charged, orbiting, kind of like how planets orbit around the sun—this is the solar system model of the atom.

Rutherford's scattering experiment is one of the great experiments in the history of physics. In fact, my dog was called Rutherford's Scattering. It seemed to be a good name for a Springer Spaniel, but the model of the atom that the experiment leads us to is a terrible puzzle. Why is that? If you think just in terms of classical physics, the orbiting electrons in the atom should radiate electromagnetic waves. When you take an electrically charged particle and you wave it around in a circle, you produce electromagnetic waves. If the atoms are continually emitting electromagnetic waves, they should lose energy. If the electrons lose energy, their orbits should spiral inward toward the nucleus. The atom should collapse inward. It should implode. How long should it take? It should take less than a microsecond. If Rutherford's model is right, then every atom in the universe should implode in a microsecond, but they don't implode. The question becomes what is it that keeps the atoms from imploding?

Along comes the second hero of our lecture, the Danish physicist Niels Bohr, who, in 1913 as a young, post-doctoral student, comes to work in Rutherford's lab. Bohr is a theoretical physicist, like me. He is a physicist that works with a chalkboard and mathematics. Rutherford, the great experimentalist, usually doesn't like theorists, but he makes an exception for Bohr. I believe he made an exception for Bohr because Bohr was also an excellent soccer player. In fact, Bohr's brother, Harald, was on the Danish national team as well as being a mathematician. Bohr comes to work for Rutherford and he tries to use the new quantum ideas of Planck and Einstein, these revolutionary ideas that are, sort of, in the air to explain atomic structure, to explain how Rutherford's solar system model could be right. This became the Bohr model. Let's talk about the Bohr model of the atom.

In the Bohr model of the atom, only discrete orbits are possible. Only certain orbits are possible for the electron. The electron can orbit in this orbit; it can orbit in this orbit, but not in between. Only certain orbits are possible. The orbits are discrete. It's a quantum effect. Bohr also said when an electron jumps from one orbit to another orbit, the electron absorbs or emits a photon. Let's think about this in a more abstract picture.

The different Bohr orbits are the rungs of a kind of ladder, but the rungs are at different heights, not in space, but in energy. The lowest rungs are low energy orbits. They correspond to the small orbits around the atom and the higher rungs correspond to larger orbits. There are only certain rungs on the energy ladder that the electron can occupy. These are the energy levels of the atom. When an electron absorbs a photon, when an electron and an atom absorb a photon, it jumps to a higher rung on the energy ladder. If an electron emits a photon, it loses energy and it jumps to a lower rung on the energy ladder. What determines the energy of the photon that is absorbed or emitted? It's the spacing between the rungs on the ladder. There are several things going on here. One is that there's a bottom rung. There's an innermost orbit and if the electron is in the bottom rung, if it's in the innermost orbit, then it can't lose any more energy. It's in its lowest possible energy. There's a stable inner orbit and this is why atoms can be stable because there's a rung below which there are no other rungs. There's a bottom to the ladder.

Bohr applied quantum ideas very cleverly and he was actually able to predict the pattern of energy levels in the hydrogen atom. Why was it the hydrogen atom? Hydrogen is the simplest type of atom. It's only got a nucleus consisting of a proton and 1 electron. You always turn to the simplest case first when you're trying out something new. Bohr was able to exactly predict the energy levels in hydrogen from quantum ideas and that energy level pattern corresponds to a set of spaces between the rungs, a set of possible photon energies that can be emitted by hydrogen.

If the electron jumps down from energy level number 3 to energy level number 2, then the photon comes out with red light. A red photon corresponds to red light. If it jumps from number 4 to number 2, it comes out green. If it jumps from 5 to number 2, it comes out kind of a deep blue. Indeed, when we look at the light that is emitted by hydrogen atoms, we find that we get some red light against green light. We get some deep blue light. What Bohr was able to do is explain the emission spectrum of hydrogen and that's a tremendous advance. Just from quantum ideas, he's able to explain the particular pattern of wavelengths that hot hydrogen gas emits.

Bohr was very ambitious. Bohr wanted to explain not just the frequencies of light emitted by hydrogen. He wanted to explain the frequencies of light emitted by all kinds of atoms like hydrogen and helium and lithium and carbon and iron and so on. He worked and worked. It was very hard and Rutherford said this is a brilliant idea; Bohr, you should publish this. Bohr said, I'd really like to work out the spectral patterns for all the elements.

Rutherford said, don't worry if you can explain hydrogen and helium, you can just let everybody else believe the rest. They'll believe everything, hydrogen and helium being the 2 simplest elements. Bohr was, in fact, not able to explain even the spectrum of helium, but hydrogen he was able to explain quite well.

This is an amazing discovery, an amazing insight into the structure of atoms. Rutherford's solar system model works. It works because the orbits are discrete and there's a lowest one. It works, but like a lot of early quantum theory, it's a bit fishy. I mean there were a few quantum ideas that Bohr sort of brilliantly worked into his analysis, but most of his analysis relied on old-fashioned classical ideas. In other words, Bohr was being quite a bit inconsistent in his way of reasoning. Sometimes he would reason this way; sometimes he would reason that way. Bohr's model, although brilliant and tremendously influential and in some respects exactly right, in other respects wasn't really well understood until de Broglie came along more than a decade later with his electron waves.

Here's the story that de Broglie told. de Broglie said the Bohr orbits are explained by standing wave patterns. What's a standing wave? If we have a wave system and we confine it in space, then we find that only certain wave patterns are even possible. Only certain wave patterns, or perhaps combinations of those, and so the simplest example that everyone talks about is a stretched piano wire. A piano wire is fixed at both ends, but in the middle it's free to vibrate. When you look at how the piano wire vibrates, the wave pattern of the piano wire must exactly fit between the 2 ends of the piano wire because the piano wire's clamped at the 2 ends and can't vibrate there. You find that half of a wavelength can fit between the 2 ends, or 1 full wavelength, or 3/2 of a wavelength, and so on. Only certain standing wave patterns are possible or combinations of those. Because only certain wavelengths are possible for the vibrations of the stretched wire, that means that only certain vibration frequencies are possible because frequency and wavelength are related. This is why a piano wire makes a definite musical note when struck. When you hit a piano wire, it can only vibrate at certain frequencies. In fact, there's a fundamental frequency it can vibrate at and it can vibrate at twice that frequency or 3 times the frequency and so on. That means that when you strike a piano string, it makes a definite musical note.

If you just knock on a door, it doesn't make a very definite musical note because it could vibrate in lots of different ways, but the stretched wire can only vibrate in certain ways. It turns out, in fact, that all musical instruments work in exactly this way. Stringed instruments work because the vibration of a wire fixed at both ends can only have certain frequencies involved. A piano or a guitar or a violin makes pure musical tones because we have a stretched wire with fixed end points, so it can only vibrate at certain frequencies. The same thing is true for wind instruments. An organ pipe or a clarinet or a trumpet work because we confine air into a tube. In that confined space, only certain sound frequencies are possible. When we cause the air to vibrate in the tube and maybe we twist the tube up like in a trumpet, when we cause the air to vibrate in the tube, we only get certain discrete frequencies. We only get certain musical tones. Almost all musical instruments work in this way.

The electron in an atom, according to Bohr, or actually according to de Broglie's picture of Bohr's model, is like the string of a violin. It can only vibrate in certain ways. It could only have certain standing wave patterns. It can only have certain frequencies and it only has certain frequencies; therefore, it only has certain energies. Only certain de Broglie wave patterns fit around the atom. Only certain wavelengths and frequencies are possible. That means that only certain electron energies are possible. The standing wave patterns around the electron are exactly Bohr's orbits.

de Broglie proposes his ideas in 1924 and it really triggers an immense creative burst in the physics community. Just 2 years later, the Austrian physicist Erwin Schrödinger provides a detailed mathematical description of de Broglie's waves. Schrödinger writes down an equation that describes how quantum waves, how the waves of electrons, move and spread out in space. This mathematical equation is exactly the tool that's needed for working out the details of atomic structure not just for hydrogen, which Bohr had explained fairly well, but also for atoms having many electrons.

I want to show you here on the screen the famous Schrödinger equation. I'm going to provide it for aesthetic value only. You see it's kind of abstruse. There are lots of parts to it. It actually, in its bones, turns out to be simply an equation about energy, but that will take us a bit too far afield to explain that. The key thing I want to explain about the Schrödinger equation is this symbol that appears in every term of the equation. The symbol representing the Greek letter ψ, psi. The Greek letter that looks like our little trident is the Greek letter psi. What is ψ? Psi is a mathematical object that physicists call the wave function. It's the mathematical object that corresponds to de Broglie's waves. It describes de Broglie's wave and the wave intensity, which is given by $|\Psi|^2$. The wave intensity at any point in space tells us the probability that the particle we're talking about is found at that location. The wave function, ψ, whose behavior is governed by the Schrödinger equation, is the mathematical object that corresponds to de Broglie's waves. It's the mathematical presentation of de Broglie's ideas. In order to find out what happens in quantum mechanics, all we need to do is solve the Schrödinger equation. That's all we have to do and we can figure out what's going to happen to atoms and molecules and electrons.

Of course, that's the trick, isn't it? Solving the Schrödinger equation can be really, really hard. It's a complicated equation. It can be really hard especially when you have many particles involved. In an atom like hydrogen, you have 1 electron moving around the nucleus, but in an atom of carbon, you have 6 electrons all moving around the nucleus and also exerting forces on each other. The Schrödinger equation becomes extremely complicated and, in a heavy atom, a uranium atom, there are 92 electrons moving around the nucleus and exerting forces on all of each other. It's a tremendously difficult problem. Physics students, when they learn quantum mechanics, spend something like 90% of their time in their courses learning to solve the Schrödinger equation. They learn to solve it in this situation and that situation and the other situation. They learn this mathematical technique and that mathematical technique for solving it, this way to approximate it. They learn a whole bag of tricks and some physicists, quantum physicists, spend 90% of their time and lots of computing power trying to solve the Schrödinger equation in complicated situations like the situations for many electron atoms. You might imagine that 90% of our business for the rest of the course will be solving Schrödinger's equation. Luckily, we don't have to do that. We can skip it. It's not that it's not an important part of the everyday quantum mechanics that a physicist uses, but we have more important things on our mind. We have more important business to attend to. We want to get at the ideas instead of the mathematical drudgery.

Let's just summarize the general result, then, what you get when you solve the Schrödinger equation. What you get when you solve the Schrödinger equation for electrons and atoms is you get standing wave patterns for the electrons and each standing wave pattern corresponds to a different energy level in Bohr's energy level ladder. The wave patterns are changed as you jump from one energy level to another when you emit or absorb a photon of light. It's a beautiful picture and it works in detail to explain all kinds of things. What kinds of things can you explain? You can explain the energy levels in atoms and molecules. You can explain what energies are possible for the electrons in those systems. You can also explain the emission and absorption of light. You can explain why a particular atom or molecule absorbs or emits the frequencies of light that it absorbs or emits.

That's pretty amazing, that's pretty astonishing, but you can do even better. You can figure out not just the photon energies, and therefore the colors of the light, but also the probabilities of making certain jumps. When you look at the light coming from, say hot hydrogen gas, you see all these different colors, all these different frequencies of light, but you also notice that some frequencies of light are more likely to be emitted than others. Some of the frequencies are brighter than others. Some of them have more photons. The Bohr model could never explain this. The Bohr model really doesn't have enough detail in it to explain why a jump from one orbit to another might be more or less likely than another jump, but Schrödinger's equation is a detailed enough picture. It allows us to calculate the probabilities of jumps and so it allows us to calculate not only the frequencies of the light that comes out of the atoms, but also the intensities of the different frequencies.

The Schrödinger equation also tells us about how atoms and their energy levels are affected by outside influences. For example, you might imagine we put an atom in an electric field and an electric field has the property that it will push the nucleus one way and it'll pull the electrons the other way. It'll stretch the atom a little bit. When you stretch the atom, how does that affect the energy levels in the atom? That's something called "the Start effect." Quantum mechanics accounts for it beautifully. Also, you might imagine that you put the atom in a strong magnetic field and that kind of twists the atom in a certain way. It makes it slightly more favorable for the electrons to go one way rather than other. How does that affect the energy levels of the atom? It's something called "the Zeeman effect." Quantum mechanics explains that, too. The Schrödinger equation is able to explain all of these things. We've got an amazing story going on here. We've got the idea of wave-particle duality, which was first glimpsed by Planck and Einstein at the very beginning of the 20th century. That idea is extended by de Broglie to cover not just light, but matter. The idea is also interpreted by Born who tells us that the waves, corresponding to an electron, are waves of probability. This explains Bohr's kind of strange theory of the quantum atomic orbits. It says that you only have discrete orbits because you only have certain discrete standing wave patterns for the electron waves about the atom. In the hands of Schrödinger, the idea becomes a sophisticated mathematical theory that explains the details of atomic structure and molecular structure and all kinds of experiments.

Quantum theory tells us that the physical world has an unexpected discreteness and also an unexpected unpredictability. The quantum wave is about both. Only discrete standing wave patterns in the atom, like the waves themselves, are waves of probability. How does that work out? Where does that lead? Next time, we're going to go on and talk about the beautiful insight of Werner Heisenberg. He said that the randomness of quantum mechanics sets a fundamental limit to the definiteness of the microscopic world. Wave-particle duality implies that the precision of our knowledge of the microscopic world is limited in a fundamental way. Heisenberg formulates the famous Uncertainty Principle and talking about the Uncertainty Principle will be our business in the next lecture. I'll see you then.

Uncertainty
Lecture 6

Our business today is to explore the implications of [the quantum idea of wave-particle duality], to say what it means for the wave to spread out, and to say what it means for the quantum wave describing a quantum particle to spread out in space. Today we're going to talk about the uncertainty principle.

Particles and waves have contrasting properties. In classical physics, a particle like an electron has both an exact location in space and a definite velocity or momentum at every moment. In other words, the particle has an exact "trajectory" through space. On the other hand, we have the basic wave phenomenon of diffraction of waves through a single slit. After passing through the slit, the waves spread out into the space beyond. The diffraction effect depends on the ratio λ/w, the wavelength divided by the width of the slit. A narrow slit (large ratio) produces a wide pattern of waves, while a wide slit (small ratio) produces a narrow pattern. This allows waves to "go around corners." A thought experiment illustrates this: A friend behind a wall speaks to us through an open door. We can hear the friend because the wavelength of the sound waves is large, and the sound waves passing through the door spread out. But we do not see the friend because light waves have very short wavelengths, and diffraction through the door is negligible.

Diffraction and wave-particle duality set a basic limit on how well a particle's properties are defined. We consider an electron, described by de Broglie waves, passing through a barrier with a single slit. If the electron passes through the slit, this means that we know the particle's lateral position (x), though not exactly. Our uncertainty in the particle position is just the slit width: $\Delta x \approx \Delta w$. Because of diffraction, the de Broglie wave spreads out past the slit. The lateral velocity of the particle is not exactly known, which means we cannot tell exactly where the particle will be found. It turns out to be easier to consider the particle's lateral momentum p. The spreading of the wave pattern means there is an uncertainty Δp in this momentum. A wide pattern means a larger Δp. The relation between slit width and diffraction spreading means there is a trade-off between Δx and Δp. The smaller one is, the larger the other must be.

Werner Heisenberg realized that this represents a basic trade-off in nature, which is his famous "uncertainty principle." Suppose Δx and Δp are our uncertainties in a particle's position and momentum. Then it must be true that $\Delta x \Delta p \geq h$ (where h is Planck's constant).

There are some important things to note. First, this is an inequality. We can always be less certain about x and p than this, but never more certain. Second, our definitions of uncertainty here are informal or "fuzzy." With more careful technical definitions, there may be a factor of 2 or 4 (or 4π!) in the right-hand side. This does not change the basic point. Additionally, Planck's constant is extremely small, so a large-scale object can have a pretty well-defined location and momentum. This is part of the reason why large-scale objects can behave like classical particles. Lastly, for microscopic particles like electrons, the uncertainty principle can be very important. An electron confined to an atom has Δx no larger than the diameter of the atom. The resulting momentum uncertainty Δp is large enough that we do not even know which direction the electron is moving in the atom!

The point is not that we do not know the exact values of x and p for an electron; the electron in fact does not have exact values of x and p.

Heisenberg argued that the uncertainty principle is actually an "indeterminacy principle." The point is not that we do not know the exact values of x and p for an electron; the electron in fact does not have exact values of x and p.

Another uncertainty principle relates time and energy. If a process happens over a period of time Δt, and the energy involved in the process is uncertain by an amount ΔE, then $\Delta E \Delta t \geq h$. ∎

1. Heisenberg used several different terms to describe his basic idea. He said that a particle's position might have "uncertainty" or "indeterminacy" or "imprecision" or "latitude" or "statistical spread." Remark on the different shades of meaning that these various terms suggest.

2. There is a classical "uncertainty principle" for any sort of wave, including sound. A musical note is a mixture of a range of frequencies Δf. If the note lasts for a time period Δt, it turns out that the spread of frequencies must satisfy $\Delta f \geq \frac{1}{\Delta t}$. (This means that very short notes do not have very definite pitch.) What version of the quantum uncertainty principle is most closely related to this fact?

Uncertainty
Lecture 6—Transcript

Welcome to the sixth lecture in our course on quantum mechanics. In the last few lectures, we've explored the quantum idea of wave-particle duality, the idea that applies to both light and matter, the idea that everything has both wave and particle properties. You have light waves, but you also have photons. You have electrons, which are particles, but the electrons also have wave properties. This idea has been quite successful at explaining things about the microscopic world, everything from the photoelectric effect to atomic structure, but it is nevertheless a very curious idea.

Particles and waves are very different. Think of a particle; here's our baseball. A baseball at each moment has an exact position in space and an exact velocity, or if you prefer, an exact momentum. Over time, the particle describes a definite trajectory through space. A definite exact path and at every point and time it has an exact location. That path that it follows through space is determined by Newton's Laws of Motion. It describes the shape of the path of the baseball but a wave is a very different sort of thing. A wave spreads out.

Our business today is to explore the implications of that fact, to say what it means for the wave to spread out, and to say what it means for the quantum wave describing a quantum particle to spread out in space. Today we're going to talk about the Uncertainty Principle, but first we need to talk about the phenomenon of diffraction. It's a wave phenomenon. Every sort of wave exhibits diffraction. We imagine that a wave hits a barrier that has an opening in it; it sounds like the 2-slit experiment, except in this experiment we only have one opening—one slit and we'll say that the width of that slit is w. Beyond this barrier, the waves that pass through the slit spread out into space and that spreading out after you pass through one slit is called diffraction. It's called "single slit diffraction." How much spreading out happens? It depends on a particular ratio—the ratio between the wavelength, λ, and the width of the slit, w. The wavelength, λ/w will determine how spread out the waves become downstream of the slit. If you have a narrow slit, then w is very small and the ratio λ/w is very large. The waves spread out in a wide pattern beyond the slit. On the other hand, if you have a very wide slit, the ratio, λ/w, is very small. The denominator's very large, so that the ratio's very small. The waves do not spread out very much at all. You have a narrow pattern of waves on the downstream side of the slit.

How can we understand this? Let's take an everyday example. Imagine that you're standing next to a wall and on the other side of the wall is a friend of yours. In the wall, there's an open doorway, but the open doorway is not exactly between you and the friend. The open doorway is off to the side. Let's suppose that the friend speaks aloud. The friend says something aloud. What happens to the sound waves? Sound waves, as we saw, are relatively long waves. Their wavelength is maybe a meter in size—maybe a little less, maybe a little more, something like a meter. The ratio of that wavelength to the width of the door is pretty large. It might even be bigger than 1. The ratio, λ/w, is large. That tells us that the diffraction effect, the spreading out of the sound waves, after the doorway, is very large. The sound waves spread out in a very wide pattern and, as a result, we can actually hear our friend's voice even though the sound has to go around the corner. The sound doesn't go around the corner so much as the sound waves spread out after they pass through the doorway. Even though our friend's on the other side of the wall, we can still hear him.

On the other hand, what about light waves? Light waves are a different sort of wave. They're electromagnetic waves instead of pressure waves, but more to the point, light waves have a much shorter wavelength. Their wavelength is a million times shorter than the wavelength of sound. The ratio of wavelength to the width of the doorway, λ/w, that ratio is exceedingly small and that means that the diffraction effect is exceedingly small. That means that the light waves do not spread out appreciably as they pass through the door. The light waves don't go around the corner an appreciable amount and that means that even though we can hear our friend, we can't see our friend because the light doesn't go around the corner because the doorway is wide and the light waves are very narrow. Diffraction effects are completely negligible.

You can understand diffraction if you understand why you can hear your friend, but you can't see your friend, around the corner. You could imagine making that door, in the wall, much, much, much narrower—thousands or tens of thousands of times narrower. Then, maybe you'd begin to have some diffraction even with the light waves, and so in fact, what you're suggesting is to do the experiment of single slit diffraction, which we've set up to do as a demonstration for you today, although you may recognize this setup. This is very similar to the setup used for Young's 2-slit experiment back in Lecture 2, when we found out that light travels as waves. Once again, we're doing a wave experiment on light about its wave properties.

It's a little bit different though, as you'll see. We have a light source using our laser again. Once again, the only thing that you need is a light source that has only one wavelength of light produced—a very, well-defined wavelength. Lasers are very convenient. We shine the laser at this little gizmo. What is it? It's a barrier and there's a narrow vertical slit in the barrier, and—this is the part I like—there's a little knob and I can make the slit wider and narrower by turning my little knob. Then, I take whatever comes out of the slit and I project it onto the screen so we can both see it. Let's look at the pattern produced by the slit. Turn the laser on. I may have to adjust a little bit and turn the knobs and put on my glasses. What we see is a broad smear of light in the middle of the screen and there are also some dimmer spots on each side of that central smear of light. The slit, I want to emphasize, is vertical. The smear smears out horizontally. That's something to remember. Also, I want to just focus our attention on the central spot. The central spot is twice as wide as any of the others and the spots on the side are much, much dimmer. In fact, the central spot is more than 20 times brighter than the ones on the side. I just want to talk about the center where most of the light is.

What I'm going to do is I'm going to vary the width of the slit. As I vary the width of the slit, we'll see what happens. Let's try a wider slit. Let's open up the slit a little wider and when we do that the pattern gets narrower. It also gets brighter because more light gets through, but the pattern gets narrower. Everything shrinks toward the center because when I make the slit wider, the ratio of the wavelength to the width of the slit becomes smaller and therefore there's less diffraction. Now let's make the slit narrower. As I make the slit narrower, the pattern gets wider. It's also gets dimmer, of course, because less light is getting through and because the pattern gets wider. It may be quite wide on the screen. Why is this? It's because the amount of diffraction depends on that ratio, wavelength to width of the slit. If the width of the slit gets smaller in the denominator of that ratio, the size of the ratio gets larger, there's more diffraction. It's a stronger effect. There's a tradeoff. The tradeoff is between the width of the slit and the width of the pattern—the narrower the slit, the wider the pattern, the wider the slit, the narrower the pattern.

We did that experiment with light, but of course, we could do the same experiment with electrons. Diffraction is an effect that is true for every kind of wave. For electrons, we could imagine the de Broglie waves of the electron passing through the barrier. They undergo diffraction and spread out on the other side. When the de Broglie waves reach the screen, what that means is that the electrons land on the screen randomly, of course, because the de Broglie waves are waves of probability. The electrons land on the screen in an unpredictable way, but they land in a pattern that's wider if the slit is narrower. The pattern is narrower if the slit is wider. The electrons, if you will, are scattered to one side or the other as they pass through the slit. They're scattered more through a narrow slit than through a wider slit. This is very strange behavior for a stream of particles.

It's so strange that, in fact, as we'll see, it has an amazing implication that wave diffraction together with the wave-particle duality of quantum mechanics sets a limit on how well the particle properties are even defined in the quantum world. Let's think about that even more carefully. Consider an electron passing through the slit. As it passes through the slit, we kind of know where the electron is, at least in the side-to-side direction. It has to actually be passing through the slit and we know where the slit is. We know its lateral position. Let's label that lateral position, x, and so we know the value of x for the electron that passes through the slit. We don't know it exactly, however, because the slit is a certain width and we don't know where the electron passed through the slit, it could be anywhere, but we know x to a certain uncertainty. There's an uncertainty in the lateral position and the uncertainty is denoted by the capital Greek letter delta. That looks like a triangle. It's the capital Greek letter delta which looks like a triangle. Δx is the uncertainty in its lateral position, and here I would say that Δx is about equal to the width of the slit. It could be anywhere in the slit.

Because of diffraction, the de Broglie wave spreads out beyond the slit and when it reaches the screen, the electron could land one place or another. It could wind up right in the middle or it could wind up a little bit to the left or it could wind up a little bit to the right because the probability pattern is spread out. In other words, after the slit, the electron could go to one side or the other side. After the slit, there's an uncertainty in the lateral velocity, the side-to-side velocity of the electron. The side-to-side velocity of the electron is 0 on average, but it could be plus or minus a little bit.

It turns out it's going to be a little bit easier to talk about, not the lateral velocity of the electron, but the lateral momentum of the electron. The electron has 0 lateral momentum, call that p. It's $p = 0$ on average, but there's an uncertainty Δp in the lateral momentum and a wide diffraction pattern means that Δp is pretty large. It means that I can't tell exactly for sure whether the electron's going to be going to the left or to the right. I have a great deal of uncertainty about that, so I don't know exactly where it's going to wind up at the screen. A wide diffraction pattern means Δp is large. A narrow diffraction pattern means the de Broglie wave is confined to a very narrow region of the screen and that means Δp must be very small. I know pretty well that the momentum is taking it from here right to that spot. There's not much uncertainty.

Because narrow diffraction patterns correspond to wide slits and vice versa, and because the width of the slit has to do with the uncertainty in lateral position, and the width of the pattern has to do with the uncertainty in lateral momentum, it turns out there's a tradeoff. There's a tradeoff between uncertainties, Δx and Δp. There are uncertainties in the position of the electron from side-to-side here and the momentum from side-to-side of the electron as it leaves the slit. The smaller one of those uncertainties is, the larger the other must be. That just follows from diffraction and because everything has wave properties according to the principle of wave-particle duality. That means everything exhibits diffraction and that means that this tradeoff between uncertainty in position and uncertainty in momentum is universal and it applies to everything.

We've now arrived where Werner Heisenberg arrived in 1927. Werner Heisenberg was a brilliant, young German physicist. He was a protégé of Niels Bohr at his Institute for Theoretical Physics at the University of Copenhagen. Heisenberg realized that there is a basic tradeoff in nature due to wave-particle duality in quantum mechanics and this basic tradeoff is called "the uncertainty principle." Let's suppose that Δx and Δp are the uncertainties in a particle's position and momentum respectively. The uncertainty principle tells us that Δx times Δp, the product of the uncertainties in position and momentum, has to be greater than or equal to h. There's Planck's constant again. Planck's constant appears in the uncertainty principle. The product of the uncertainty of position and the uncertainty of momentum has to be greater than or equal to Planck's constant. This means that no particle can have a definite position and a definite momentum at the same time. It means that the more definitely we know where the particle is, Δx being smaller, the less definitely we can know where it is going, Δp is larger.

There are a couple of important points about this great principle of physics. The first is that the relationship is in an inequality, not an equation. In other words, we can always be more uncertain than the uncertainty principle tells us. We just cannot be less uncertain. Nothing prevents you from being as uncertain as you like but the uncertainty principle tells you that you cannot be more certain about both position and the momentum than the principle allows. The second point is that our definitions of uncertainties, the Δx and the Δp, are pretty vague and fuzzy. You may have noticed that we didn't work really hard to define that exactly. Maybe that's appropriate. Maybe it's appropriate that our definition for uncertainty is a little bit uncertain but in fact, it is possible to define uncertainty in a more mathematical way, more exactly. If you do that, then the right-hand of the uncertainty principle might look a little bit different. The right-hand side would still involve Planck's constant, h, but it might include some numerical factors like 2 or 4 or pi or something like that. However, it works out the basic point is unchanged. There's an inescapable tradeoff between uncertainty in position and uncertainty in momentum.

Note that Planck's constant is extremely small, as we've seen. In ordinary units, Planck's constant is 6.6×10^{-34} joule seconds. In decimal notation, that would be 0.000..., 33 zeros, 6.6 joule seconds. That means if you take a large-scale object, like our baseball, we can easily know the baseball's position and its momentum to 12 or 15 decimal places each and still respect the uncertainty principle. The uncertainty principle is peanuts for a large-scale object like a baseball and so a macroscopic object like a baseball can have a well-defined position and momentum, pretty well defined at every point and time. It can follow a pretty well defined classical trajectory and so classical physics applies pretty well to a baseball. But for a microscopic particle like an electron, the uncertainty principle is a big deal.

For example, consider an electron inside an atom. Δx, the uncertainty in position of the atom, can be no larger than the diameter of the atom. We know that the electron is in there somewhere. Its uncertainty is very tightly confined by the fact that's it bound to the nucleus of the atom and because Δx has to be pretty small. The result in Δp, the result in uncertainty in momentum, is pretty large especially for a tiny electron. How large is it? For an electron in an atom, we cannot even tell which direction the electron is moving. The electron might be moving this way or that way or any way and it might be moving as fast as a few percent of the speed of light. The uncertainty in momentum for an electron in an atom is quite substantial because the electron is confined to a very small space.

Here's another question for the uncertainty principle and, in fact, this is a question I remember well. As you may know, one of the steps you go through in getting a Ph.D. is you have an oral examination with your doctoral committee—your panel of imminent scientists, in my case—who get to ask you questions about whatever they want. I remember very vividly a question that was asked to me on my own Ph.D. oral exam and the question is, how big is a photon? Of course, my instinct was to answer that a photon is really, really tiny, but I smelled a trap. Luckily, I gave the matter a little bit more thought before I answered. Of course, we think of a photon as being really, really tiny because atoms are tiny and photons, we said, were tiny, but what we meant when we said that photons were tiny is that a photon carries a very tiny amount of energy. There's a very tiny amount of energy in one photon, but the question was not about how much energy is in a photon. The question is, what is its size in space? How much room does it occupy? What I mean by how much room does it occupy, I mean something about what is our uncertainty about its location in space? How well do we know its spatial location?

Let's think about the light from a laser. We know actually the side-to-side uncertainty and position of the photon pretty well because the photon has to get out the little aperture at the front of the laser and this aperture is a couple of millimeters across. The uncertainty in lateral position is no more than a couple of millimeters. What about its uncertainty in position this way? How long is a photon? The light from a laser is extremely well defined in wavelength. That's the beauty about a laser. It's extremely well defined in frequency and wavelength and, from wavelength, we can determine the momentum. The photons that come out of this laser have an extremely well defined momentum. The uncertainty in momentum, Δp, is exceedingly small for a laser photon. As a result, the uncertainty in position for a laser photon is extremely large and, if you work the numbers, it's astonishingly large. The uncertainty in position for a laser photon may be as much as a meter or more.

How big is a photon? It's about this big. The general lesson here is that when you say that something is small, that requires a little careful thought. First of all, small in what sense? Do you mean small in energy? Do you mean small in size? Secondly, small compared to what? Do you mean small compared to our everyday scale? Small compared to the atomic scale? When we talk about the uncertainty principle, we should keep in mind a couple of nice extreme examples. One is the electron and the atom because the electron is inside the atom, its Δx is really tiny. Its Δp is huge, especially compared to an electron. Its velocity is this way or that way, we don't know, and maybe a few percent of the speed of light. That's really, really fast. The other extreme is the photon from a laser because the laser's wavelength is so well defined, the Δp, the uncertainty in momentum of a laser photon, is extremely tiny. Its uncertainty in position is extremely large, maybe a meter or more.

As an aside, I should mention that there's another uncertainty principle in addition to the position momentum uncertainty principle. There's an uncertainty principle that relates to time and energy. Let's mention that. Let's suppose a process that happens over a very short period of time, Δt. We know that it happens sometime in the period of the time, Δt. For example, suppose we have an electron in an atom that jumps from one energy level to another. We know that happens in some short period of time, Δt. There's an energy involved in that process and that energy is well defined within an uncertainty, Δe. Then it turns out there's an uncertainty principle that relates the 2. It must be that Δe times Δt is greater than or equal to h, Planck's constant again. That time-energy uncertainty principle tells us that things that happen very fast, things for which Δt is extremely small, have very poorly defined energy. Δe is very large. Our uncertainty in energy is very large. For example, very short lived energy levels in an atom. Energy levels that a particle leaves rapidly, say it jumps down to a lower energy level very, very rapidly, those very short lived energy levels in an atom are actually not very sharply defined. Those energy levels have a considerable uncertainty in their energy. The light from a laser, of course, is very well defined in energy. The photon comes out very well-defined in energy and that means that the light from a laser actually comes from long lived atomic energy levels, which is an interesting point.

This is the time-energy uncertainty principle, a tradeoff in our uncertainty about energy and time—analogous to the position-momentum uncertainty principle, a tradeoff in our uncertainties of position and momentum. Why do I bring up the time-energy uncertainty principle? As we'll see later on, this is an uncertainty principle that is of huge, maybe even cosmic, importance, as we'll see in Lectures 17 and 18. Stay tuned for that.

Wave-particle duality and diffraction lead us to a fundamental tradeoff. The more we pin down a particle's position, the less well we know its momentum. That's the uncertainty principle. Heisenberg argued that this really was not an uncertainty principle; it's an indeterminacy principle. What do I mean? He meant that an electron is not the sort of thing that has exact values of position and momentum at the same time. An electron is the sort of thing for which x and p, position and momentum, are always a little bit indeterminate. Sure, we call an electron a particle. We use the particle language to talk about electrons, but a quantum particle is not quite as perfectly particle-ish as our thinking suggests. Our ordinary particle language that we inherited from our experience with classical physics has limits set by the uncertainty principle.

That's kind of a big claim that Heisenberg is making. There's a big difference between saying the particle has exact values for x and p, but we don't know them and saying the particle does not even have exact values for x and p. It's one thing to say that the particle follows a trajectory through space, but we don't know what trajectory it is, and saying there is no exact trajectory for the particle to follow. What's the difference? It's kind of a philosophical difference, but let me try to get at it this way. One of them is a statement. We don't know; it's a statement about our ignorance. We might hope by being clever to find out more about the particle's position and momentum. There is, after all, more to find. There's an exact position and an exact momentum. We could hope, by means of a very clever experiment, to beat the uncertainty principle. The other statement, the statement that it does not have definite position and momentum, says that nature itself is truly fundamentally irreducibly and inescapably fuzzy and indeterminate. That statement will require a more radical revision of our thinking about the world.

Which is it? Are the uncertainties in quantum mechanics due to our own lack of knowledge or due to nature's own lack of definiteness? That's a perplexing question. It's at the center of a long passionate debate about the meaning of quantum mechanics, a famous debate. The debaters were 2 of the founders of quantum mechanics, Niels Bohr and Albert Einstein. This debate was one of the most influential and important debates in the history of science. That's our business next time. We'll talk much more about the debate over the meaning of uncertainty next time. I'll see you then.

Complementarity and the Great Debate
Lecture 7

This lecture is about an argument. The protagonists are 2 giants of 20ᵗʰ-century science, Albert Einstein and Niels Bohr. They're 2 of the founders of quantum theory and the subject of their argument is the meaning of quantum mechanics. At stake, are our most fundamental ideas about the nature of nature.

Albert Einstein was the father of the idea of wave-particle duality, but he found much to criticize in quantum mechanics. In his view, one key flaw was that quantum mechanics failed to answer the question of why a particle ended up in one place rather than another. The theory only predicts probabilities. Einstein believed this to be a flaw—he thought a theory should explain individual events, not just tendencies. Also, he was predisposed to "determinism," the idea that the future of the universe is completely determined by the present. He said, "God does not play dice with the universe." Additionally, he at first thought that quantum mechanics was not logically consistent.

Niels Bohr was a deeply philosophical thinker and a powerful personality. Much of quantum mechanics was developed by his followers and worked out at his theoretical physics institute in Copenhagen. Bohr believed that the new quantum theory required physicists to abandon old concepts, including determinism. He said, "Einstein, stop telling God what to do." Bohr worked out a sophisticated framework of concepts for using quantum ideas without contradictions. This framework came to be called the "Copenhagen interpretation" of quantum mechanics and has been the principal way that physicists have made sense of quantum theory. (We will see other approaches later.)

The Copenhagen interpretation rests on Bohr's "principle of complementarity." This is a subtle idea that requires a careful explanation. Bohr says that we must consider 2 physical realms. There is a microscopic realm of electrons, photons, etc., that cannot be described in "ordinary language." There is also a macroscopic realm of large objects, people, etc., that can be described in "ordinary language" and in which classical physics is approximately valid. To make a measurement of the quantum realm, we must always "amplify" the result to the macroscopic realm, so that we can record it and communicate it in ordinary language. This act of amplification is crucial!

Every experiment on a quantum particle is an "interaction" between the experimental apparatus and the particle, not just a passive observation. Interaction goes both ways, and the particle is always affected in some way. How the quantum particle responds depends on what interaction occurs. Different types of experiments are logically exclusive—we can do one or the other, but not both at the same time. The uncertainty principle tells us that we cannot exactly measure the position and momentum of a particle at the same time. Why not? The interaction needed for a position measurement is not the same as that needed for a momentum measurement. They are complementary quantities. Measuring one logically excludes measuring the other at the same time. Consequently, when we try to use ordinary language to describe the quantum world, we must use different complementary descriptions in different situations—but the mathematics of quantum mechanics guarantees that we can do this without contradiction.

Einstein proposed several puzzles and paradoxes designed to show some loophole in quantum mechanics. Bohr responded to them one by one, in each case trying to expose the flaw in Einstein's thinking and defend quantum mechanics.

Bohr and Einstein engaged in a long-running debate about the validity and meaning of quantum mechanics. Much of the debate centered on a series of thought experiments. Einstein proposed several puzzles and paradoxes designed to show some loophole in quantum mechanics. Bohr responded to them one by one, in each case trying to expose the flaw in Einstein's thinking and defend quantum mechanics. This might appear to be a debate about details and examples, but it was really a profound argument about basic principles.

The debate reached its crescendo at the Solvay Conferences of 1927 and 1930. Einstein proposed several clever thought experiments to try to prove that the uncertainty principle could be beaten. We will examine one of these.

Einstein asked us to suppose a particle passes through a barrier with 1 slit. This gives us a lateral position uncertainty Δx, which implies a minimum lateral momentum uncertainty Δp. But if the barrier is moveable, then the deflection of the particle will cause a sideways recoil of the barrier. By measuring this recoil, we should be able to determine the particle's new momentum. We can violate the uncertainty principle!

Not so fast, replied Bohr. We must also consider how the uncertainty principle applies to the moveable barrier, which has position X and momentum P. To measure the recoil precisely, then our uncertainty ΔP in the barrier's momentum must be extremely small. But then the barrier's position is uncertain by a large ΔX. The uncertainty Δx in the particle's position cannot be smaller than our (large) uncertainty ΔX in the location of the slit. The uncertainty principle is not violated.

After 1930, Einstein was forced to accept that quantum mechanics was a consistent theory of nature. Nevertheless, he was still dissatisfied and kept looking for clues to a deeper view. The Bohr-Einstein debate shifted but did not end. ■

Questions to Consider

1. De Broglie's original view was that both waves and particles existed at the same time and that the wave exerted quantum forces that guided the particle through space. The particle thus had a definite trajectory, though the trajectory would be complicated and difficult to predict. Would this idea have appealed more to Einstein or to Bohr?

2. In a 1928 letter to Schrödinger, Einstein referred to complementarity as a "tranquilizing philosophy" that merely allowed quantum physicists to avoid uncomfortable questions. Is this fair? How would you respond to—or defend—Einstein's remark?

3. Should we think of Einstein's sharp critique of quantum theory as an obstacle or a spur to its development? What is the role of criticism in the creation of new ideas?

Complementarity and the Great Debate
Lecture 7—Transcript

Welcome to the seventh lecture in our course on quantum mechanics. In many ways, this is the most dramatic lecture so far because drama means conflict. This lecture is about an argument. The protagonists are 2 giants of 20th-century science, Albert Einstein and Niels Bohr. They're 2 of the founders of quantum theory and the subject of their argument is the meaning of quantum mechanics. At stake, are our most fundamental ideas about the nature of nature.

Our setting is the 1920s. It's the culmination of a quarter century of continuing development of quantum theory beginning with Planck and Einstein's theories about light quanta, about photons, and Bohr's theory of atomic structure. His discrete electron orbits, his quantum jumps between orbits. All this culminates in de Broglie's radical idea that pieces of matter have wave properties and this is really the breakthrough because in the few years after de Broglie's discovery, discover after discovery comes in rapid succession. You have Schrödinger's wave patterns that determine atomic structure. You have Born's interpretation of quantum waves as waves of probability; the intensity of the wave gives the probability of finding the particle. You have Heisenberg's uncertainty principle and you have many other discoveries that we haven't even mentioned.

George Gamow, a Russian physicist who was part of that story, one of the pioneers of quantum theory, wrote a book about the years 1900–1930 and he called the book, *Thirty Years That Shook Physics*. Between 1924 and 1927, you have 3 years that were a pretty powerful earthquake all by themselves. Out of vague, fishy, miscellaneous sets of quantum ideas there was the birth of a solid framework, quantum mechanics, essentially the same theory that we use today. This all amounts to a dramatic turning point in the history of physics. Of course, the new physics, the new quantum mechanics, posed many conceptual and philosophical challenges that the physicists of the day had to come to grips with and that's our story.

Our protagonists are, first, Albert Einstein, the greatest physicist of his age, maybe the greatest physicist ever. He's tremendously famous and he deserves to be tremendously famous. His contributions are too numerous to mention but he's also a deeply philosophical man. He's a man who cares not just about the mathematics, he cares about the meaning of the physics and he's a solitary thinker in many ways. He certainly thinks of himself as a solitary thinker. Over the years, he has comparatively few students and relatively few collaborators on his work. His way is to ponder a problem and think it through himself and to follow the guidance of his own intuition, that profound intuition about physics, that almost miraculous and magical intuition of his. Einstein is also, in his way, very stubborn and it's stubbornness that allows him to work years and years on the hardest problems in physics and see them through. That led him to some of his greatest discoveries. Einstein, of course, is the father of wave-particle duality and his analysis of the photoelectric effect; just because light travels as waves doesn't mean that light can't behave as a string of particles in the photoelectric effect.

In the 1920s, Einstein realizes that the new quantum mechanics was an important advance. In fact, he nominates Heisenberg and the rest for the Nobel Prize. Yet, Einstein finds much to criticize in quantum mechanics. For example, in an experiment like the two slit experiment, why does the particle wind up in one place rather than another? Quantum mechanics gives no answer at all. It only predicts the probabilities that a particle lands here and here, but quantum mechanics says nothing about why one possibility is realized and another one is not. Einstein sees this as a tremendous flaw in quantum mechanics.

Einstein thinks that a theory should explain individual events, not just general tendencies. Also, Einstein is philosophically disposed to determinism. Determinism is the idea that the future is completely determined by the present. Newton's theory of motion is like this. If you know completely the positions and velocities of all particles at a certain time, say the present, then you can use the forces between the particles to predict exactly where the particles will be and what they'll be doing in the future. This idea of Newton's theory, this determinism, is not changed by the introduction of Einstein's relativity. Relativity is also a deterministic idea of the universe. In quantum mechanics, of course, there's the uncertainty principle, which prevents us from having that kind of exact knowledge, but Einstein's intuition is unwilling to abandon determinism. He thinks determinism is right. He says, "God does not play dice with the universe." Finally, Einstein, at first thinks that quantum mechanics may not quite be logically consistent. It may have an inconsistency somewhere and so he tries to find it.

Our second protagonist, Niels Bohr, is another figure of tremendous importance in the history of science and, also like Einstein, a deeply philosophical man. He's a man who cares about meaning as well as mathematics, and Bohr is also a powerful personality. I don't mean that Bohr was an overbearing man. Let me see if I can explain. Einstein was regarded with awe and admiration by his peers not only for his scientific genius, but also because he was a man of great ethical character. But, in many respects, Bohr inspired not just respect but love among his followers. Bohr's style of thinking is very different. Bohr developed his ideas in dialogue, dialectically, in conversation with other people. He was forever bringing other people into his office and wrestling with ideas considering all sides of the question and every objection that could be raised. Bohr was also quite stubborn in this process. He could wear his colleagues out with his relentless drive to understand.

Let me tell you something about Einstein and Bohr's writing, their different styles of writing. Both, of course, are brilliant and insightful. Einstein is lucid and elegant. Bohr is subtle and nuanced and sometimes a little obscure. You can think of Einstein as the lone genius. Bohr is the leader of a movement. Einstein is the prophet. Bohr is the pope. In fact, his students sometimes teased him by calling him "the pope." As a matter of fact, much of quantum mechanics was developed by followers of Bohr and much of it happened at the Institute for Theoretical Physics at the University of Copenhagen where Bohr was the director.

What's Bohr's thinking about quantum mechanics? Bohr thinks that new quantum theory requires physicists to abandon their old ideas. Among those ideas that should be abandon is the idea of strict determinism. Einstein says, "God does not play dice with the universe." Bohr says, "Einstein, stop telling God what to do." Bohr works out a framework for using the ideas of the new quantum mechanics without contradiction and this came to be called "the Copenhagen Interpretation" of quantum mechanics. The Copenhagen Interpretation has been the principal way that physicists have made sense of quantum theory ever since the 1920s. Of course, there are now approaches other than the Copenhagen Interpretation, and we'll talk about those other approaches in the next to last lecture of the course.

For now, let's find out about Bohr's Copenhagen Interpretation. The Copenhagen Interpretation rests on Bohr's principle of complementarity, and the principle of complementarity is a very subtle idea. It's almost obscure. It's very Bohr-like. It's not boring or boorish, and so it needs a lot of explanation. The principle of complementarity is founded on the distinction between the microscopic and the macroscopic realms. The microscopic realm, the electrons and photons, cannot be described in ordinary language. After a few mind-bending lectures on quantum physics, maybe you agree. In any case, the macroscopic realm, the realm of large objects, laboratories, people, and so on, can be described pretty well in ordinary language. A thing is so or it is not. We have simple cause and effect. Classical physics is approximately valid when we deal in the macroscopic realm with large objects and so on.

Whenever we measure the microscopic quantum realm, we always amplify the result to the macroscopic realm. There's always an electrical signal, or a pointer position on a dial, or maybe the click of the detector. Perhaps you remember me talking about doing the experiment of counting photons one at a time in a 2-slit experiment and we arrange the apparatus so that an audible click was made every time a photon hit the detector, one photon becoming an audible click that could be heard all across the room. That's a tremendous act of amplification and Bohr says that this amplification that happens in a measurement is no accident. There must be amplification because we have to have it for the result to be recorded and communicated in ordinary language in the macroscopic realm. The act of amplification is crucial. It's how we, macroscopic beings, get at the microscopic realm of the quantum world. Of course, that may be cause for some worry because the rules of microscopic and the macroscopic realms don't exactly match. The microscopic realm is quantum mechanical and the macroscopic realm to a good approximation is classical. We're going to have to be very careful and Bohr's principle of complementarity is a way of being very careful.

Let's suppose we make some measurement on a quantum particle. A measurement is not just a passive observation. A measurement is an intervention. A measurement is an interaction between the particle and the experimental apparatus and that interaction goes both ways. The particle is always affected in some way by that interaction and how the particle responds to the interaction depends on what interaction occurs. It depends on what measurement we make because, of course, different measurements will need different experimental setups and will involve different kinds of interactions. That means that different measurements are logically exclusive of each other. We can do one kind of measurement or we can do another kind of measurement, but we cannot do both at the same time because they involve mutually exclusive physical arrangements of our laboratory equipment.

For example, take the uncertainty principle. The uncertainty principle is that we cannot measure position x and momentum p at the same time. Was it a physical question? Why not? The answer is the interactions that we need for the 2 measurements, the physical arrangement of experimental apparatus that we need for the 2 measurements, those 2 arrangements are very different. They're logically exclusive. Doing one measurement logically excludes doing the other measurement at the same time, and so Bohr would say that means that position and momentum are complementary quantities. When we use ordinary language, the language of everyday life where a thing is so or not, when we use ordinary language, we must use different complementary descriptions in different situations depending on what measurements are actually made.

This is, in fact, Bohr's way of thinking about wave-particle duality. When you do an experiment about wave propagation, you can get a wave answer. When you do an experiment about particles exchanging energy, you get a particle answer. You have to have 2 complementary pictures and the mathematics of quantum mechanics almost miraculously guarantees that we can do this without ever running into a contradiction. We never have to use 2 different ordinary language descriptions at the same time. We always get to choose which one we're going to make, which one we're going to apply, which experiment we're going to construct, which measurement we're going to make.

To sum it up in a few words, which is a difficult job, the problem with quantum mechanics, as Bohr sees it, is trying to fit together these different pictures like the wave picture and the particle picture. Bohr says we only find out about the microscopic world from doing experiments and amplifying the results and because of complementarity different experiments are mutually exclusive. We never actually have to use both pictures at once. That means that quantum mechanics might sound paradoxical at first but no actual contradiction ever arises. The moral of the story is the exact experimental arrangement in a particular case determines what it is that's being measured and what's being measured determines what picture is appropriate.

Now we turn to the great debate between Bohr and Einstein. What's the debate about? It's about basic questions. Is quantum mechanics logically consistent? Is quantum mechanics valid? What's the meaning of quantum mechanics? What is quantum mechanics trying to tell us about the nature of the microscopic world? Much of the debate between Bohr and Einstein centers on a series of thought experiments. Remember thought experiments, they're idealized experiments that might be hard to perform in practice, but we use them to clarify our thinking about physics ideas. Einstein proposed a series of puzzles and paradoxes. Each one of his puzzles is designed to show some loophole in quantum mechanics, some flaw in the theory, some way around the theory. Bohr responds to Einstein's ideas one by one. He tries to expose the flaw in Einstein's thinking. He tries to defend quantum mechanics from the attack. That means that it might appear that this is a debate about a series of special examples, but really it's a profound argument about basic principles.

In this argument, Bohr is at a strategic disadvantage. He's got to figure out what's wrong with every one of Einstein's paradoxes. Einstein only needs to succeed in one example. In succeed, I mean he needs to show an un-resolvable problem with quantum mechanics. Einstein is on the attack; Bohr is defending. The debate reaches its climax at the Solvay Conferences of 1927 and 1930. The Solvay Conferences are periodic gatherings of the world's best physicists to discuss the most important physics problems of the day. They go on to this day. Both the 1927 and 1930 conferences centered on the new quantum mechanics. During the day, you had lectures and formal discussions and so on, but outside of that during meals, in the evenings, the real business went on. Einstein would propose clever thought experiments to show that quantum mechanics does not make sense or that the uncertainty principle can be evaded. Einstein believes that a particle should have definite position and momentum and that, if we were very clever, we might be able to find them both out at the same time. On the other hand, Bohr is trying to show why Einstein's clever ideas won't work. To give you some flavor of the debate, I want to examine one particular example, one particular thought experiment proposed by Einstein and answered by Bohr. I've actually simplified the example somewhat, but I think I've captured the essential physics. Einstein says suppose a particle passes through a barrier with one slit. We're doing the single slit diffraction experiment. A particle passes through a barrier with one slit and because the barrier has one slit, when the particle passes through, we know that the particle lateral position with an uncertainty, Δx we called it, which is the width of the slit, let's say. The slit has some width. We know where the particle is because it passes through the slit.

Of course, we saw that the de Broglie waves spread out on the other side of the single slit because of diffraction and that means that the particle might be deflected this way or that way as it passes through the barrier. We don't know how it's deflected this way or that way. We have uncertainty about the momentum. We just know it might be knocked a little bit to the left, thrown to the right, and that means we can predict as well where the particle winds up. But Einstein says suppose we construct the barrier so that it can move from side to side. It's free to move. Then, if the particle is deflected as it passes through the barrier, that deflection of the particle will actually push the barrier the other way. If the barrier is knocked to the right, that means the particle was deflected to the left. If the barrier was pushed to the left, that means the particle was knocked to the right. If we see how the barrier moves, we can work out exactly what the particle deflection was as it passed through the slit.

That means, of course, if we know how the particle's momentum was changed, its momentum is no longer uncertain. If we can take into account the effect of the slit on the particle, then it's no longer random. We'll know that the particle passed through the slit and we'll know where it's going to wind up on the screen because we know the recoil of the barrier and we can work it out. We know x, the lateral position of the particle with a very small Δx. We made a very narrow slit. We know p, the lateral momentum of the particle with a very small uncertainty, Δp. By doing the experiment very carefully, Einstein argues, we can make both of the uncertainties as small as we like. We can beat the Heisenberg uncertainty principle, which says that the product of the uncertainties has to be at least as big as Planck's constant. If we can beat the uncertainty principle, quantum mechanics cannot be 100% right. There has to be something wrong with it.

What's Bohr's response? Bohr's response is to say, not so fast. He says you have to also consider how the uncertainty principle applies not just to the particle but also to the movable barrier. The movable barrier has its own position and momentum from side to side. We can call its position capital X and its momentum capital P. To measure the recoil precisely, to measure very precisely how much the barrier is knocked to the left or to the right, then we have to at the outset have a very small uncertainty in the barrier's momentum. We just have to know very precisely that it wasn't moving to start with; otherwise, we won't know what the affect of the particle was.

To do this experiment, we must make the uncertainty in the side-to-side momentum of the barrier, ΔP, very tiny. On the other hand, to do the experiment we have to know the position of the slit in the barrier very precisely because if we don't know where the slit is then the fact that the electron passed through the barrier doesn't really tells us where the electron was. In order to get the electron's position uncertainty very small, we have to make ΔX, the position uncertainty of the barrier with the slit in it, we have to make that uncertainty very small, but the uncertainty principle for the barrier tells us that its uncertainty in position and its uncertainty in momentum cannot both be tiny at the same time.

What's Bohr's response? Bohr's response is, essentially, Einstein is cheating. He neglects to apply the uncertainty to the barrier itself, but the uncertainty principle applies to everything. Einstein's thought experiment won't work. Quantum mechanics is saved, but notice how it's saved. Quantum mechanics is saved because it applies to everything. If there's anything in the universe that is truly not quantum mechanical, that anything in the universe for which the uncertainty principle does not hold, we could use that to defeat quantum mechanics. Quantum mechanics is saved because it is universal.

The Bohr-Einstein argument goes on round after round. Bohr is always able, eventually, to find the flaw in Einstein's proposed thought experiment. Einstein's no dummy. The flaws in his proposed thought experiments are often extremely subtle. Sometimes Bohr has to think overnight to figure out what's wrong with them, but the flaws are always there. After 1930, Einstein is forced to accept that quantum mechanics is a consistent theory of physics. Is he satisfied? No, Einstein is not satisfied. He is not satisfied with quantum mechanics. He still believes in determinism. He still thinks quantum mechanics has flaws. He thinks quantum mechanics is correct as far as it goes, but he believes that it is incomplete. Einstein goes on looking for clues to a deeper view of nature. That means that after 1930, the Bohr-Einstein debate shifts but it does not end. There's another chapter, an even more amazing chapter yet to come. We'll talk about it in Lectures 15 and 16 on quantum entanglement, but this lecture must come to an end here.

In fact, at this point, the first section of our course comes to an end. In this section, we've traced the development of quantum ideas leading up to the development of quantum mechanics. Now we're going to turn to something even more ambitious. Now we're going to try learning not just about quantum mechanics, but learning quantum mechanics itself. Our goal for the next few lectures is to learn the abstract language that physicists use to describe the microscopic world. That abstract language is a kind of mathematics. It's not terribly difficult mathematics, but it is very unfamiliar.

We're going to learn a simplified form of quantum mechanics. We're going to learn quantum mechanics stripped to its essentials and we're going to use a couple of helpful examples to guide us on our way. The first example we're going to talk about is to take the phenomenon of interference that we saw in the two slit experiment, and we're going to show how it works in the simplest conceivable situation. We're going to set up our thought experiment. We're going to analyze it. We're going to explore it. We're going to play with it. We'll also discover a few surprises and that's going to be our business beginning in the next lecture. The next few lectures may be a little challenging, but the payoff will be considerable. The payoff is to make the tremendous insights of quantum mechanics our own and that task begins next time. I'll see you then.

Paradoxes of Interference
Lecture 8

In the first section of the course, we've been tracing how a generation of the most brilliant scientists in human history created the theory of quantum mechanics and wrestled with its perplexities. ... In the second section, we embark on the task of introducing the theory itself, quantum mechanics in a simplified form.

To begin to look at quantum mechanics, we will use an interferometer as a simple conceptual "laboratory." An interferometer is an optical apparatus made up of several components. A light source generates a beam of light with a definite wavelength as input to the apparatus. The intensity of the light can be reduced so that only 1 photon is traveling through the apparatus at a time. Photon detectors can be placed to register any photons that strike them. (Our detectors are somewhat idealized.) Mirrors are used to guide the light beams in various directions.

The crucial components of an interferometer are "half-silvered mirrors." A half-silvered mirror splits a beam of light into 2 beams of equal intensity. These mirrors are also sometimes called "beam splitters." It's important to note that light waves that reflect from the silvered side of the mirror are inverted—that is, the electromagnetic fields are reversed in the reflected waves. If we send a single photon through a beam splitter, photon detectors do not both register "half a photon." Instead, the entire photon is registered in one place or the other, each with probability $\frac{1}{2}$.

Our apparatus is a Mach-Zehnder interferometer. An incoming light beam is split at a half-silvered mirror. The 2 beams are then recombined at a second half-silvered mirror, and the output beams are observed. If everything is set up properly, all of the light emerges in 1 beam. This is because the light constructively interferes in that direction but destructively interferes in the other. If we send 1 photon at a time through the interferometer, the photon is always registered in 1 beam rather than the other. The probabilities exhibit constructive and destructive interference!

We can explore quantum ideas by thought experiments using the single-photon version of the Mach-Zehnder interferometer. Interference can only happen if the photon travels "both ways" through the interferometer. Suppose we block 1 beam with our hand; 50% of the time, the photon hits our hand. Otherwise it travels along the other beam to the second half-silvered mirror and is registered by each detector 25% of the time. Suppose we introduce a nonabsorbing detector into 1 beam. This tells us which beam the photon traveled, but in so doing we completely lose the interference effect. Each detector registers the photon 50% of the time. For interference to occur, the photon must leave no "footprints" behind that would tell which way it went.

"Both ways" and "which way" experiments illustrate the principle of complementarity. With the second half-silvered mirror present, we find interference effects. The photon must have traveled "both ways" through the interferometer. If we remove the half-silvered mirror, the photon detectors tell us "which way" the photon traveled through the interferometer. We must choose which experiment to do, and we cannot later say what would have happened if we had done the other one. Keep in mind Asher Peres's quantum motto: "Unperformed experiments have *no* results." In 1978, John Wheeler proposed the "delayed-choice experiment": We decide whether to leave the mirror in or take it out when the light has already traveled 99% of the way through the apparatus. We decide whether the photon went "both ways" or "one way" after it has almost completed its journey! Wheeler's quantum motto is "No phenomenon is a phenomenon until it is an *observed* phenomenon."

Wheeler's quantum motto is "No phenomenon is a phenomenon until it is an *observed* phenomenon."

The Elitzur-Vaidman bomb problem leads us to even stranger conclusions. In this scenario, a factory produces bombs with extremely sensitive light triggers. Some bombs are "good" and some are defective. We want to test them. A good bomb will explode if even 1 photon hits the trigger. But a defective bomb lacks the trigger mechanism and photons pass through. Suppose we send just 1 photon into a bomb to test it. A good bomb will explode and a defective one will not. This tests the bomb, but only by blowing it up. Can we ever find out that a bomb is good without exploding it? This seems impossible!

A quantum trick solves the puzzle. Elitzur and Vaidman suggested that we put the bomb in 1 beam of a Mach-Zehnder interferometer and send 1 photon through. If the bomb is defective, then the light shows interference. The photon always winds up in one detector and never in the other. If the bomb is good, then 50% of the time it will explode. But the other 50% of the time, the photon travels the other beam to the second beam splitter. Thus 25% of the time it will strike a detector that would be impossible if the bomb were defective. We can certify some good bombs without exploding them! ∎

Questions to Consider

1. In our interferometer experiment, suppose we flip the second beam splitter so that its metal coating is on the other side. How would this affect the constructive and destructive interference? What if we flip both beam splitters?

2. In the bomb-testing experiment, one possible outcome is inconclusive, since both working and defective bombs can produce it. Suppose we repeat the test once more if this happens. What percentage of working bombs are (a) blown up, (b) certified as working, and (c) still undetermined in this double test? Suppose we repeat the test as many times as necessary to achieve a conclusive result. What percentage of the working bombs are blown up?

Paradoxes of Interference
Lecture 8—Transcript

Welcome to the eighth lecture in our course on quantum mechanics. In the first section of the course, we've been tracing how a generation of the most brilliant scientists in human history created the theory of quantum mechanics and wrestled with its perplexities. We've told how Planck and Einstein and Bohr introduced quantum ideas into the theory of light and matter. We've heard how de Broglie and Schrödinger and Born and Heisenberg built that into a complicated, sophisticated mathematical theory, the theory of quantum mechanics. In the second section, we embark on the task of introducing the theory itself, quantum mechanics in a simplified form. We're going to begin with an idealized thought experiment. It will be our laboratory, if you will, to explore the concepts of quantum mechanics and that idealized laboratory is the interferometer.

Interferometer is an optical apparatus with several components. Let's talk about the components of an interferometer. First of all, there's a light source. The light source generates a beam of light with a definite wavelength, which we direct into the apparatus. We might use a laser but any light source will do. The intensity of the light source though can be reduced so that only one photon at a time is in the interferometer. We'll be asking what will that one photon do, where will it go, how will it behave. That's what's at the front end of the interferometer. At the back end of the interferometer, we have photon detectors, devices that can register any photons that strike them. Our photon detectors will be somewhat idealized. For example, they will be 100% efficient. Whenever a photon hits them, they will certainly register a photon and real photon detectors are not quite that efficient, but we'll assume it's 100% efficient. Another thing is that, generally, real photon detectors actually absorb the photons they detect. For example, they might detect the photon by the photoelectric effect in which a photon is absorbed and an electron is produced. The photon is at once detected and destroyed, but we could imagine, if we like, super-duper detectors that can register a photon without actually destroying the photon. Such detectors would be very, very hard to build, but they're possible in principle. Whenever we need a super-duper non-destroying photon detector, we'll allow ourselves to use it. Many photon detectors are the technological descendants of the old fashioned

Geiger counters. We've all seen those in movies. They're detecting radiation with an audible click and so we say that a photon detector goes click when a photon is detected. That's much like the photon detectors that I told you about in the experiment that I did with the two slit experiment, Young's 2-slit experiment, doing one photon at a time. The photon detector that I used made an audible click whenever a photon was detected. We have the light source. We have the photon detectors. What's in between? One of the things that we find in between is a mirror. We find several mirrors in the experiment and these mirrors are used to guide the beam around in various directions. We'll mostly ignore the regular mirrors. They're not very important for the operation of the interferometer, but the most important components of the interferometer are the half-silvered mirrors, also called beam-splitters. A half-silvered mirror is a partially reflecting mirror. It's a piece of glass with a little bit of metal evaporated onto one side, instead of a lot. When you shine a beam of light at a half-silvered mirror, it splits the beam—that's why they're called beam-splitters—into a transmitted beam and a reflected beam. Each one of which has exactly half the intensity of the original beam. Half of the energy goes one way, half of the energy goes another way.

There's one detail about half-silvered mirrors that I'd better put out. It's a trivial sounding detail but it turns out to be very important. The half-silvered mirror is a piece of glass. It has a little bit of metal coating one side and if you have light incident on the silvered side, on the side with the metal coating, then that light is reflected. The reflected light wave is actually reversed. It's actually inverted. The electromagnetic fields are reversed in direction in the reflected wave. This doesn't happen with the light that is transmitted. It doesn't happen either with the light that is reflected from the other side, the side without the metallic coating. This is a funny little fact that the light rays from the silvered side, the lights waves are inverted. It turns out to be a crucial fact as we'll see and it will show up later on as a kind of minus sign for those light waves.

What happens when a single photon is incident on a beam-splitter? What happens to the photon? Let's imagine an experiment. We have a very weak light source. It produces one photon at a time. We have a beam-splitter, which would split the light beam into 2 directions and we have a couple of photon detectors to see where the photon goes. A photon cannot be divided into 2 pieces. The photon is the indivisible quantum of light. What happens? What happens is either detector might click. One of the detectors will click. In fact, each detector has a probability of 1/2, 50%, of detecting the photon. We see an illustration of the Born rule. The wave intensity, half the intensity goes each direction, gives the particle probability. The particle has a probability of 1/2 of ending at one detector or a probability of 1/2 of ending at the other detector. It looks at first glance as if what a beam-splitter really does is it chooses randomly. A photon reaches a beam-splitter and, so to speak, flips a coin. Heads, you reflect. Tails, you transmit. That's a naive picture of what a beam-splitter does but we better be careful because as we'll see things are not so simple at a beam-splitter.

Let's take all these components, the light source, the mirrors, the photon detectors, and put them all together. Here we have our model of interferometer. It's called a "Mach-Zehnder interferometer" and this is not a real interferometer. It's just a model. It's made out of foam board and glue and wood and plastic. It doesn't really work but it's a great interferometer for a thought experiment because I can point at the pieces and we can figure out how things go.

Here's our Mach-Zehnder interferometer. Here's the layout. The incoming beam comes from the lower left hand corner and it strikes a half-silvered mirror in that corner. The first mirror here is a half-silvered mirror. The beam is split in 2 and the 2 beams go to the 2 corners where we have full-silvered mirrors, regular mirrors to reflect the beams back together and the beams are recombined at a second half-silvered mirror. Then the resulting beams from the second half-silvered mirror are directed into these 2 photon detectors. The output beams are measured by these 2 photon detectors and for convenience we may refer to this path, the upper left-hand path as the upper path and the other path that the light might travel as the lower path.

If you set this up properly and you get everything aligned just so and you send in a beam of light, you can find out where the light goes and it turns out that all of the light emerges in one beam. All of the light, 100% of the light intensity, winds up at the green detector, the upper detector. Why is this? Of course, the answer has to do with interference. That's why we call it an interferometer. The light reaching the green detector can come along 2 paths.

One of them is the upper path that is reflected at the first half-silvered mirror and reflected at the second half-silvered mirror and the other is at the lower path that is transmitted at the first half-silvered mirror and transmitted at the second half-silvered mirror.

Now I need to tell you, if I want to tell you how things are reflecting, which sides of half-silvered mirrors have the metal coating on them. I've chosen to put the metal coatings on my half-silvered mirror on the lower side. The lower right-hand side of the mirror is on this side of the interferometer and that means that whether a light wave is reflected twice or transmitted twice, it never is reflected off of the silver side of the half-silvered mirror. That means that it's not inverted. The 2 light waves, therefore, arrive in unison, they add up together, you get constructive interference. What about in the other direction? In that direction, you can get there 2 ways. You can reflect off the first mirror and be transmitted at the second mirror—No inversion, no minus sign. Or, you can be transmitted by the first mirror and then reflected by the second mirror. Being reflected off the bottom side of the second mirror gives you a minus sign. The 2 waves arrive at the second detector exactly out of sync. They cancel each other out. No light reaches the second detector. You get destructive interference.

Notice the importance of that fiddly little minus sign. Without it, we'd get constructive interference both ways, which can't happen because then more light would come out of the interferometer than went into it. The interferometer is really a highly simplified version of Young's 2-slit experiment. There are 2 alternatives. There are 2 different beams you can follow versus 2 slits you can go through in Young's experiment. You have constructive and destructive interference affects—constructive interference at one detector, destructive interference at the other. That means 100% of the light goes one way and 0% goes the other. It's a super simplified Young's 2-slit experiment.

Let's consider some quantum experiments that we can do with our Mach-Zehnder interferometer. Let's send one photon at a time through the interferometer. The photon is always registered by one detector or the other but the probabilities exhibit constructive and destructive interference. We know that from the Born rule. The wave intensity gives the particle probability and all of the wave intensity winds up at the upper detector. That means that the photon lands in the upper detector all the time and never in the lower detector. This means whatever's going on in a beam-splitter, it's just not a coin flip for the photon because the photon could flip the coin and get heads and be transmitted by the first beam and then flip the coin and get tails and be reflected from the second mirror and wind up at the blue detector. That could happen. That's a possible way to flip the coins, but since that never happens we know that what's going on at the half-silvered mirrors is something more than just a random choice.

If we have a single photon in the interferometer, we have somehow interference between the beams even though there's only one photon in the interferometer, which means that the beam must somehow travel both ways. The beam must somehow figure out both ways in the interferometer. It must explore both ways in the interferometer. It knows to interfere at the second half-silvered mirror and wind up at the green detector. The photon has to travel both ways. That seems very strange. Photons seem like particles. Particles should make a choice. They should go one way or the other. What we have is simply the fact that the photon's location in the interferometer is indeterminate.

Let's do another experiment. Let's imagine we have the beams going and I'm going to now block one of the 2 beams with my hand. I'm going to put my hand in right like this. What happens to the light? Now, 50% of the time the photon that I send through will actually hit the back of my hand and if my hand were a few trillion times more sensitive than it is, I might actually feel the photon hit my hand. I might go "ouch," and so with the probability of 1/2, the photon hits my hand but the other 50% of the time with a probability of 1/2, the photon goes the other way, it misses my hand. It reaches the second half-silvered mirror and if this photon reaches the second half-silvered mirror along the upper beam then the half-silvered mirror will just reflect it or transmit it with equal probability. That means 50% of the time it hits my hand, 25% of the time it reaches the green detector, and 25% of the time it reaches the blue detector, which is kind of interesting because it never reached the blue detector before that. By blocking one of the beams, I actually make the light brighter at the blue detector. Of course, we did something very similar with the two slit experiment—by blocking one of the slits we were able to increase the intensity of light at some places on the screen.

Let's suppose we don't actually block the photon. Let's just suppose we detect it. We use one of those super sensitive, non-absorbing photon detectors in the lower beam and we see whether the photon goes by there. We find out that 50% of the time the photon travels along the lower beam. When the photon travels on the lower beam, it winds up at the green or the blue detectors with equal probability. That means 50% of the time we don't see the photon go this way. We know the photon went the other way and if that happens, then 50% of the time it winds up at the blue detector or at the green detector. In other words, each detector will register the photon 50% of the time whether the photon went in the lower beam or not. There's no interference effect. Each detector fires with a probability of 1/2. There's no constructive and destructive interference. It goes away. Why did it go away? Just because I measured the photon to see which beam it traveled in. The important point here is that any sort of which way detector, any sort of detector that tells you which way the photon traveled, will wipe out the interference effect which relies on the fact that the photon could be going both ways. Just observing the photon is enough to change how it behaves in this experiment.

Conversely, for interference to occur there must be no measurement at all. That means the photon has to leave no footprints behind. No evidence of which way it went because if there were any trace of which way the photon went, we'd be able to use that as a measurement of which way the photon went. No detective looking at the interferometer afterwards, even examining the mirrors and so forth atom by atom, no detective could find any evidence of which way the photon went. The choice of the photon's path would be the perfect crime. It's undetectable by any method.

Let's say some more about complementarity. We've got 2 kinds of experiments. There's a both way experiment where we get interference and there's a which way experiment where we detect which path the photon traveled. That nicely illustrates Bohr's principle of complementarity. In fact, there's a neat way to switch experiments here. I can actually take the second beam-splitter and do something with it. If I leave it in, then I get interference. The photon went both ways and somehow figured out to wind up always in the green detector 100% of the time, 0% of the time at the blue detector. The photon sort of acts as a wave. On the other hand, suppose I actually remove the second half-silvered mirror. Then the beams, instead of recombining at the mirror simply cross each other and the detectors will actually tell us which way the photon went. If the photon went along the lower path, it'll wind up at the green detector. If it went along the upper path, it'll wind up at the blue detector. So the detectors themselves will tell us which way the photon went. The light acts as a particle. It chooses a definite path.

We must choose which experiment to do. We can take the mirror out, make a particle experiment, or we could put the mirror in and do a wave experiment. We make the choice. Whichever experiment we do, we can't later say what would have happened if we had done the other experiment instead. It's too late. We didn't do that experiment. We could do another experiment where we change the position of the mirror but we can't do the old one. We can't say what the result would've been. I like the way that Asher Peres, the late Israeli physicist put it. He said that unperformed experiments have no results. Unperformed experiments have no results.

Let's add a new wrinkle here. This is an idea due to John Wheeler and this is called the "delayed choice" version of the interferometer experiment, which he proposed in 1978. Wheeler was a disciple of Niels Bohr. Bohr and Wheeler worked together on the first theory of nuclear fission, for example. They were close collaborators and Wheeler was a deep thinker about quantum mechanics and the meaning of complementarity. This is not the last time we'll be discussing his thinking in this course. Wheeler's idea is to decide whether to put the mirror in or take it out after the photon has already gone most of the way through the experiment. Can you imagine making this experiment not this big, but maybe 100 million miles on a side? It takes 15 minutes for the photon to go from the first half-silvered mirror to the second half-silvered mirror and after all but the last few seconds have transpired, and the photon has almost reached the second half-silvered mirror, we decide whether to put it in and do a wave experiment or take it out and do a particle experiment. After the photon has already gone 99% of the way through the experiment, we can decide whether it will have gone one way as a particle or both ways as a wave.

That seems very strange, but essentially it's a language problem. The point is that we can't give a sensible account in plain language of what happened to the photon until after the measurement is made. Wheeler's motto for quantum mechanics is this: No phenomenon is a phenomenon until it is an observed phenomenon. No phenomenon is a phenomenon until it is an observed phenomenon. Wow, what do you mean by observed? What is an observer? Actually any physical record will do. Consider the old chestnut. If a tree falls in the forest and nobody's there to hear it, does it make a sound? Wheeler would say, in fact did say, suppose you'd look at the trees near that tree. Perhaps in one of the trees there's a leaf and another leaf is just touching that leaf. The sound vibrations from the falling tree made one leaf vibrate and make a tiny scratch on the other leaf, visible only through a microscope. Nevertheless, that's a physical record of the sound and so the tree did make a sound. We can tell afterwards. Any physical record can count as an observation.

The interferometer is about the simplest example of quantum physics. You really can't make it any simpler. It has interference. It has probabilities, but even this simple of a contraption can still astonish us. To prove that I want to tell you one of my favorite thought experiments. This is one devised by Avshalom Elitzur and Lev Vaidman, 2 Israeli physicists, and it's called "the bomb testing problem." We must imagine there's a factory and the factory makes bombs with very sensitive photon detector triggers. Imagine my fist here is the bomb and my finger is the trigger. If one photon hits the trigger the bomb will explode. It's that sensitive. However, some bombs made by the factory have defective triggers that can't detect a photon. The photon just passes through. The detectors, the triggers, are defective. Elitzur and Vaidman invite us to put ourselves in the position of the manager of the factory. We like to test the bombs in order to see if they're in working order. That's our problem.

First of all, why bombs? There are 2 reasons for bombs. One is their explosions are very exciting. Remember the key idea in quantum mechanics, in quantum measurements, is that a measurement amplifies the microscopic world and if you have one photon turning into an entire explosion that's really amplification. The second reason is that once a bomb explodes we cannot reuse it and that emphasizes the irrevocable nature of our choice of experiment. We can do another experiment on another bomb but once the bomb explodes the world has changed. We can't go back and do a different experiment. That's complementarity. We have to make a choice and then for that particular physical system, that's the choice we've made. The bomb may be at risk of exploding. We want to test our bombs. Of course, the naïve testing method is to take a bomb and send a photon through it. If it does not blow up, it's defective. If it does blow up, it's a working bomb. Or, rather, it was a working bomb. This is not completely useless. In this way, we can study the quality control at the bomb factory. We can say, oh yes, the factory is producing 10% defective bombs, but it really doesn't help us for our problem. What we want to do is we want to identify working bombs, bombs that are guaranteed to explode, at least we're really sure they will explode, without actually blowing them up because we'd like to tell our customers, yes, we're sure this bomb will actually explode.

When you think about it, that seems impossible because if you send a photon through and the bomb is working, it will blow up. If you don't send a photon through then you can't test the bomb. It seems impossible; however, there is a way: The Elitzur Vaidman method. The idea is to the put the bomb in one arm of a Mach-Zehnder interferometer. We'll put the bomb in one arm of the Mach-Zehnder interferometer. We'll put it over here on this arm and let's suppose the bomb is defective. We send one photon through. The photon goes through. If the bomb is defective, it will not register the photon. It will not measure the presence of the photon and so no measurement on the photon is made. There's interference and only one detector could possible click. The photon always winds up at the upper detector, the green detector.

Suppose we include a working bomb. Put the detector right there in the beam. Now, 50% of the time the bomb blows up. That's too bad, but what happens the other 50% of the time? Well, 25% of the time if the bomb doesn't blow up, the photon must have traveled the upper beam. So, 25% of the time, the photon winds up in the green detector again and we can't really tell. We can't tell whether the bomb is good or bad because the green detector could click either way but 25% of the time the other detector clicks—the blue detector, something that could never happen if the bomb were defective because if the bomb's defective there's interference. Destructive interference at the blue detector, there's no probability of winding up there. So, 25% of the time the blue detector clicks and then we are sure we can certify for sure that the bomb is in working order even though it did not actually blow up.

What this means is that for photons, it's not just a question of whether a photon went through or did not, whether a photon hits the detector or does not. There are actually other possibilities. The photon could be not localized in space. It could be spread out across the interferometer. Our one photon interferometer is a great conceptual laboratory for exploring quantum ideas. It is simple. It illustrates constructive and destructive interference. It illustrates the relation between wave intensity and probability. It illustrates the principle of complementarity and so on. It has a few surprises to keep us on our toes. Let's not forget about the interferometer. We're going to return to the interferometer whenever we need to use it to make things clear. Whenever things get a little bit fuzzy, we'll run back to the interferometer.

What's our next task? Our next task is to develop a symbolic language for describing quantum situations. We're going to introduce abstract symbols and some rules for using those abstract symbols to describe situations like the interferometer. We're going to be able to analyze the interferometer or, in fact, any other quantum physics experiment using our new abstract language. What we're going to putting together is a small toolbox, if you will, of essential ideas and methods for doing quantum mechanics. That's next time; I'll see you then.

States, Amplitudes, and Probabilities
Lecture 9

Now we want to formulate symbolic ways of working with quantum ideas. We want to introduce a kind of mathematical language. I mean, after all, if we want to explore Mongolia, it's a good idea to learn some Mongolian, especially if the best maps are all written in Mongolian. Our destination is a place that's even more exotic than Mongolia. Our destination is the microscopic world.

Our aim here is to introduce a formal language to describe quantum ideas. First we introduce a few terms and abstract symbols. A "system" is any piece of the quantum world that we wish to consider. For example, we might consider a single photon in an interferometer. A "state," on the other hand, is a physical situation of some system. We represent a state by a "ket," like so: $|state\rangle$. What we put inside the ket $|\cdots\rangle$ is just a convenient label for the state. A "basis" is a set of distinct states that cover all of the outcomes of some measurement. For example, the photon in the interferometer would be found in one beam or the other, so the 2 states $|\text{upper}\rangle$ and $|\text{lower}\rangle$ make up a basis. There can be different possible measurements, so there can be different possible basis sets for a quantum system.

Besides basis states, there are also "superposition" states. The term superposition is meant to suggest a composite, like 2 pictures "superimposed" on one another in a double exposure. We represent a superposition as an abstract sum:

$$|state\rangle = a|\text{upper}\rangle + b|\text{lower}\rangle .$$

The numerical factors a and b are called "amplitudes." In full quantum mechanics, these amplitudes might include imaginary numbers (like $\sqrt{-1}$). We can omit this complication, but we will use both positive and negative amplitudes. We define the number $s = 0.7071 \ldots$, for which $s^2 = \frac{1}{2}$.

(We give this number a special name for convenience because we will use it a lot in our examples.)

Next, we need rules for working and interpreting the abstract quantum symbols. The "rule of superposition" says that a superposition of 2 or more basis states is also a quantum state. This means that a quantum system has more possibilities than we might expect. For the photon in the interferometer, besides $|\text{upper}\rangle$ and $|\text{lower}\rangle$ states, we also have lots of superposition states $a|\text{upper}\rangle + b|\text{lower}\rangle$ for many different choices of amplitudes a and b. A superposition state represents the photon divided among the beams in some way, as happens in an interferometer. The amplitudes determine the details.

Quantum mechanics only predicts probabilities, not definite results. What is probability? For any event, its probability P is a number between 0 and 1.

The "rule of probability" (also called the Born rule) says that if we make a measurement, the probability of any result is determined by the amplitude for that result:

$$\text{probability} = |\text{amplitude}|^2 .$$

Quantum mechanics only predicts probabilities, not definite results. What is probability? For any event, its probability P is a number between 0 and 1. The value $P = 0$ means the event is impossible, and $P = 1$ means that it is certain. An intermediate value like $P = 0.37$ means that, if we tried the same experiment many times, the event would happen about 37% of the time. Probabilities predict statistics. Both positive and negative amplitudes give positive probabilities.

Suppose our photon is in the state $a|\text{upper}\rangle + b|\text{lower}\rangle$. If we make a measurement to find which beam the photon is in, we will get results with probabilities:

$$P(\text{upper}) = |a|^2 \text{ and } P(\text{lower}) = |b|^2 .$$

This means we must have $|a|^2 + |b|^2 = 1$, since probabilities must always add up to 1.

In the state $s|\text{upper}\rangle + s|\text{lower}\rangle$, each beam has probability $|s|^2 = \frac{1}{2}$. The same thing is also true for the different quantum state $s|\text{upper}\rangle - s|\text{lower}\rangle$, because:

$$|s|^2 = |-s|^2 = \tfrac{1}{2}.$$

There are 2 "update rules" that tell how the state changes when something happens to the system. Update rule I says that when there is no measurement, the state changes in a definite way that maintains any superposition. If we know how to update the basis states, we can determine how to update superposition states. Update rule II says that when there is a measurement, we use the results to find the new state. In this case, the state is updated randomly.

We will now look at an example for update rule II. In our example, the photon is in the state $a|\text{upper}\rangle + b|\text{lower}\rangle$, and we use photon detectors to determine which beam it is in. Then:

$$a|\text{upper}\rangle + b|\text{lower}\rangle \quad
\begin{cases}
|\text{upper}\rangle & \text{with } P = |a|^2 \\
\\
|\text{lower}\rangle & \text{with } P = |b|^2
\end{cases}$$

These are (almost) the only rules of quantum mechanics!

To understand the meaning of the quantum rules, we apply them to the photon in an interferometer. At a beam splitter, the basis states change in this way:

$$|\text{upper}\rangle \;\Rightarrow\; s|\text{upper}\rangle + s|\text{lower}\rangle.$$
$$|\text{lower}\rangle \;\Rightarrow\; s|\text{upper}\rangle - s|\text{lower}\rangle.$$

This is an example of update rule I, since no measurement is made. The minus sign indicates reflection from the silvered side of the mirror.

In the interferometer, we keep track of the quantum state at each stage to figure out what happens to the photon. The photon starts out in the upper beam, so its state is $|\text{upper}\rangle$. At the first beam splitter, the state changes: $|\text{upper}\rangle \Rightarrow s|\text{upper}\rangle + s|\text{lower}\rangle$. The beams recombine at the second beam splitter. We apply the beam splitter state change to each part of the superposition, according to update rule I:

$$s|\text{upper}\rangle + s|\text{lower}\rangle$$
$$\Rightarrow s(s|\text{upper}\rangle + s|\text{lower}\rangle) + s(s|\text{upper}\rangle - s|\text{lower}\rangle).$$

We now multiply amplitudes and combine terms as we would in an ordinary algebraic expression. This gives us the final state:

$$(s^2 + s^2)|\text{upper}\rangle + (s^2 - s^2)|\text{lower}\rangle = |\text{upper}\rangle.$$

At the end, the photon is certain to be in the upper beam. Constructive and destructive interference take place in the amplitudes. The quantum amplitude keeps track of the wave properties of the photon. ∎

Questions to Consider

1. One of the questions for the last lecture asked what happens when the second beam splitter is flipped so that its metal coating is on the other side. Write down how a flipped beam splitter affects the $|\text{upper}\rangle$ and $|\text{lower}\rangle$ basis states, and work out the final quantum state for the photon. Does this agree with your previous answer? (It should.)

2. If we simply allow the 2 beams to cross without a beam splitter, this simply exchanges the basis states: $|\text{upper}\rangle \Rightarrow |\text{lower}\rangle$ and $|\text{lower}\rangle \Rightarrow |\text{upper}\rangle$. Use this fact to find the final quantum state if the second beam splitter is removed (as in Wheeler's delayed-choice experiment).

3. Suppose we place a nonabsorbing detector in one of the beams of the interferometer. Using both update rules, explain what happens to the quantum state at various stages of the apparatus.

States, Amplitudes, and Probabilities
Lecture 9—Transcript

Welcome to the ninth lecture in our course on quantum mechanics. Last time we began to introduce the theory of quantum mechanics in a simplified form. We used the example of the photon in an interferometer to explore how quantum probabilities work. We saw quantum interference and we saw a few of the paradoxes of quantum interference. Now we want to formulate symbolic ways of working with quantum ideas. We want to introduce a kind of mathematical language. I mean, after all, if we want to explore Mongolia, it's a good idea to learn some Mongolian, especially if the best maps are all written in Mongolian. Our destination is a place that's even more exotic than Mongolia. Our destination is the microscopic world.

This may be the most technical lecture in our course. It's not terribly difficult, but what we do will be very unfamiliar. It's like Mongolian. I want to tell you not to be concerned if you don't get it completely at first. You have several things going for you. First of all, in later lectures, we will mostly speak English. If you don't get this lecture completely, you've just missed the parts that are in Mongolian or quantum-ese. You could skip this lecture and still understand most of what is said later on. What would you miss? What you would miss would be some of the logical connections and we really want those. Let's try to get the hang of quantum-ese in this lecture. The second thing you have going for you is that as you use the new language in the later lectures, you'll find that it will make more and more sense. You'll find that this new language actually expresses the same ideas that we've been talking about since the beginning of the course. Finally, you have one more thing going for you. You can always return and review this lecture. In fact, if you are doing so, welcome back. Let's embark on speaking quantum-ese.

First, we need a few basic terms and abstract symbols. The first term is a system. A system is any piece of the quantum world that we wish to consider in itself. A photon in an interferometer was an example of a quantum system. An electron in an atom is an example of a quantum system. We can imagine a pair of particles may even be separated in space as one quantum system. Any piece of the quantum world that we want to consider in itself, that's a system. The second term is the idea of a state. A state is a physical situation of some quantum system. We have a special symbolism for representing states and it's called, for obscure historical reasons, a "ket." A ket looks like this: $|state\rangle$. There is on the left-hand side, there's a vertical line, and then there's something in between. Then on the right hand-side, there's an angled bracket. What's inside those funny little brackets is just a label. We can put numbers, words, funny little pictures. We can put whatever we like in there. The whole purpose is to identify the physical situation that is being described. We generally don't put really long labels. We generally choose very simple labels but we can put anything you like. It's just a description.

What else? We also need the idea of a basis. A basis is a set of distinct states, a collection of distinct states that cover all of the possible results of some measurement. For example, let's consider a photon in the interferometer, in the middle of the interferometer. If we look for it, if we make a measurement of the photon's location, we either find it in one beam, the upper beam, or the other beam, the lower beam. It's either in the upper beam or the lower beam. We can make states, upper and lower. Write them as "kets." Ket upper, $|upper\rangle$, and ket lower, $|lower\rangle$, and those together make up a basis for the photon and the interferometer. It's a key fact about quantum systems that there is more than one different sort of measurement that you can make on a system. That's just the key part of the principle of complementarity. There's more than one different sort of measurement and that means that a given system has more than one possible basis. More than one possible collection of basis states and we'll talk a lot more about that later.

Beside the basis states, there are also so-called "superposition states." The term "superposition" is meant to suggest a composite like 2 photographic images superimposed in a double exposure. In the interferometer example, a superposition state would be where we had the photon occupying both beams. There's the basis state where the photon is in the upper beam. There's the basis state where the photon is in the lower beam, but there's the superposition state where the photon is occupying both beams. In our symbolism, we write the superposition as an abstract sort of sum of the basis states. We would write it like this: $|state\rangle = a|upper\rangle + b|lower\rangle$. The state is a times the upper state plus b times the lower state. What are those things, a and b? They're numerical factors. They're very important and they're called "amplitudes," quantum amplitudes. Those are the numerical factors in a superposition sum. We'll interpret this and learn how to work with it in a little bit as we go, but for right now, we can always write a superposition as a sum of basis states with amplitudes.

Let me just make a couple of remarks. First of all, in full quantum mechanics, if you were reading a quantum mechanics textbook you would find that the amplitudes are not just ordinary numbers but might include imaginary numbers like the square root of -1. It's a curious fact about quantum mechanics that it makes use of these imaginary numbers. We're going to simplify and just use ordinary numbers including positive and negative numbers. That'll be good enough for our purposes but I have to tell you this is a simplification. In fact, I was recently talking with Dan Styer, a colleague of mine at Oberlin College, and Dan is one of the authors of a book that I'm recommending for you to read along with this course. I mentioned that I was going to leave out the possibility of imaginary numbers in the amplitudes and Dan was very concerned. He thought that was a very extreme simplification. Nevertheless, I think it's an allowable one for our purposes. If you want to learn how things work out with imaginary numbers included in the amplitudes, you can go read Dan's book. It's not very long. It's an excellent and accessible read.

The second remark I want to make is I want to introduce you to a convenient number. We're going to call this number s and s has the value 0.7071, etc. In fact, it's the number that if you square it you get $1/2$. It's the square root of $1/2$. Why am I giving this number a special name? I'm giving this number a special name because it happens to show up in lots and lots of examples that we're going to be considering. Since it shows up in so many examples that we consider, we're going to make up our own special private name for it. This is not a name in the books. You see the letter s in a book; it means something else. We're just going to use it in this course but it will save us from having to write the square root of $1/2$ over and over again.

Now we have a basic vocabulary. We have quantum systems. We have quantum states. We have both basis states associated with the outcomes of a measurement. We have superposition states, which are combinations of the basis states. These are represented symbolically by these funny kets and the numerical factors in the superposition states are called amplitudes. Now we need some rules for working with these and rules for giving them meaning. What do these symbols mean? Let's begin by giving the rules. Our first rule is the Rule of Superposition and it states that a superposition of 2 or more basis quantum states is also a quantum state. It says that superposition states are just as good as basis states. For example, besides the upper and lower states of the interferometer, there are also the superpositions like *a* upper plus *b* lower. For different choices of the amplitudes *a* and *b*, we get different superpositions. That means that the photon may be divided among the beams in many different ways and the amplitudes will tells us the details of how that's happened. Superpositions are just as good as basis states. You can have many different choices of amplitudes for the superpositions.

Our second rule is the Rule of Probability, but in fact, that's a rule we've seen before. It's the Born rule named after Max Born who introduced it. You'll remember the Born rule. The Born rule says that the wave intensity determines the particle probability. The intensity of the wave in any location determines how likely it is that the particle is found there. In our new language, the Born rule is as follows, the Rule of Probability, if we make a measurement the probability is determined by the amplitude according to the formula where probability is equal to the absolute value of amplitude squared. Remember quantum mechanics only tells us probabilities. It doesn't tell us the actual results of the measurements. Those are random but the Rule of Probability tells us how to calculate those probabilities. We just take the absolute value of the amplitude and we square it and that's the probability.

Let's take that apart a little bit. First of all, let me remind you, or perhaps tell you for the first time, some of the basic facts about probability. Any event has a probability, which is a number we'll call *p* between 0 and 1. The probability is a number between 0 and 1. If the probability is 0 that means that the event is impossible. It can never happen and if the probability is 1 that means that the event is certain. It must happen. If your probability is in between, it's bigger than 0 but less than 1, that means that it's possible but not certain—maybe so, maybe not. That's what probabilities in between mean.

What does it mean to have a particular specific probability? Suppose your probability is 0.37. What does that mean? That means that if you did the same experiment over and over again many times then the event that you're talking about would happen about 37% of the time in the long run on average. If the probability is 1/2, then if you do the same experiment over and over again, about 50% of the time you would expect that event to happen. In short, probabilities predict statistics.

Now that we know what a probability is, let's go back to the Born rule. The probability is the absolute value of the amplitude squared. Both positive and negative amplitudes will then give us positive probabilities which is part of the answer to why we put in that absolute value symbol to remind us that both positive and negative amplitudes both give us positive probabilities. Also, it's to make Dan Styer happy because, if we include imaginary numbers as our amplitudes, we'll need the absolute value signs for sure but let's let that pass.

Let's imagine that our photon state in our interferometer is this state a, amplitude a times upper, plus b times the state lower. It's $a|\text{upper}\rangle + b|\text{lower}\rangle$. So a and b are the amplitudes for being in the upper state and the lower state. Let's make a measurement to find out where the photon is. Then, the probability that we find out that it's in the upper beam will be the magnitude of a^2 because that's the amplitude for being in the upper beam. The probability that we find the photon in the lower beam is the magnitude of b^2 because b is the amplitude for being in the lower beam. Probability is the magnitude of the amplitude squared. By the way, that means that magnitude of a^2 plus the magnitude of b^2 must be 1 because probabilities have to add up to 1. Why is that? The photon must be somewhere. The probability that it's here plus the probability that it's here has to be 1. It's certain to be somewhere.

Let's consider another special state. Let's use our handy number, s. Suppose we have the state s times upper plus s times lower. In that case, each being would have a probability of the magnitude of s^2, which we said was 1/2. Each being would have a probability of 1/2. Interestingly though that same thing is true for a completely different quantum state, which is s times upper minus s times lower. The amplitude for upper is s but the amplitude for lower is $-s$. Why is this? It's because when you take the magnitude of s^2, you get that same thing as the magnitude of $-s^2$. You get 1/2. These 2 states, s upper plus s lower, and s upper minus s lower, they look the same for this measurement, but in fact they're really not the same quantum state but they happen to predict the same probabilities for this particular measurement. For some other measurement, maybe not.

What else do we need? We've got the Rule of Superposition and we've got the Rule of Probability, the Born rule, which tells us what the amplitudes mean. What else do we need? What we need are update rules. How does the quantum state change when something happens to the system? This is a key requirement; after all, mechanics is the science of motion, the science of how things change. Quantum mechanics had better include rules about how the quantum state changes. In fact, there are 2 rules for how the quantum state changes. This is very interesting. I'm going to introduce them and I'm not going to give them fancy names. I'm going to call them Update Rule I and Update Rule II.

Update Rule I says that when there is no measurement on a system, the state changes in a definite way that maintains any superposition. The state changes in a definite way that maintains any superposition. There are 2 key things there. One is that there is no randomness in the way that the state changes. The state itself may represent some indeterminate state of the world. I don't know whether the photon is in one beam or the other but the way the state, the quantum state, changes is not random at all. The second thing is the way the quantum state changes kind of respects any superpositions. This means that if you know how to update the basis states, you'll automatically know how to update the superposition state. That sounds confusing, but that's OK. We're going to give an example in a few minutes that will show you exactly how this works.

Next we have Update Rule II. Update Rule II is the rule that applies when there's a measurement on the system. It states that when there is a measurement on a quantum system, the result determines the new state. The state is updated randomly depending on the outcome. The state is updated randomly. What do I mean? Let's go back to the interferometer. We always run back to the interferometer when we're a little confused. If we go back to the interferometer and we imagine that the state of the photon in the interferometer is a times the upper beam state plus b times the lower beam state, we can imagine making a measurement of which beam the photon is in.

We'll use special non-absorbing photon detectors to determine which beam it's in. Suppose we measure it and we find that the photon is in the upper beam. What's the new state? The new state is upper and what probability does that occur with? It's the magnitude of a^2. Conversely, if we find that the photon's in the lower beam, the new state of the photon is lower. It must be in the lower beam and what's the probability that that occurs? It's the magnitude of b^2, the magnitude of the amplitude squared. What the new state is is a bit random. It depends on the measurement result. We can't tell for sure, in advance, which state it's going to wind up with. It's a gamble. That's Update Rule II.

Now we have some rules. We have the Rule of Superposition. We have the Rule of Probability. We have 2 Update Rules, whether or not there is a measurement or not, depending on whether there's a measurement. We have one rule or the other. It turns out that these rules are almost the only general rules of quantum mechanics. We'll actually add one more rule in Lecture 15. We almost have it all down.

How are we doing in quantam-ese? We have some vocabulary. We have some definitions to give some meaning to the vocabulary. We have some grammar including some rules for how to use the language. We really need to begin speaking quantam-ese. We're going to use our new language for our favorite example, the photon in the Mach-Zehnder interferometer. We're now going to describe, using the quantum language, what we described in the last lecture. It should sound very familiar. On the other hand, it may sound a bit unfamiliar because we'll be using a new language. At the start, the photon will pass from the upper side to the first beam-splitter. We're going to have to first decide how a beam splitter affects a quantum state. This is how it works. The upper state is updated to a state that's a superposition of upper and lower because the beam-splitter splits the beam. The upper state turns into s, our favorite number s, times upper plus s times lower. That's what the beam-splitter does to an upper state. How does the beam-splitter work if the light comes from the other direction? There it does the same thing. It's split into a superposition of upper and lower, but remember the mirror has its silvery coating on the lower side and so when the wave reflects off that side, there's a minus sign that shows up. The wave is inverted. In fact, the lower state, the lower basis state updates to s times upper $-s$ times lower, which we said was a different state. This is an example of Update Rule I. There is no measurement made at the half-silvered mirror. This is Rule I. If we know how the basis states work, we know how everything works and furthermore, the minus sign that shows up is an indication that we reflect from the silver side of the mirror on the bottom and that's where that minus sign comes from. As we already saw, that minus sign turns out to be important. Knowing how the basis states behave, in fact, tells us how superpositions behave.

Let's see this in action. We're going to analyze the Mach-Zehnder interferometer. We're going to keep track of the quantum state at each stage—the input state, the state in between the half-silvered mirrors and the state that comes out of the second half-silvered mirror. First of all, what's the initial state? What's the input state? It comes in from this way, so the initial state is the state upper, the basis state upper. The photon reaches the first half-silvered mirror and we know what a half-silvered mirror does. We know that the half-silvered mirror will take the state upper and turn it into s times upper plus s times lower. After the first half-silvered mirror, that's the state of the photon, s times upper plus s times lower. It's a superposition of being in the upper beam or the lower beam. The photon comes around and it reaches the second beam-splitter and the beams recombine. At the second beam-splitter, we use the rule for the beam-splitter again. It's Update Rule I because there's no measurement. We come into the second beam-splitter in the state s times upper plus s times lower. How do we apply the update rule?

Update Rule I maintains the superposition. All I have to do is apply the update rule to each term in the superposition independently. The s times upper state, or s times upper term, becomes s upper plus s lower. The s times lower state coming into the beam-splitter becomes s times s lower minus, or s upper minus s lower. The superposition of upper and lower comes out as a more complicated superposition of upper and lower. There are 4 terms in the superposition. It's s times s times upper plus s times s times lower plus s times s times upper minus s times s minus lower.

$$s|\text{upper}\rangle + s|\text{lower}\rangle$$
$$\Rightarrow \ s\big(s|\text{upper}\rangle + s|\text{lower}\rangle\big) + s\big(s|\text{upper}\rangle - s|\text{lower}\rangle\big).$$

What is that lined up with? It turns out that now we're going to apply the familiar rules of algebra to this. You just combine the terms and you simplify. I said there were 4 terms; 2 of them involve the upper state, so I'll combine them together. I get s² + s² because I have $s \times s$ each time, $s^2 + s^2$ times upper. What about the lower beam terms? I get $s^2 - s^2$ times lower because one of those terms has a minus sign. The lower terms cancel. The lower term goes away and the upper term is just $2 \times s^2 \times$ upper, but s is our favorite number. It's the square root of 1/2. If I take s_2, that's 1/2, I multiply it by 2, I get 1.

$$\left(s^2 + s^2\right)|\text{upper}\rangle + \left(s^2 - s^2\right)|\text{lower}\rangle = |\text{upper}\rangle.$$

wSo the final quantum state is upper. That means that at the end of the interferometer the photon must be in the upper beam. It must hit the upper detector and that's exactly right. That's exactly what we concluded last time, but we got it by means of this abstract language. Notice that the constructive and destructive interference in the interferometer applies to the amplitudes. In some of the terms of the state, the amplitudes cancelled out and you had destructive interference and in other terms, they augmented each other and you had constructive interference. It's the amplitudes that keep track of the photon's wave properties in this analysis.

Let's step back. What have we accomplished? Well, we've introduced a new abstract language, quantam-ese, to describe quantum physics. This abstract language has some basic rules. There are superposition states and these superpositions are just as good as basis states. A photon can be in the upper beam or the lower beam. It can also be in a superposition of upper and lower. For a photon that's no more uncomfortable than being in the upper beam or the lower beam. The photon likes it just as well. They're just as legitimate as quantum states. We found that the amplitudes that occur in the superpositions give us the probabilities. You just square the magnitudes. It's the Born rule. We found that the quantum state changes in 1 of 2 different ways depending on whether there's a measurement or not and we saw examples of both of those changes. In one of them, the Update Rule I, that was like the change that occurred to the amplitude at a half-silvered mirror. The other one, Update Rule II, was the kind of change you had if you did a non-destructive measurement of the location of the photon in the middle of the interferometer. We've used this language and these rules to describe the photon in the interferometer, this experiment. Along the way, we made a correct prediction about constructive and destructive interference. We were able to correctly predict which detector the photon would wind up in. That's not a bad piece of work for one lecture.

Of course, it all seems very abstract, but we're describing a strange microscopic world. We don't have a lot of everyday experience to go on. Specific examples help us understand what we're doing. The photon in the interferometer is a good and I hope a helpful example. We'll need more examples to aid our intuition. That's what we're going to do next time. We're going to apply our new quantum language to a different system, a system we haven't talked about so far. We're going to talk about a particle with internal spin. Some of the details will be different, but the basic rules will be exactly the same. We'll use the same quantum rules for all quantum systems. That's next time; I'll see you then.

Particles That Spin
Lecture 10

This time, we're going to take up a new example. We're going to use lots of 3-dimensional geometry, lots of angles and directions. We'll get to practice our spatial skills. This time we're going to talk about the physics of spin.

The physics of "spin" offers us another example of the quantum rules. An electron in orbit is analogous to a planet moving around the Sun. Each planet moves through space and also rotates on its axis. Something similar is true for quantum particles like electrons. They not only move through space—they also have internal spin. Spin is a kind of angular momentum, a physical measure of the amount of rotation in a particle.

Classical spins can have any value for any component. A "spin component" is the degree of spin a particle has along a particular axis. Classically, this depends on (1) the total amount of spin, and (2) the angle between the rotation axis and the axis we are interested in. For a classical spinning object, a given spin component can have any value, and all spin components have definite values at the same time.

Quantum spins have quite different characteristics. We can measure any component of a particle's spin by a "Stern-Gerlach apparatus," which measures the deflection of the particle in a nonuniform magnetic field. The orientation of the apparatus determines which spin component we measure. For electrons, the measurement of any spin component only can give 2 possible results, the values $\pm\frac{1}{2}$ (in units of $h/2\pi$). Electrons are said to be spin-$\frac{1}{2}$ particles, as are protons and neutrons. Other quantum particles can be spin 0 (no spin at all), spin 1, spin $\frac{3}{2}$, etc.

> **A "spin component" is the degree of spin a particle has along a particular axis. Classically, this depends on (1) the total amount of spin, and (2) the angle between the rotation axis and the axis we are interested in.**

Let's look at measurements and states for a spin-$\frac{1}{2}$ particle. We can measure an electron's spin along any axis in space. Two axes that we are especially interested in are the perpendicular axes z and x. A z measurement gives us 2 basis states $|\uparrow\rangle$ and $|\downarrow\rangle$, corresponding to the results $z = +\frac{1}{2}$ and $z = -\frac{1}{2}$, respectively. We call these "spin up" and "spin down." An x measurement gives us different basis states $|\rightarrow\rangle$ and $|\leftarrow\rangle$, corresponding to the results $x = +\frac{1}{2}$ and $x = -\frac{1}{2}$, respectively. We call these "spin right" and "spin left." We can write the x basis states as superpositions of z basis states and vice versa:

$$
\begin{aligned}
|\rightarrow\rangle &= s|\uparrow\rangle + s|\downarrow\rangle \\
|\leftarrow\rangle &= s|\uparrow\rangle - s|\downarrow\rangle
\end{aligned}
\quad \text{and} \quad
\begin{aligned}
|\uparrow\rangle &= s|\rightarrow\rangle + s|\leftarrow\rangle \\
|\downarrow\rangle &= s|\rightarrow\rangle - s|\leftarrow\rangle
\end{aligned}
.
$$

We call x and z "complementary quantities" for the electron. The x and z measurements are mutually exclusive—the Stern-Gerlach apparatus must be aligned one way or the other. There is an uncertainty principle for spin. A particle cannot have definite values for both x and z at the same time. For z basis states, z is definite but x is indeterminate; for x basis states, x is definite but z is indeterminate. The complementarity of different spin components for large-scale spinning objects (baseballs, planets) is negligible because h is so small.

From here we can extend the theory of spin $\frac{1}{2}$. There are other spin components besides z and x. Consider the spin component at an angle α from the z-axis (in the x-z plane). The basis vectors for this spin component can be called $|\alpha +\rangle$ and $|\alpha +\rangle$. For instance, $|\rightarrow\rangle = |90° +\rangle$. Suppose we prepare $|\alpha +\rangle$ and measure spin component z. What is the probability P that we obtain the result $z = +\frac{1}{2}$? Here is a table:

α	0°	45°	90°	135°	180°
P	1.00	0.85	0.50	0.15	0.00

(The values for 45° and 135° are rounded off here.) This table helps us calculate the probabilities if we have a spin with a definite component along any axis and then measure it along another axis at an angle α.

What happens to the spin of a particle if we rotate it in space? We can rotate an electron spin (or the spin of a proton or neutron) by using magnetic fields. Since no measurement is involved, the spin state should change according to update rule I. Suppose we rotate around the y-axis by 90°. How do basis states change?

$$|\uparrow\rangle \;\Rightarrow\; s|\uparrow\rangle + s|\downarrow\rangle \;=\; |\rightarrow\rangle.$$
$$|\downarrow\rangle \;\Rightarrow\; -s|\uparrow\rangle + s|\downarrow\rangle \;=\; -|\leftarrow\rangle.$$

From this, we can also find the following:

$$|\rightarrow\rangle \Rightarrow |\downarrow\rangle \text{ and } |\leftarrow\rangle \Rightarrow |\uparrow\rangle.$$

Why the minus sign in the rotation of $|\downarrow\rangle$? We cannot work things out consistently without it. But it should not matter. Because of the rule of probability, the states $|\leftarrow\rangle$ and $-|\leftarrow\rangle$ will yield exactly the same probabilities in any measurement. The 2 kets $|state\rangle$ and $-|state\rangle$ describe equivalent physical situations.

To rotate the spin by 360°, we can do it 90° at a time:

$$|\uparrow\rangle \;\Rightarrow\; |\rightarrow\rangle \;\Rightarrow\; |\downarrow\rangle \;\Rightarrow\; -|\leftarrow\rangle \;\Rightarrow\; -|\uparrow\rangle.$$

This curious minus sign does not worry us—but we will remember it. It turns out to be very interesting and significant later on! ■

Questions to Consider

1. In a Stern-Gerlach experiment, a beam of particles with spin is deflected by a magnetic field. The amount of deflection depends on the z component of the spin. In the real experiment, quantum particles emerge in just 2 different directions, corresponding to spin components $+\frac{1}{2}$ or $-\frac{1}{2}$. But imagine a world in which these particles had "classical" spin, like the spin of a top. How would the experiment turn out?

2. Here is an algebraic exercise suggested in the lecture. We gave formulas for the x basis states written in terms of the z basis states:

$|\rightarrow\rangle = s|\uparrow\rangle + s|\downarrow\rangle$ and $|\leftarrow\rangle = s|\uparrow\rangle - s|\downarrow\rangle$. Starting only with these, figure out the formulas that give the z basis states in terms of the x basis states. (You will need to remember that $s^2 = \frac{1}{2}$.)

3. Show that we cannot "do without" the funny minus signs in the rotation rule for spins. It would be nicer if a 90° rotation worked something like this: $|\uparrow\rangle \Rightarrow |\rightarrow\rangle \Rightarrow |\downarrow\rangle \Rightarrow |\leftarrow\rangle \Rightarrow |\uparrow\rangle$, with no minus signs at all. Show that this "nice rule" is inconsistent with update rule I. (Hint: Write $|\rightarrow\rangle$ and $|\leftarrow\rangle$ as superpositions of the basis states $|\uparrow\rangle$ and $|\downarrow\rangle$.)

Particles That Spin
Lecture 10—Transcript

Welcome to the tenth lecture in our course on quantum mechanics. Last time, we introduced a new abstract language to the microscopic world, a symbolic way to represent and work with situations in quantum physics. We established some vocabulary for the language and some rules for using it. We applied our language to our favorite example, a photon in a Mach-Zehnder interferometer. We predicted constructive and destructive interference. This time, we're going to take up a new example. We're going to use lots of 3-dimensional geometry, lots of angles and directions. We'll get to practice our spatial skills. This time we're going to talk about the physics of spin.

What is spin? An electron in orbit in an atom is analogous to a planet moving around the sun. That was the analogy that Ernest Rutherford made and that played a role in Bohr's model of the atom. Of course, we know that what's really going on with an electron and an atom is much weirder but let's just take this analogy for what it's worth. Each planet moves through space but it also rotates about its axis. It turns out there's something similar going on for quantum particles like electrons. They not only move through space but they also have internal spin. Spin is a kind of angular momentum, a physical measure of the amount of rotation in a particle. It's analogous to ordinary momentum. What I'm telling you is that electrons have a tiny amount of angular momentum just due to some kind of internal property of the electron.

We're going to be working in 3-dimensional space. We're going to use the famous Cartesian coordinates, x, y, and z to describe our space. How are we going to visualize these coordinate axes? The answer is we can always use our right hand. If you use your right hand and you spread apart your first and your second fingers, you stick out your thumb, then you have an x, a y, and a z axis. The x axis is in the direction of your fore finger, the y axis is in the direction of your middle finger, and the z axis is in the direction of your thumb. They are approximately right angles—x, y, and z axes. You have a set of Cartesian axes wherever you go. You shouldn't use your left hand. Things work out a little bit wrong for your left hand, but on your right hand, x, y, and z. We usually point the thumb upward because that's more comfortable.

When we talk about the z direction, z points toward the ceiling; z is up. That will help us keep things straight with our ordinary language.

A classical spinning object, a classical spin, for example, like a spinning planet or a spinning top, is always rotating about some axis but the axis can be pointing in any direction. The axis can be tilted in any way. How are we going to describe this? In fact, the way we're going to describe this is by specifying 3 spin components. A spin component is the degree of spin an object has along the x, y, or z axes in 3-dimensional space. This depends on the total amount of spin, but it also depends on the angle of the actual rotation. If this pencil is the rotation axis, it depends on which direction in space that rotation axis is. Whichever direction it is, the rotation is about that axis.

Let's imagine we have a spinning top and it's exactly upright. Its axis is parallel to the z axis. Then the z spin component is actually the total spin. The x and y spin components are both 0 because the axis is parallel to the z axis and is completely perpendicular to these. Let's take another example. Let's suppose that the spin axis is tilted over a little bit between the x axis and the z axis. The x and z spin components are both non-0. Each has a part of the total spin, but the y spin component is still 0 because it's still perpendicular to the direction of the axis of the rotation. That's sort of how spin components work. For a classical spinning object, each spin component can have any value whatsoever from 0 to something tremendously huge. All the spin components, all 3 spin components, can have definite values at the same time because the spin axis is a definite direction in space, but for quantum spins, both of these classical facts are false.

I say that quantum particles like electrons have spin. How do we know? How can we measure a quantum spin? It turns out that any component of a quantum spin can be measured by something called "a Stern-Gerlach apparatus" named after the physicist who originated it back in the 1920s. In a Stern-Gerlach apparatus a particle passes through a non-uniformed magnetic field, a magnetic field that's stronger on one side than the other. It turns out that different spins are deflected in different directions depending on their spin component and the deflection depends on just one of the components of the spin. It's the overall orientation of the apparatus. It's the angle of the magnets in space that determines which component of the spin we're measuring. These big Stern-Gerlach apparatuses, which are big magnets that allow us to deflect the particles in a beam, will allow us to measure the spins of those particles.

Let's think about electrons. If we measure the spin of an electron, if we measure any spin component of an electron, it turns out that that measurement can only give us 1 of 2 possible results. Angular momentum, like energy, is quantized. It comes in quantum amounts and the values that we can get for the spin component of an electron are either $+1/2$ or $-1/2$ in the basic units of h, Planck's constant, divided by 2π. That's the basic unit of angular momentum. There's Planck's constant again. Forgetting the exact units, the value can either be $+1/2$ or $-1/2$. Those are the only 2 possible values for a spin component for an electron. Electrons are called spin-1/2 particles because their spin components can only be $\pm 1/2$. It turns that protons and neutrons also happen to be spin-12 particles. Indeed, there are other particles which have different spins. There are spin-0 particles. There are particles with no spin at all. There are spin-1 particles. There are spin-3/2 particles and so on. It's an interesting feature of quantum mechanics that you can only have spins that are an integer divided by 2; 0, 1/2, 1, 3/2, 2, and so on.

In this lecture, we're going to stick with the spin-1/2 particles like the electrons and the protons and the neutrons in this lecture. Notice, by the way, the spin-1/2 particles are terribly important because all of the common constituents of ordinary matter are spin-1/2 particles.

What kind of quantum states are there for a spin-12 particle? What kinds of measurements can we make on a spin-1/2 particle like an electron? To start out with, let's realize that we can measure the electron's spin along any axis in space and 2 especially interesting axes are the x axis and the z axis—x and z. What about y? Remember in the last lecture how we said we weren't going to consider the possibility that quantum amplitudes were imaginary numbers like the square root of -1. It turns out that to describe spin components around the y direction, we would need those imaginary amplitudes, and so to keep on the safe side, we're going to leave y alone and stick to x and z.

If we make a spin component measurement along the z axis or the spin component measurement along the x axis by orienting our Stern-Gerlach apparatus this way or this way, then those measurements give us basis states. For a z basis state, the z measurement, the basis states are what we can call "up" and "down." We write them with little arrows inside the kets ($|\uparrow\rangle$ and $|\downarrow\rangle$). Remember inside the kets it's just a label. We can put whatever we like. We can put numbers or letters or funny pictures and so we'll put little arrows to remind us, spin up and spin down. Spin up corresponds to a measurement of the z spin component of $+1/2$. Spin down corresponds to a measurement of the z component of the spin of $-1/2$; a basis spin up, spin down. How about an x measurement? Then our basis states are spin right and spin left. Spin right corresponds to a measurement result of $+1/2$. Spin left corresponds to a measurement result of $-1/2$. Spin right or spin left, we represent them by little arrows pointing to the right or to the left inside our ket ($|\rightarrow\rangle$ and $|\leftarrow\rangle$). Either the z basis states, up and down, or the x basis states, right and left, are perfectly good basis states for the electron spin. We can write the x basis states as superpositions of the z basis states and vice versa if we want to. Let me just go ahead and show you how that works out. Once again, we're going to be using our favorite number, s, the square root of $1/2$. That shows all the time in this lecture, so we'll be using it.

Let's look at the x basis states in terms of the z basis. We're going to write spin to the right in terms of spin up and spin down. It turns out that spin to the right is just s times spin up plus s times spin down. It's a superposition of spin up and spin down. Spin left, the other x basis state, can be written in terms of the z basis by s spin up minus s spin down. Recalling the s squared is $1/2$. We know that if we had spin to the right for example, and we measured its z component of spin, we would get to the 2 possible values with equal probability. Probability 12 because that's the magnitude of s squared.

$$\begin{aligned} |\rightarrow\rangle &= s|\uparrow\rangle + s|\downarrow\rangle \\ |\leftarrow\rangle &= s|\uparrow\rangle - s|\downarrow\rangle \end{aligned}$$

We can write the x states in terms of the z basis, but we can also write the z states, up and down, in terms of the x basis. If you're clever and you remember some high school algebra, you can actually work it out from the equations that we've just given. It's like solving 2 equations and 2 unknowns, but I'll just give you the answer and I'll let you see if you can work it out on your own. I'll give you answer—spin up is s times spin to the right plus s times spin to the left. Spin down is s times spin to the right minus s times spin to the left. We can write the z states in terms of the x basis.

$$|\uparrow\rangle = s|\rightarrow\rangle + s|\leftarrow\rangle$$
$$|\downarrow\rangle = s|\rightarrow\rangle - s|\leftarrow\rangle$$

There's a relation between x and z. The spin components x and z are complementary quantities for the electron. They're like position and momentum. You see measurements of x and z are mutually exclusive. We have to take our Stern-Gerlach magnets and align them one way or the other. We have to choose and this means that there's a kind of uncertainty principle for spin. We can't know both the x component of the spin and the z component of spin at the same time. An electron cannot have definite values for both spin components at the same time. So in a z basis state, either up or down, z is completely definite.

We know exactly what the z component but x is completely indeterminate. If we made a measurement we would not be able to predict at all what the outcome would be. It could be $+1/2$, it could be $-1/2$ with equal probability. Similarly, if we had a state that had a definite value of the x component of spin, either right or left, then it's x component of spin would be completely definite but it's z component of spin would be completely indeterminate. There may be other states which are a bit indeterminate for both x and z, but the point is that we can't know x and z components of the spin exactly at the same time. They are complementary quantities.

What about macroscopic spinning objects? What about a planet or a top or something like that? How does this quantum mechanics work for gigantic things? Of course, the complementarity of different spin components is negligible for planets and spinning tops and so on. Why is this? It's the usual reason. Planck's constant is so small. The quantum effects depend on the size of Planck's constant and it's a really, really tiny number when we write it out in usual units. It's a decimal point then 33 zeros before you get to the first non-zero digit. It's a really tiny number. Remember our discussion of position and momentum, for large objects both can be pretty well defined. Even though they're related by an uncertainty principle, both position and momentum can be very well defined for a macroscopic object because Planck's constant is so small. In a similar way, for macroscopic spinning objects all the spin components can be pretty well defined at the same time and so the macroscopic has a definite axis of spin, a definite direction about which it's spinning.

Let's extend our discussion. We can do z states. We can do x states. Let's extend to doing some other things. Let's consider other spin components besides z and x. Let's stay away from y though because we don't want to consider imaginary numbers. What we're going to do, we're going to stay in the x, z plane. Let's imagine we want to look at the spin component of an electron along a direction that is at an angle α from the z axis in the x, z plane. this is 0. Here's 45°. Here's 90°, some angle α in the x, z plane. To measure this we'll have to take our Stern-Gerlach magnets and we'll have to tilt them at the angle α but that's okay. When we do that, that measurement will have basis vectors in the usual way. The basis vectors we can have are $\alpha+$ or $\alpha-$. If we measure the spin component then the $\alpha+$ state corresponds to getting $+1/2h$ or $+1/2$ units of Planck's constant over 2π or $-1/2$ in the same units.

For an example that actually includes what we've already talked about, the x states are actually just where α is equal to 90°. Spin to the right is 90° plus because the x axis is at 90° and spin to the right is the $+1/2$ state for the x component measurement. We can actually talk about spin states in any direction and all of those spin states can be written as superpositions of z basis state or as superpositions of x basis state as convenient. Here's our experiment. We're going to start out with the state $\alpha+$. This is the state that you get if you knew that the spin component at the angle α was in the plus direction. Loosely speaking, I can identify it with a pencil pointing this way.

This is our spin component, our spin state $\alpha+$. Let's measure not that spin component but the z component. Our Stern-Gerlach magnets are going to be oriented so we measure the z component of the spin. The spin is prepared along one axis and it's measured along another and there's an angle α

between them. My question what's the probability, call it p, that we get the z component to be $+1/2$.

If we know to start out with the spin component being plus along this axis, what's the probability that we'll find that the spin component is plus along this axis at an angle α ? It turns out we can work out table for various angles and so let me show you the table now. On one side we have the various angles—0, 45°, 90°, 135°, 180°. On the other side we have various probabilities. We have a probability of 1 for 0° and then the probabilities get smaller and smaller until at 180°, the probability is 0. Here's the table.

α	0°	45°	90°	135°	180°
P	1.00	0.85	0.50	0.15	0.00

Now we have to understand what's in the table.

Let's first of all understand what's easy to understand. If the angle is 0 that's easy to understand because the angle 0, then the spin state we made was up. It's up along the z axis, at 0° from the z axis and we measured spin along the z axis. The z component of spin and so we found up always. The probability that we got up was 1. With 0°, that's easy; of course, you get 1. Another one that's easy is at the bottom of the table. The other end of the table and that's what happens if our angle α is 180°. We prepare the spin to have a spin component plus in a direction that is the opposite direction from the z direction, which means that we're making spin down. So if the spin is spin down; then we measure the z component of spin, we never get that the spin is up and so the probability is 0. Another one that's easy is 90° because at 90° we're just making spin to the right. When we write spin to the right as a superposition, s up plus s down, then we square the amplitudes to get the probabilities. We just get 1/2 for the probability that if we prepare it to the right and we measure it in the up-down direction; we'll find spin up.

Those are all really easy to understand. The tricky parts are the other 2 rows in the table—45° and 135°. There's a diagram that will help. Let me show you. In the diagram there's a half circle, which represents the various angles from 0° to 180° that are marked on there. Then, next to the half circle, is a vertical line and that vertical line represents the range of probabilities from 0 to 1. We can see that 0°, we can just look horizontally in the diagram to go from 0° angle to the probability 1. For 180°, that's at the bottom, we can go straight horizontally on the diagram from 180° over to 0 and the same thing works for 90°. We can go horizontally from 90°, halfway down the semi-circle over to the line and get .5, the probability exactly halfway between 0 and 1.

When we look at the angles 45° and 135°, we find that at 45° the probability should be between 0.5 and 1.0 and it's actually closer to 1.0 because of the way the circle sits. We actually get a 0.85 for the probability and similarly, for 135° that's between 0 and .5. It's a little closer to 0 than it is to 0.5. It's actually 0.15 and if you remember a little high school geometry, you can derive these numbers for yourself and you'll find that 0.5 or 0.85 and 1.5 are actually rounded off a little bit. I give you the challenge of finding out what the next decimal place is.

Exactly why does this semi-circle and line trick work? The explanation is a little involved. We can work it out from what we've said but the point here is just to make the point that we can work out any angle we choose. We can figure out the probabilities for measurement results if we prepare the spin along one direction and we measure the spin along another direction. Indeed, there's nothing sacred about the z direction here. The table lets us calculate the probabilities if we have a spin with a definite component along any axis and it's measured along some other axis. This table will allow us to compute the probability that we get the plus result for that problem. We just need to know the angle α between the spin state and the spin measurement. It's a pretty handy table and we'll make use of it later on.

Let's extend the theory a little bit more. What happens if we rotate a spin? What does it mean to rotate a spin? Isn't the spin already rotating? What I mean by rotating a spin is I want to turn the spin axis in some way. I want to twist the spin around in some way. I can actually do this physically with electrons and protons and neutrons using magnetic fields. It turns out that the spins of these particles act as tiny magnets. If you will, the poles of the magnet are along the spin axis of the particle and the external magnetic field twists the particles around like a compass needle is twisted around by the earth's magnetic field. We can rotate the spins of these particles in the process; there's no measurement involved.

The rotation of the spin is an example of Update Rule I, how a state changes when there's no measurement involved. To make something definite, I'm going to imagine we rotate the spin by about the y axis by 90°. Wait a second. Aren't we staying away from the y axis? Yes, we're staying away from the y axis because if we rotate around the y axis then the x and z axes always stay in the same plane. That's the safe plane and so we'll make our rotations around the y axis because that keeps x and z well behaved.

Suppose we rotate the spin about the y axis by 90°. How do the z basis states change? Remember if we have Update Rule I, if we know how the basis states change, we'll be able to figure out how every state changes. If we have the rotation around the y axis by 90°, a spin up state changes to s times up plus s times down which is just spin to the right and sure enough, spin up changes to spin to the right. That makes sense.

Now let's see how spin down changes. When we work it out we get - s times spin up plus s times spin down and that looks kind of like spin to the left but there's an extra minus sign in both terms. In fact, this is minus spin to the left. This is kind of funny. This is just −1 times the spin to the left ket. It's the spin to the left basis state times a −1 amplitude. This is not the same thing as spin to the right; −1 times spin to the left is not spin to the right. Spin to the right is something completely different. It's a funny thing. It's very abstract. It's a −1 amplitude times the basis state spin left. Then, from these 2 facts, we can also work out how spin to the right and spin to the left are affected by the rotation because we can just apply the rule, Update Rule I: Spin to the right is a superposition of up down; spin to the left is a superposition of up and down and we can just apply the rule. We find that spin to the right becomes spin down and spin to the left becomes spin up.

All of that makes sense except the funny minus sign. Why is there a funny minus sign when you take spin down and rotate it around to spin left? Why doesn't it just go to spin left? Wouldn't that be nicer? Why does it go to minus spin left? It turns out that you can't get by without a minus sign somewhere. You can't do without it and still be mathematically consistent and obey Update Rule I. There has to be a minus sign somewhere. On the other hand, the minus sign really shouldn't matter. Remember the Rule of the Probability. In the Rule of the Probability, we always square the magnitude of the amplitudes to get the probabilities. If you have a positive amplitude or a negative amplitude it doesn't matter. You get the same probabilities. The states left and minus left have exactly the same amplitudes except the one for minus left are all negative. It's amplitudes of the negatives of the amplitudes for left and so when we calculate probabilities, we always get exactly the same probabilities for any measurement for the states left and negative left. Those states look exactly the same. ($|state\rangle$ and $-|state\rangle$) Those 2 kets represent thus equivalent physical situations. State and minus state describe equivalent physical situations. It's a little weird, but it's OK.

What if we wanted to rotate the spin by 360° going 90° at a time? We could do it like this. We'd start with spin up and then rotate by 90° and we get spin to the right. Then we rotate by 90° again and we get spin down. We rotate by 90° again and we get minus spin left. That's the funny minus sign. Then we rotate by 90° again using Update Rule II. We have minus spin left and since left goes to up, minus spin left goes to minus up. We start with spin up and we rotate by 360° and we get minus spin up. It's a funny result. If you take a spin and you rotate it by 360° it doesn't quite come back to the same quantum state. That seems funny but it doesn't really worry us because the state up and the state minus up look exactly the same. They correspond to physically equivalent situations. They get exactly the same results for every experiment. They're pretty much the same but we should keep in mind this curious minus sign that's connected to rotation. I've gone into it because it actually turns out to mean something. That minus sign is going to show up again later in a very surprising place.

Here's a quick recap. We've studied the quantum mechanics of spin-1/2 particles like electrons, protons, and neutrons. We say we can measure any spin component and get either +1/2 or −1/2 for the result. The different spin components are complementary quantities. Only one can be definite at a time. We considered the basis states for z and x, the up and down states and the right and left states and we saw how these were related. Each set of states is a superposition of the other set. We can also work out the rules for spins along any angle α in between *x* and *z*. Finally, we saw how to rotate a spin using a magnetic field and we found this funny, odd minus sign after we rotated a spin by 360°, but the minus sign is not too much of a worry.

That concludes Section Two, our initial look at the theory of quantum mechanics. It may not seem as if we have done much. We have a few rules. We have a couple of examples, but in fact, we've actually put together a very powerful toolkit for discussing quantum mechanics. In the next few lectures, we'll see the ideas we've discussed in these 3 lectures again and again. We'll see systems and states and amplitudes and probabilities. We'll use our language over and over. Next time, we'll begin Section Three, which is a tour of the quantum realm. Our first stop on the tour is the physics of identical particles. That's next time; I'll see you then.

Quantum Twins
Lecture 11

Now we'll be moving into ... several different particular topics in quantum theory. We'll begin ... with ... the theory of identical particles. All electrons are identical. All photons are identical. What does this mean? How can quantum theory describe that? What are the implications? This is an amazing story that we'll be telling. ... Here's our essential point: Macroscopic classic objects and microscopic quantum particles have a different sense of identity.

Macroscopic objects obey the "snowflake principle": No 2 are exactly alike. Every object can be uniquely identified, at least in principle. No 2 snowflakes are alike (though some appear quite similar). Even identical twins have slightly different fingerprints. If we put 2 pennies in a box and then draw 1 out, it makes sense to ask which penny we have. There are always microscopic differences that can be used as identifying marks, like the serial numbers on currency.

In contrast, quantum particles do not obey this snowflake principle. All electrons are exactly identical to each other. They may differ in location and spin, but they are otherwise exactly the same. If we put 2 electrons in a box and then draw 1 out, it does not make sense to ask which electron we have. There are no microscopic differences to be used as serial numbers. The same is true for 2 photons, or 2 protons, or even 2 atoms of the same type.

The point here is not simply a philosophical one; it changes how we apply the quantum rules. We already know the quantum rules for a single-particle system. We imagine 2 "boxes," A and B. A quantum particle can be in either of the 2 boxes. Thus 1 particle has basis states $|A\rangle$ and $|B\rangle$ (and could be in any superposition of these).

"Distinguishable" quantum particles have simple rules. These particles can be discriminated in some way. For example, in a 2particle system, our first particle might be a proton and the second one an electron. The 2-particle states $|AB\rangle$ and $|BA\rangle$ are distinct physical situations. In $|AB\rangle$, the first particle is in box A and the second in box B; in $|BA\rangle$, they are reversed. We can tell these situations apart. Distinguishable particles might also be in the same box, as in the states $|AA\rangle$ and $|BB\rangle$.

"Identical" particles force us to reexamine our assumptions. For 2 electrons, the states $|AB\rangle$ and $|BA\rangle$ do not represent distinct physical situations. We can express this by using the "SWAP" operation, which exchanges the 2 particles. For instance, $SWAP|AB\rangle = |BA\rangle$. (If we had more particles, we would have a SWAP operation for each possible pair.) For any state of 2 identical particles, $|state\rangle$ and $SWAP|state\rangle$ must be physically equivalent. If we swap twice, we must return to the original situation: $SWAP^2|state\rangle = |state\rangle$.

Quantum particles come in 2 possible types, depending on how the SWAP operation works: [Bose-Einstein particles, or "bosons," and Fermi-Dirac particles, or "fermions"].

Quantum particles come in 2 possible types, depending on how the SWAP operation works. First we will consider Bose-Einstein particles, or "bosons," named for Satyendra Bose and Albert Einstein, who did groundbreaking work related to them. The boson rule says that for a pair of identical bosons, $SWAP|state\rangle = |state\rangle$. The quantum state is completely unchanged when we swap the particles. Examples of bosons include photons and helium atoms.

Next we will consider Fermi-Dirac particles, or "fermions," about which Enrico Fermi and Paul Dirac did important work. The fermion rule says that for a pair of identical fermions, $SWAP|state\rangle = -|state\rangle$. The quantum state acquires a negative sign when we swap the particles. Two swaps still cancel out:

$$SWAP^2|state\rangle = -\left(-|state\rangle\right) = +|state\rangle.$$

Examples of fermions include electrons, protons, and neutrons. Notice that the basic constituents of ordinary matter are all fermions.

Consider the 2 boxes again, with 1 particle in each. For distinguishable particles, we have distinct states $|AB\rangle$ and $|BA\rangle$. For bosons, there is only 1 distinct state, which is $s|AB\rangle + s|BA\rangle$. This is called a "symmetric" state because it is unchanged if we swap the particles. For bosons there is also only 1 distinct state, which is $s|AB\rangle - s|BA\rangle$. This is called an "antisymmetric" state because it acquires a minus sign is we swap the 2 particles:

$$\begin{aligned} \text{SWAP}\left(s|AB\rangle - s|BA\rangle\right) &= s|BA\rangle - s|AB\rangle \\ &= -\left(s|AB\rangle - s|BA\rangle\right). \end{aligned}$$

If 2 (or an even number) of identical fermions combine to make a "composite" particle, then the result is a boson, because swapping 2 fermions yields 2 minus signs. This is why ordinary helium atoms (with 2 electrons + 2 protons + 2 neutrons) are bosons. ∎

Questions to Consider

1. Think of the 2 most nearly identical macroscopic objects in your house. How could they in fact be distinguished?

2. If we have 3 identical particles (labeled 1, 2, and 3), then there are at least 3 different SWAP operations: SWAP(12), SWAP(13), and SWAP(23). Show how SWAP(23) can be created out of a combination of SWAP(12) and SWAP(13). Also show how to use these pairwise SWAPs to create the "cyclic" swap that takes $1 \Rightarrow 2 \Rightarrow 3 \Rightarrow 1$.

3. A composite particle of several fermions can act like a boson. Can we have the opposite—a composite of bosons that acts as a fermion? If so, how? And if not, why not?

Quantum Twins
Lecture 11—Transcript

Welcome to the eleventh lecture in our course on quantum mechanics. We had just finished our introduction to simplified quantum mechanics. Now we are experts at, or at least acquainted with, quantum systems, quantum states, superpositions of states, amplitudes, probabilities, and so on. We've used our new quantum language to explore 2 physical systems in depth, the photon and the interferometer, and particles like electron with intrinsic spin.

Now we'll be moving into Section Three of the course, a look at several different particular topics in quantum theory. We'll begin Section Three with a look at the theory of identical particles. All electrons are identical. All photons are identical. What does this mean? How can quantum theory describe that? What are the implications? This is an amazing story that we'll be telling. It's so amazing that it will keep us busy for the next 4 lectures. Let's begin.

Here's our essential point: Macroscopic classic objects and microscopic quantum particles have a different sense of identity. Macroscopic objects obey the snowflake principle. No 2 macroscopic objects are exactly alike. How do we know about snowflakes? It's a common saying, but is it really true that no 2 snowflakes are alike? In fact, scientists have actually caught and photographed many thousands of snowflakes. There's a researcher at Cal Tech that has perfected the technique and been doing for this years. It's real science. It aims at categorizing the crystal patterns formed in snowflakes and relating those patterns to different cloud conditions in which the snowflakes form. The pictures that they come up with are beautiful. Very rarely, 2 extremely simple snow crystals, which are just hexagonal in shape, do look similar but in fact, no 2 snowflakes are exactly alike.

That's a general principle about the world. Every macroscopic object can be uniquely identified at least in principle, for example, identical human twins. We call them identical, and indeed they're genetically identical, but they're different individuals. For example, they have very similar but different fingerprints. Similar whorl patterns, but different in detail. They can be identified by their fingerprints. Or suppose we consider 2 pennies.

Imagine we put these 2 pennies in a box and we shake it up and we draw one out. It actually makes sense to ask which penny did we pull out because the 2 pennies are actually a common everyday situation in which this is not true. Let's suppose we deposit 2 pennies in your bank account. Then the next day you go to the bank and you withdraw one penny. Which penny did you withdraw? The question doesn't even make sense. Bank accounts are not shoeboxes with your name on it in the back with cash in it. Bank accounts are a more abstract reality and in fact that's true about money in the modern age in general. Money is actually a representation of abstract accounting information. It's not tied to ordinary physical tokens. Pennies lose their individuality in the banking system. If we wanted to sum up the situation about classical microscopic objects and quantum particles, we might say that classical objects are like money in your pocket. You might have this coin or that coin and you can tell the difference. On the other hand, quantum particles are like money in the bank, less tangible but still real.

I want to take a bit of a detour because this problem of identity, the identity of different objects whether they can be identical or whether they are distinguishable, actually came up in the late 19th century in the context of classical physics and that's an interesting story. I think it's worth telling here. Let's consider a container of gas, a tank of gas. This tank has a partition in the middle, a wall that prevents the gas on one side from getting into the other side. Let's suppose that we're able to remove the partition, if you will, open the valve, remove the partition, and put it back again as we like. This is our situation; the container that has 2 halves. There's a partition in the middle, it can be removed and put back in, and it contains gas.

Now let's suppose that we put different gases in each side of the container. Let's suppose we put nitrogen in one side and oxygen in the other side. Of course, we're looking at this from a point of view of a 19th-century physicist, so we know that the gases are made out of atoms or in this case, molecules, because oxygen and nitrogen are in diatomic molecules. There's nitrogen molecules on one side, oxygen molecules on the other. The 2 elements are separated. We remove the partition and we allow the gas molecules to move around. The gas molecules fly around. The gases mix together and after awhile, we replace the partition. When we replace the partition, half of the gas is on one side and half of the gas is on the other, but now the situation is actually very different. We have nitrogen and oxygen mixed together on both sides of the container. It might be a lot of trouble to separate the gases again. We might have to lower the temperature of the container. At about 190° below 0, the oxygen will liquefy and the nitrogen wouldn't. Then we can draw off the nitrogen and we can put the oxygen in the other side. It would take a lot of work. It would be a big mess to un-mix the gases.

Let's try the experiment again, except let's put the same gas on each side. Let's put nitrogen on each side. We have nitrogen molecules on the left and nitrogen molecules on the right. If we remove the partition, the gas molecules move around. The gases mix together. Now we replace the partition. The new situation is really no different from the old situation. We still have a tank with nitrogen molecules on both sides of the partition.

The 2 experiments, experiment number 1 with 2 different gasses and experiment number 2 with the same gas on each side, seem to lead to very different results. In experiment number 1, there's what's called "irreversibility." That doesn't mean that we actually can't restore the original situation but it does mean that a change has occurred that we'll have to work at to undo. We'll have to do work on the system to restore the original. There's an irreversible change in that sense. Whereas in experiment 2, when we put the partition back into the gas, we've actually restored what is essentially the same situation we started with. We've made no real change. That is a reversible situation.

This set of thought experiments was pondered in the last decades of the 19th century by the American physicist, Josiah Willard Gibbs. He said if nitrogen molecules had distinct identities, if nitrogen molecules had little serial numbers on them so that you could tell one nitrogen molecule from another, then both experiments, he said, are irreversible. Experiment 1 is obviously irreversible because we mix the gas together but experiment 2 is also irreversible, Gibbs said, because we've mixed up the left hand and right hand molecules. There was a certain set of molecules on the left hand side of the tank at first. Perhaps somewhere, someone has an enormous list, which is a list of all the serial numbers of all the nitrogen molecules on the left-hand side. Similarly, there were certain nitrogen molecules with their serial numbers on the right-hand side. But then we withdraw the partition and the molecules get mixed up, and when we replace the partition those lists are no good anymore. There's a new situation.

If nitrogen molecules have an individual identity, said Gibbs, both experiments involve irreversible changes, but in experiment number 2, we observe as a practical matter that we haven't made any difference to the overall properties of the gas. That is a practical matter. Nobody can really tell that we did this. Nobody can tell that we removed the partition and put it back in because the molecules are distributed in exactly the same way.

Gibbs drew the following interesting conclusion. He said in order to think about this correctly, we should consider all nitrogen molecules to be exactly the same. We should consider mixing around the nitrogen molecules to be exactly the same as doing nothing because if we exchange the position of 2 nitrogen molecules nobody can tell. That makes no difference in the physics of the situation. This was a very strange conclusion to draw and, in fact, this thought experiment came to be called "Gibbs Paradox." It was a somewhat mysterious aspect of classical physics until the invention of quantum mechanics and the concept of identical particles.

That brings us back to our story. In quantum mechanics, as we've said, it is possible for 2 particles, 2 electrons say, to be really and truly identical. This is not just a philosophical point. This actually affects the way we apply the quantum rule; the way we apply the language of quantum mechanics. We already know how to apply the quantum rules for a system consisting of a single particle.

Let's imagine 2 boxes, A and B. A particle can be in either in this box or that box. We imagine that we have 2 basis states for a quantum particle, a single quantum particle. There's the basis state A which corresponds to being in box A and there's the basis state B which corresponds to being in box B. These are basis states because there's an observable feature, namely, the what-box-are-you-in observable feature which has these as the 2 outcomes. Of course, the particle also has quantum states which are superpositions of A and B. We mustn't forget that. Superpositions of A and B mean the particle might not be in a definite box. It might be, somehow, distributed among 2 boxes just as the photon was distributed among 2 beams in the interferometer.

That's how a single particle behaves. That's the quantum language for a single particle. What about a pair of distinguishable particles, that is to say, particles that can be discriminated in some way? For example, the first particle is a proton and the second particle is an electron. They're easy to tell apart. The protons, a couple of thousand times more massive than the electron; the proton's positively charged. The electron's negatively charged. They are no problem to tell apart. Let's suppose the first particle and the second particle can be distinguished like a proton and an electron. Among the 2-particle quantum states there's a state, which we might call AB in which the first particle's in A and the second particle's in B. Then there's also a state, which we might call BA in which the first particle's in B and the second particle's in A. These 2 quantum states, which we can represent by kets, represent distinct physical situations. In AB it's the first particle that is in A, the other particle's in B. In BA it's the first particle that's in B and the other one is in A and because we can tell the particles apart, we can tell the 2 states apart. We can tell the 2 physical situations apart. We can ask the question which particle is it in? Of course, in a pair of distinguishable particles, there might also be some other states. For example, the state AA where both particles are in the same box or BB and there might be superpositions of all of these things. We'll talk a little bit later in the course about how to think about all those states. For now, let's just think about AB and BA.

Now let's turn our attention to a pair of identical particles, like a pair of electrons. The identical particles, the identicalness of the particles, forces us to reexamine our assumptions. You see for 2 electrons AB and BA do not represent distinct physical situations. If I say the first electron is in A and the second electron in B or the first electron's in B and the second electron's in A, you may very reasonably ask what do you mean the first electron? What physical meaning can you ascribe to the statement, oh this electron is the one that's in A and that electron's in B? Electrons don't have serial numbers. They aren't labeled 1 and 2. All we know is that there's an electron in A and an electron in B. Then, AB and BA cannot be distinct quantum states. There's a very neat way to express this mathematically. We're using something called the SWAP operation and what this does is we imagine exchanging 2 particles. If we act with the SWAP operation on the state AB, we get the state BA. You take the 2 particles and you exchange them. If you take SWAP acting on BA, you get AB. The SWAP operation just exchanges.

That's how it works out for 2 particles. What if you had more than 2 particles? You may have noticed there are more than 2 particles in the universe, more than 2 electrons. What if you had many particles? Then you actually need lots of SWAP operations. You need a different SWAP operation for every pair of particles. You need to be able to exchange that pair of particles.

Let's go back to 2 particles. For a state, which we represent, of course, by a ket, $|state\rangle$, of 2 identical particles then it must be the case that the state and SWAP acting on the state must be physical equivalent quantum states because the particles are identical. They're indistinguishable. Remember, our penny swapping game. If we'd played the penny swapping game with 2 electrons, you turn your back and I either exchange the electrons or I didn't, you'd lose. You wouldn't be able to tell whether I exchanged them or not because the electrons are identical. There's no physical difference between the physical situation with the electrons this way and the physical situation with the electrons that way. The state and SWAP the state must be physical equivalent quantum states. What happens if you SWAP twice? What happens if you SWAP the states, SWAP the particles and then you SWAP them again? Then, you must return to the original situation and symbolically we can write that SWAP^2 acting on the state which SWAP acting on SWAP acting on the state. Just gives you back the state. SWAP^2 is the same as doing nothing.

What possibilities does quantum mechanics admit? It turns out that quantum particles come in 2 possible types depending on how the SWAP operation works. The first type was identified by Satyendra Bose and Albert Einstein, and they're called "Bose-Einstein particles," or "bosons." The boson rule is very simple. If you have a pair of identical bosons then SWAP acting on the state gives you the state. SWAP doesn't affect the state. The quantum state is completely unchanged when we SWAP the particles. There are actual particles that are bosons that follow the Bose-Einstein rules. Some examples of bosons are photons. Photons are bosons it turns out and if you consider helium atoms, entire helium atoms. They can act as bosons as well. The other possibility was discovered by Enrico Fermi and Paul Dirac, 2 of the great early quantum physicists. They're called "Fermi-Dirac particles," or "fermions." The fermion rule is that for a pair of identical fermions if you SWAP the state, SWAP acting on state, what do you get? You get the negative of the state. You get the -1 amplitude times the state. The quantum state acquires a negative amplitude when you SWAP the particles.

Of course, we saw this negative amplitude business before. We know that if you multiply the state by -1 it doesn't change any of the probabilities of any measurements. We know that state and minus the state are actually equivalent physical situations. This is okay. This is a possible quantum rule. You can have an electron and an electron. When you SWAP it, we get a state that has a minus sign out front, but that minus sign has no observable consequences and so that's OK. It's still the case that 2 SWAPs cancel out because if I SWAP twice I just get 2 minus signs. Two minus signs make a plus sign. SWAP^2 acting on the state gives me the state just as it should. There are lots of examples of fermions. Electrons are fermions. Protons are fermions. Neutrons are fermions. Notice, once again, that all of the basic constituents of ordinary matter are all fermions.

Let's sum it up. There are 2 boxes again. There's A and B. Let's suppose we know that there's one particle in each box. What's the situation if there particles are distinguishable? There are 2 distinct states. There's the state AB where the first particle's in one box and the second particle's in the other. There's the state BA in which the particles have exchanged position. These are distinguishable situations quantum mechanically. They're distinct states. Of course, superpositions of these things are also allowed. There's more than one physically distinct state for a pair of a distinguishable particles in this situation. Let's suppose we're talking about bosons. Then it turns out there's only distinct state and that one distinct state turns out to be, remembering our favorite number s, the square root of $1/2$. So s times AB plus s times BA ($s|AB\rangle + s|BA\rangle$) and this is called a symmetric state since if we apply the SWAP operation to it, AB becomes BA and vice versa. This state actually just becomes itself. The state is exactly unchanged if we apply the SWAP operation and so it's called a "symmetric state."

What about fermions? Again, for a particle in each of the boxes there's only distinct state and that distinct state is s times AB minus s times BA ($s|AB\rangle - s|BA\rangle$). If we apply the SWAP operation to it, SWAP of AB becomes BA, SWAP of BA becomes BA. When we apply the SWAP operation to it, we actually get from the state to the negative of the state. The SWAP of the state is $-s$ times AB plus s times BA. This state, which is the only possible state of these 2 fermions, one in each box is called an "anti-symmetric state" since we get a minus sign when we apply SWAP. Anti-symmetric, it's kind of symmetric, but you pick up a minus sign, that's the anti part.

We have bosons and we have fermions. Those are the only 2 types of particles we can have in quantum mechanics. There's actually one final wrinkle. If you take 2 identical fermions or indeed, an even number of identical fermions, and you combine them together to make a composite particle then the result is actually not a fermion but a boson. Why is this? When you SWAP 2 fermions, that yields 2 minus signs, which cancel. An ordinary helium atom has 2 electrons, 2 protons, and 2 neutrons in it. Ordinary helium atoms collectively act as bosons. You can make fermions together act like bosons. The reverse is not true. You can't make a composite particle of bosons and have it act like a fermion. That's kind of interesting. Quantum particles come in 2 varieties. There are bosons and fermions. The difference between bosons and fermions is just a single minus sign. The minus sign is in the SWAP operation and it seems like a small thing but as we'll see this has tremendous consequences.

Let me indulge a couple of minutes in sort of personal philosophical observation about this subject. That is macroscopic objects, the objects of our experience, or direct experience, they obey the snowflake principle, the principle that no 2 of them are exactly alike because they are immensely complex. The electrons and so on that inhabit this microscopic realm we're exploring do not obey the snowflake principle. They're not like tiny baseballs. They're not like tiny pennies. It's hard to escape the conclusion that electrons are somehow radically simple. They're almost too simple for us to comprehend. We've never experienced in our everyday life anything that simple. What do I mean?

Recall the old Greek idea about atoms. The Greek Atomists said everything we see is made of smaller pieces and those pieces are made of smaller pieces and so on but maybe, the Atomists said, there's a bottom to this process. Maybe you can finally get down to a level where there are basic things that really are not made of other things, indivisible things. The Greek atoms, and the whole point for the Atomists, for the Greek Atomists, is that these atoms are simple. All of the complexity of the world arises from complicated configurations of atoms but that the atoms themselves are simple, like nothing in our direct experience. To me the story of identical particles offers the most persuasive sort of evidence that in quantum mechanics we are really getting down to a fundamental level of reality—a level at which objects are really simple, they're so simple they can be identical to one another.

For the next 2 lectures we're going to learn all about bosons and all about fermions. We're going to do bosons first. We're going to learn about everything from lasers to superconductors and that'll be next time. I'll see you then.

The Gregarious Particles
Lecture 12

We're going to be considering bosons, the symmetric ones, and examples of bosons include photons, the particles of light, helium atoms. ... Where did all this boson stuff come from originally? It's actually rooted in the same thing that quantum theory itself is rooted in; remember the original impetus for quantum theory was to explain black body radiation.

Because of the boson rule, 2 identical bosons can exist in the same state. In fact, they prefer it that way. We consider a pair of particles in 3 boxes: A, B, and C. A single particle has basis states $|A\rangle$, $|B\rangle$, and $|C\rangle$. A pair of distinguishable particles has 9 basis states:

$$|AA\rangle, \ |AB\rangle, \ |AC\rangle, \ |BA\rangle, \ |BB\rangle, \ |BC\rangle,$$
$$|CA\rangle, \ |CB\rangle, \ |CC\rangle.$$

In $\frac{1}{3}$ of these states ($|AA\rangle, |BB\rangle, |CC\rangle$), the particles will be found in the same box. Just by chance, we would expect to find the particles together $\frac{1}{3}$ of the time.

If the 2 particles are bosons, there are fewer basis states, since the states must be symmetric under a particle swap. A pair of identical bosons has 6 symmetric basis states:

$$|AA\rangle, \ s|AB\rangle + s|BA\rangle, \ s|AC\rangle + s|CA\rangle, \ |BB\rangle,$$
$$s|BC\rangle + s|CB\rangle, \ |CC\rangle.$$

In $\frac{1}{2}$ of these states, the particles are found in the same box. Just by chance, we would expect to find the particles together $\frac{1}{2}$ of the time, more often than we would a pair of distinguishable particles. Bosons have a "gregarious" streak, not because of some special force but simply because they are bosons. This effect gets stronger when more bosons are together.

The boson rule explains how a laser works. Einstein identified 3 ways that an atom can interact with a photon. An atom can absorb a photon, if one is present with the right energy. The atom jumps to an excited state. Alternatively, an atom already in an excited state can emit a photon spontaneously, which then emerges in some random direction. Another possibility is stimulated emission: Suppose we have an excited atom, and there are already some photons present that are moving in a particular direction. Because photons are bosons, the atom has a greater probability of adding its own photon to this group.

Stimulated emission is what enables us to build lasers.

Stimulated emission is what enables us to build lasers. Here is the simplified version of how it works: First, get a lot of atoms together. Add some energy so that most of the atoms are excited. This is called "optical pumping." We need to have more excited atoms than unexcited ones—called a "population inversion"—since otherwise absorption will defeat us. Next, make sure that we have some photons around that are moving in a particular direction. This is usually done by bouncing the light we want back and forth with mirrors. Because photons are bosons, lots and lots of photons will be emitted in that same direction. ("laser" stands for "light amplification by stimulated emission of radiation.") The result will be a highly directional beam of light having just 1 wavelength. This is called "coherent light."

The boson rule also explains some amazing low-temperature phenomena. Our first example is superfluid helium. Helium atoms are bosons. Helium gas liquefies at about 4° above absolute zero, and the resulting liquid is called Helium I. At about 2° above absolute zero, helium forms a superfluid (Helium II). A superfluid can flow without any friction, leak through tiny pores less than 1 millionth of a meter across, and literally "creep" out of an open container. The superfluid state represents trillions of helium atoms in a single quantum state—a macroscopic example of the quantum gregariousness of bosons.

Our second example of amazing low-temperature phenomena is superconductivity. In metals, electric current is carried by the flow of electrons. But there is some friction in the form of electrical resistance, which is why a current-carrying wire can heat up. Under some circumstances, the electrons can combine into "Cooper pairs." Cooper pairs can carry electric current, but they are bosons. Near absolute zero, Cooper pairs flow as a superfluid in the metal. Electric current can be carried with zero resistance! This is called "superconductivity." If we set up an electric current in a superconducting circuit, it will continue to flow for millions of years without any addition of energy. This has many technological applications, especially to make powerful electromagnets. A lot of research involves looking for superconductors that work at higher temperatures.

Our third example is a Bose-Einstein condensate. In this example, a supercold cloud of atoms can be created in which thousands or millions of atoms are in exactly the same quantum state. These atoms act like a single quantum system. This state of matter was first predicted in 1925 but was not created in the lab until 1995. ∎

Questions to Consider

1. Three particles each have 4 basis states $|A\rangle$, $|B\rangle$, $|C\rangle$, and $|D\rangle$. If the particles are distinguishable, how many 3-particle basis states are there? If they are identical bosons, how many basis states are there?

2. Helium III is a rare isotope of helium that only has 1 neutron in its nucleus, so that helium III atoms are fermions. Nevertheless, at extremely low temperatures (only $\frac{1}{400}$ of a degree above absolute zero) it is observed that helium III can become a superfluid. How is this possible?

The Gregarious Particles
Lecture 12—Transcript

Welcome to the twelfth lecture in our course on quantum mechanics. As you will recall from the last lecture, quantum particles are quite different from classical macroscopic objects. Large objects obey, what we call, the snowflake principle. No 2 of them are ever exactly alike. There are always tiny differences that would enable you to distinguish one large object from another large object.

Quantum particles can be truly identical. All electrons are identical with each other. All photons are identical with each other. When we considered this idea carefully, we found that there could be 2 possible types of quantum particles and it depended on the operation of the SWAPping 2 identical particles affected the quantum state. For bosons, the SWAP operation acting on the state just gave us the same state. Bosons are said to be symmetric if we exchange the 2 particles but for fermions the SWAP operation acting on the state returned the negative of the state. The amplitude -1 times the state. Fermions are said to be anti-symmetric if we exchange particles. So in this lecture we're going to be considering bosons, the symmetric ones, and examples of bosons include photons, the particles of light, helium atoms, and several other examples that we'll see before the end of the lecture.

Where did all this boson stuff come from originally? It's actually rooted in the same thing that quantum theory itself is rooted in; remember the original impetus for quantum theory was to explain black body radiation. To marry together the theory of heat with the theory of light and explain how warm objects emitted electromagnetic radiation. That was Planck's motivation in introducing the quantum hypothesis. Then over the next couple of decades, Einstein made many contributions to this subject and in his contributions, he always in a very clever way was able to weed together wave and particle ideas about light. Then in 1924, an Indian physicist named Satyendra Bose came up with a very strange idea. Bose said you can actually explain black body radiation by just treating light as if it were made of particles provided you treat them as identical particles. In other words, exchanging 2 photons gives you a physical situation that is the same as the original one. It doesn't change the physical state of the assembly of the photons. So this is a somewhat different approach from Planck and from Einstein, but yet it gives the same answer.

Bose writes a paper on this and he sends it off to Einstein in Germany. Einstein reads the paper. He thinks it's a great idea and he makes sure that Bose's paper is published in the leading German journal of physics. Also, Einstein turns his hand to extending Bose's idea to other particles, to atoms and so on. They're a little different from photons. Photons can be easily created or destroyed in being emitted or absorbed whereas atoms are conserved. Atoms persist over time and so the mathematics is a little bit different but Einstein was able to extend Bose's idea to this new situation. The particles that obey these ideas that Bose and Einstein worked out are called "Bose-Einstein particles," or "bosons," for short, and they follow the Bose-Einstein statistical law, which we will call "the boson rule." That's what we're about today, particles that follow the boson rule.

Here's how it works. Imagine that you have 3 boxes. We'll call them A, B, and C. A particle can be in any one of the boxes. Our quantum mechanical measurement is to find out where the particle is and there are 3 basis states for this measurement. There's the state, A, meaning the particle is in box A; the state B, meaning the particle's in box B, and the state C, meaning that the particle is in box C. Of course, as we know from the rule of superposition there are also superpositions of these basis states. Those are also possible, always equally valid. The particle's location need not be determinate. The particle could be spread out among 2 or 3 boxes just as the photon's position in an interferometer is spread out among 2 or more beams. The purpose of the 3 boxes is just to provide us with 3 basis states for our measurement and make our conversation easier.

First of all, we've already figured out everything there is to know about the quantum mechanics for one particle. That's great. We can be in the basis state A or B or C or a superposition, but suppose there are 2 particles and suppose that the measurement we make is where the 2 particles are. How does it work out? How does the quantum mechanics work out for 2 particles? First of all, let's suppose that the particles are distinguishable. That way we can call the particles number 1 and number 2. We know which particle is number 1 and which particle is number 2.

Let's consider the basis states for this measurement. There are 9 basis states in all. First of all, there are basis states in which the particles happen to be in the same box. There's the *AA* state. There's the *BB* state. There's the *CC* state. Particles are both together in 1 of the 3 boxes. Those are 3 basis states. Then there are 6 basis states that correspond to situations in which the particles are in different boxes. There's the *AB* state, which means number 1 is in *A* and number 2 is in *B*. There's the *BA* state, which means number 1 is in *B* and number 2 is in *A* and so on. There's *AC* and *CA* and *BC* and *CB*. There are 6 states where they are in different boxes, 6 basis states and, of course, all of these correspond to distinct physical situations because the particles are distinguishable from one another and as usual there are also superpositions of these states, but these are the states that correspond to the outcomes of our measurement.

There are 9 basis states all together and of these basis states, 3 of them correspond to the particles being in the same box, *AA*, *BB*, or *CC*. In 1/3 of the basis states, the particles are in the same box. You can imagine an experiment where you set up a system at random. The particles are just put into the boxes willy-nilly and then we do the measurement to locate the particles. By chance then, we would expect to find the particles in the same box about 1/3 of the time, about 33% of the time because there are 9 possible basis states and 3 of them correspond to the particles being in the same box. If the particles if distinguishable they're in the same box about 1/3 of the time on average, if we prepare things randomly.

Let's do the same experiment for 2 identical bosons. The measurement's same, but the boson state must be symmetric if we SWAP the particles. What does that mean? The same box states, the states in which the particles are in the same box, they're still OK. *AA* is exactly the same if you switch *A* and *A*, *BB*, *CC*; those are all perfectly good boson states, but what about the different box states, the states in which the 2 particles lie in different boxes? Then there are only 3 basis states. Remembering that our favorite number, *s*, which is the square root of 1/2, the 3 basis states are *s* times *AB* plus *s* times *BA*, *s* times *AC* plus *s* times *CA* and *s* *BC* plus *s* *CB*. What do those mean? Each of these states involves the particles being in 2 different boxes, but because they're bosons you can't tell which particle is in which and each of those states is symmetric under the SWAP operation because the SWAP operation takes *AB* to *BA* and vice versa and each of these are symmetric states. These are the 3 possible symmetric states, which have a particle in each of 2 boxes.

How many basis states are there? There are 6 of them. In how many of these basis states are the particles in the same box? It's in half of them, 3 out of the 6. That means if we set the system up at random and we measure where the particles were, by chance we would expect to find the bosons in the same box 50% of the time. So, 50% is more than 33%. If the particles are bosons, they're more likely to wind up in the same box just at random. This is an observable difference between a pair of distinguishable particles and a pair of identical bosons. The bosons wind up together more easily than we would've expected. They have a gregarious streak. They like to hang out together. Why is this? It's not because of some special attraction. It's simply because they are bosons and the affect gets stronger, actually, when more bosons are involved. If you work it out, if you have 3 particles and 3 boxes, what's the likelihood of them all being together in the same box? If they're distinguishable particles, well let's see, there are 27 ways to arrange the particles. In 3 of them they're all in the same box. That's 3 out of 27, which is a probability of 1/9, about 11% of the time you would expect the particles to be in the same if they were distinguishable.

On the other hand, if they're identical bosons it turns out that there are only 10 ways, 10 basis states that are symmetric. There's one basis state in which there's a particle in each of the 3 boxes. There are 6 basis states in which there are 2 particles in 1 box, 1 particle in another and 0 particles in the third box. There's 6 ways to do that and there are 3 ways that the particles could all be in the same box. That means the probability of finding them together, if you just prepare it randomly, is 3 out of 10, about 30%. It's almost 3 times as likely for the particles to be all together if they are bosons.

The boson rule explains a host of phenomenon including some pretty exotic stuff, as we'll see, but let's begin with something that's actually fairly commonplace, the laser. We're talking about photons. In 1917, Einstein identified 3 ways that an atom can interact with a photon and we'll simplify our treatment of the atom. We'll just imagine the atom has 2 energy levels, a ground state and an excited state. The first way that a photon and an atom can interact is that the photon could be absorbed, the process of absorption. You got an atom that starts out in its ground state. A photon comes along with just the right energy; the atom can absorb the photon. The photon goes away and the atom jumps up to the excited state. That can happen.

The second thing that can happen is something called "spontaneous emission." That's where the atom's already in an excited state and then, just at random, it can jump down to the lower state, the ground state, and emit a photon. It emits the photon in some random direction in space. This is called spontaneous emission but there's a third way that Einstein realized in 1917. That's called stimulated emission. You got an atom in an excited state. But now, there already are some photons present with the right energy moving in some particular direction and because photons are bosons, because they're gregarious, because it's more likely for them to wind up together, it's much more likely for the atom to add its own photon to this group moving in that direction. This process of stimulated emission is quite remarkable. Indeed, it's this process that allows us to build a laser.

How do you build a laser? The first laser was built in 1960, but they're so ubiquitous now that you have lasers all over the place. How do you build a laser? You get a lot of atoms together and you add some energy so that most of the atoms are in excited states. This is called "optical pumping" and the way you add the energy to the atoms, there are lots of ways to do it. You might have an actual bright light that you shine on it or electrical discharges or chemical reaction or all kinds of things. It can even be another laser. If you already have another laser, you can use it to optically pump this laser.

We need to arrange it so that there are more excited atoms than unexcited atoms, more atoms in their excited energy level than in their ground state. This is a called "a population inversion." There are more excited atoms than unexcited atoms. We have to have that because otherwise the absorption process will actually defeat us in trying to make the thing turn into a laser. We need to make this special population inversion. We've got some excited atoms. They're ready to emit photons. We make sure that we have some photons flying around that are moving in a particular direction that we want. This is usually done by putting our collection of atoms between a pair of mirrors. The photons that we want bounce back and forth between the mirrors many times. One of the mirrors will be partially silvered like with the half-silvered mirrors we talked about before. Sometimes the photon can escape, but mostly they bounce back and forth.

Photons are bosons. There are lots and lots of them bouncing back and forth in the laser cavity, it's called. The atoms in the laser will be much more likely to admit their photons to be part of the same game. Pretty soon you have lots and lots and lots of photons moving in this direction and the result is that you have a highly directional beam of light coming out through the partially-silvered mirror, highly directional having just one wavelength. So-called "coherent light" and that's a laser, which is actually an acronym that stands for "light amplification by stimulated emission of radiation."

Of course, we've already seen a laser in this course. This is our laser. It's what's called a "helium neon" laser. Let me just quickly tell you how it works. Inside this laser is a tube of gas containing helium and neon atoms. Actually it's kind of clever; we excite the helium atoms and the helium atoms collide with the neon atoms and transfer energy to them. Then the neon atoms are excited and we're interested in the neon atoms as we get a population inversion in the neon atoms. When those neon atoms decay, they produce photons of red light as we saw and there are mirrors on either end of our tube. A fully-silvered mirror in back, a partially-silvered mirror in the front, so that the light bounces back and forth and what happens is a beam escapes through the partially-silvered mirror and this laser emits about 1500 trillion photons each second.

That's actually much less than an ordinary light bulb. This only emits about half of a millawatt of energy, but all that light is in one direction, all of it's at one wavelength, so this is a very special, very intense kind of light source for light of that wavelength. There are of course all sorts of lasers. There are gas lasers, solid state lasers, and so on. Some operate with short pulses, others continuously. They can be built at all kinds of different wavelengths. Some lasers are even tunable; you just adjust the wavelength, which is kind of very clever and very complicated. They're immensely useful in our technology, everything from telecommunications to eye surgery. They all depend on the fact, the quantum fact, that photons are bosons. Because photons are bosons it is comparatively easy to get lots and lots of photons with the same wavelength, the same energy traveling in the same direction in a beam. That's how a laser works. It's all about the boson rule.

So much for photons. The boson rule also explains some amazing phenomena that occur at extremely low temperatures. Temperatures near to absolute zero, which is 273° below 0 Celsius. The first example I want to talk about is the example of liquid helium. Remember I mentioned that helium atoms are bosons. Helium gas becomes a liquid at the unbelievable low temperature of 4° above absolute zero. Helium is very hard to liquefy but at 4° above absolute zero you can make liquid helium and this liquid is called "helium I" as you'll see there's also another kind of helium. If you cool this liquid down at about 2° above absolute zero, the liquid changes. It becomes a different sort of liquid. It becomes something called a "superfluid." That's called "helium II." What is a superfluid?

A superfluid is something that can flow without any friction at all. It can seep through pores less than 1 millionth of a meter across. If you have any holes whatsoever even ones that are almost too small to see with a microscope, helium can leak through them, liquid helium II can leak through them. Helium II conducts heat perfectly. It's impossible to have a temperature difference between one part or another part of your superfluid. It has all kinds of strange properties; zero friction, infinite thermal conductivity. In fact, helium can even creep out of a container, an open container. If there were liquid helium in my cup then the helium could crawl over the side of the cup and down the wall and fill up whatever this was rested on. This is a very unfamiliar and very peculiar state of matter. It's unlike anything that we know in ordinary temperatures. The way it works is that it represents trillions of helium atoms in a single quantum state. It's an example of the quantum gregariousness of the bosons because the helium atoms are all moving together in the superfluid, in the same quantum state. They do not collide with each other. They don't produce the friction in the flow and so on because they are perfectly in unison. They behave not as a liquid we're familiar with but as a superfluid.

Here's a second example of the importance of the gregariousness of bosons. That example is superconductivity. Metals are conductors. An electric current is carried because electrons inside the conductor, inside the metal, move, they move and that carries electric charge from place to place. That's an electric current. In an ordinary conductor, there's always some form of friction. There's always some form of electrical resistance into the flow of current. This is why a current carrying wire can heat up. This is why a source of power is required to keep the current flowing because there's always this friction to electric current called "electrical resistance." It turns out that for some metals and some other materials, this electrical resistance actually goes to zero not just really small, but all the way to zero at low temperatures. Temperatures close to absolute zero. The metal turns into a superconductor.

This phenomenon was discovered a long time ago, actually in 1911, but it wasn't explained until the late 1950s, 1957, by the introduction of something called "the BCS theory." The BCS theory is named after John Bardeen, Leon Cooper, and John Schrieffer, who developed the theory. In the BCS theory, the electrons in the conductors—which are not themselves bosons, they're fermions—the electrons combine into pairs called "Cooper pairs." The Cooper pairs can move around together and they carry electric current because they can carry charge from place to place. But the Cooper pairs, a pair of electrons bound together, a Cooper pair is a boson. The Cooper pairs at low temperatures can flow in the metal like a superfluid and because you have a superfluid flow you have current without resistance. You have electrical flow without friction and that's the phenomenon of superconductivity.

All kinds of amazing things happen because of superconductivity. If you set up an electric current in a superconducting loop, it doesn't lose its energy to friction. Without any additional power that electric current will continue to flow for millions of years. This is a thing with lots of technological applications especially useful for making very powerful electromagnets. In electromagnets, you need to run electric currents through loops of wire and if you use ordinary wires, you need a lot of power because there's friction to that electric current. You produce a lot of waste heat so the electromagnet must be continually cooled. If you can manage to make the whole thing a superconductor then you'd get the current going and then you'd just stand back and it stays going forever. There's lots of research going on right now to find superconductors that work at higher temperatures or that can support stronger magnetic fields. There are some superconductors that work at more than 100° above absolute zero, which is amazing and a wonderful discovery, but it's still a long way from room temperature. It's still pretty darn cold.

We've talked about superfluids and we've talked about superconductors. Both of these examples show that the boson rule can lead us to new states of matter at very low temperatures, states of matter with unfamiliar properties. Both of these examples illustrate the tendency for bosons to join together in the same quantum state and act in concert, they act together. Not because of forces that act between the bosons, but just because of the fact that their states are symmetric when particles are exchanged. Actually, these examples that I've mentioned are not as straightforward as we would like because both of these examples, the superfluids and the superconductors, are condensed systems; liquids and solids. The atoms are really close together and the particles we're talking about, the Cooper pairs and the helium atoms, are actually exerting considerable forces on each other. They're right next to each other. This really complicates things and this is a technical matter. It makes it harder to say this effect is due to that cause.

Let me give you a third and much cleaner example, a much purer example of the Bose rule in action. What you do is you create a sparse cloud of boson atoms. Sparse means merely a vacuum, just a few billion atoms floating in space. The first experiments for this used rubidium atoms. They turn out to be very convenient. What you do is you suspend the cloud in a vacuum sitting there in your laboratory. Just suspend it in space with a magnetic field and some lasers. Then you cool the atoms down. This is the hard part. You cool the atoms down to an astoundingly low temperature. There's almost no heat energy left. The cloud of bosons is about one 10 millionth of a degree above absolute zero. A 10 millionth of a degree above absolute zero, and when you do that, the cloud of atoms will form what is called "a Bose-Einstein condensate."

In the Bose-Einstein condensate, thousands or millions of atoms can all be in exactly the same quantum state. They're bosons. They like being in the same quantum state. Because all of these atoms are in the same quantum state the atoms act like a single quantum system, the whole cloud is described by a single de Broglie wave. The whole cloud exhibits constructive and destructive quantum interference effects. This is a remarkable state of matter.

It was predicted in 1925 but it was not created in the lab until 1995, 70 years later. These Bose-Einstein condensates count as both, an astounding prediction of quantum theory and a real tour de force of experimental physics, a real triumph to actually make these things after so many decades.

We've been exploring the strange physics of bosons, the quantum particles whose states are symmetric when you exchange them, when you SWAP the particles. That symmetry led us to conclude that identical bosons have a peculiar tendency to collect together in the same quantum state, to be in the same box to use our original example. This tendency, which is pretty weird in itself, is not due to special forces acting between them but just to the fact that they're bosons and it led us to some remarkable conclusions.

We saw how the boson rule for photons led to stimulated emission of light and thus to the laser. We found how the gregariousness of bosons led to some really wild states of matter, unexpected things near absolute zero, superfluids that flow without friction, superconductors that can carry electric current without resistance, and Bose-Einstein condensates where you have a whole cloud of ultra-cold atoms described by a single quantum wave. Next time, we're going to tell the other side of the story. Next time, we're going to talk about fermions, the other type of quantum particle. The properties of fermions are just as remarkable, but they are closer, in fact, to our everyday experience. Fermions are next time; I'll see you then.

Antisymmetric and Antisocial
Lecture 13

Last time we talked about bosons and their curiously gregarious behavior. It was a lecture full of laser physics and exotic states and super cold matter. Lots of particles were always doing the same thing. ... This time we're going to discuss the other kind of quantum particle, the fermions. The fermions include electrons, protons, and neutrons. They're anything but rare. ... They are very different from bosons.

Because of the fermion rule, 2 identical fermions can never exist in the same state. Consider again 2 particles in 3 boxes: A, B, and C. For a pair of identical fermions, there are only 3 antisymmetric basis states:

$$s|AB\rangle - s|BA\rangle, \quad s|AC\rangle - s|CA\rangle, \quad s|BC\rangle - s|CB\rangle.$$

We cannot have states with the fermions in the same box, because those states cannot be antisymmetric: $s|AA\rangle - s|AA\rangle = 0$, which is no state at all.

This is the basis of the "Pauli exclusion principle" discovered by Wolfgang Pauli in 1925 as he investigated atomic structure. Pauli said that no 2 electrons can be in exactly the same quantum state. The same principle holds for any sort of fermion (e.g., protons and neutrons). Fermions are antisocial simply because they are fermions—no actual "repelling forces" are involved.

The exclusion principle for electrons explains many of the properties of ordinary matter. The structure of atoms with many electrons depends on Pauli's principle. An atom has various energy levels corresponding to standing wave patterns. If electrons were bosons, they could all just collect in the bottom level. The Pauli exclusion principle means that the electrons can "fill up" the lower rungs on the ladder. Note that, since electrons also have spin, there can be 2 electrons for each standing wave pattern. The chemical properties of the various elements depend on how the electrons have filled the energy levels. Generally, only the outermost electrons (on the top rungs) are involved in chemical reactions.

The structure of atomic nuclei works in a similar way. There are 2 kinds of fermions involved: protons and neutrons. Both are called nucleons. The way that nucleons fill their nuclear shells determines nuclear properties. For instance, certain numbers of nucleons make unusually stable nuclei, while others make unstable nuclei.

The Pauli exclusion principle explains why matter occupies space.

The Pauli exclusion principle explains why matter occupies space. A gas is easily compressible. It is not very hard to push twice as much gas into the same volume. A liquid or a solid is much, much less compressible. It is almost impossible to push twice as much material into the same volume. Why is solid matter solid? Electric repulsion between electrons cannot be the whole story, since ordinary matter contains both positive and negative charges and thus attracts and repels the same amount. To push 2 solid objects into the same volume, we would have to add more electrons into the same region of space. To do this, we must give the electrons a very high energy, since all of the low-energy states in that volume are already occupied. Thus, it takes a lot of energy to get twice as many electrons into the same space. The Pauli exclusion principle affects almost everything we see around us. ■

Questions to Consider

1. Three particles each have 4 basis states $|A\rangle$, $|B\rangle$, $|C\rangle$, and $|D\rangle$. If the particles are distinguishable, how many 3-particle basis states are there? If they are identical fermions, how many basis states are there?

2. Look around the room and begin to make a list of the phenomena you can see that are directly affected by the Pauli exclusion principle. (You may stop your list after you reach a dozen items. That should not take long!)

Antisymmetric and Antisocial
Lecture 13—Transcript

Welcome to the 13th lecture in our course on quantum mechanics. Right now we're in the middle of discussing the properties of identical quantum particles. You'll recall that we've found that such particles come in 2 basic types, bosons and fermions. Bosons are particles whose state is symmetric when the particles are exchanged. Fermions are particles whose state is anti-symmetric when the particles are exchanged. Last time we talked about bosons and their curiously gregarious behavior. It was a lecture full of laser physics and exotic states and super cold matter. Lots of particles were always doing the same thing; bosons are gregarious. They favor doing that. This time we're going to discuss the other kind of quantum particle, the fermions.

The fermions include electrons, protons, and neutrons. They're anything but rare. They include the basic constituents of matter. They are very different from bosons. Let's consider once again the example of particles in 3 possible boxes—boxes A, B, and C. One particle can be in any of the 3. There's a basis for particle states, a basis with state A, state B, or state C. We can write any state has a superposition of those 3 and that will tell us how the quantum particle is inhabiting the boxes, but suppose we have not just 1 particle in the boxes but 2 particles. Suppose those 2 particles are identical fermions. Remember the fermion rule. The fermion rule is that if you apply the SWAP operation, that exchanges 2 particles, to the quantum state you should get back the negative of the quantum state, the amplitude minus 1 times that state. If we exchange the fermions the state picks up a minus sign and that minus sign is why we call it an "anti-symmetric state."

For a pair of identical fermions, this means that there are only 3 distinct basis states for 2 identical fermions living in the 3 boxes and those basis states are $sAB - sBA$, where s, of course, is our square root of $1/2$, our favorite number. There's $sAC - sCA$ and there's $sBC - sCB$. ($CBsBCsCAsACsBAsABs$---,,) Since the SWAP operation takes AB to AB and so on, it exchanges the 2 particles. If you examine those 3 states you'll see that the SWAP takes each one to its negative, their anti-symmetric, states as required but notice that all of these states have one particle in each of 2 boxes. Can we have a fermion state in which both particles are in one box, say, box A? The answer is no, we can't. The state *AA* is symmetric, not anti-symmetric. If we exchange the 2 particles we get the same state back. It can't be a legitimate fermion state. If we try to make something out of it, if we try to make something anti-symmetric like *sAA* – *sAA* we just get 0—no state at all.

The conclusion is that 2 identical fermions can never be found in the same box. What we've done is we've established the Pauli exclusion principle, one of the great principles of physics. It was discovered by the Austrian physicist, Wolfgang Pauli, in 1925, as he investigated atomic structure. Pauli said that no 2 electrons in an atom he was considering, no 2 electrons can be in exactly the same quantum state. This same principle holds for any sort of fermion, for protons and neutrons and so on. No 2 identical fermions can be in the same quantum state. The implications of Pauli's were worked out almost at once within about a year of his suggestion by the Italian physicist, Enrico Fermi and the English physicist Paul Dirac. They're called "Fermi-Dirac particles" or "fermions" for short, and they obey the Fermi-Dirac statistical rules, which we'll just call "the fermion rule." Fermions of the same species are identical and they obey the Pauli exclusion principle.

If bosons are gregarious particles that like to hang out together, then fermions are anti-social particles. They're never found in exactly the same place doing the exactly the same thing. They're loners. Once again this is not because of any special repelling forces. It's not that fermions push each other away by means of forces, it's just because they are fermions and their quantum state must be anti-symmetric under particle exchanges as we've described. That's where it comes from and that implies the Pauli exclusion principle.

Pauli was interested in atomic structure. Let's begin with that. Let's see how the Pauli exclusion principle for fermions applies to the electrons in an atom. As we saw some lectures ago, the electrons in atoms can only exist in certain discreet energy levels. These energy levels correspond to standing wave patterns for the electron about the atom, to solutions to Schrödinger's equation describing the waves around an atom. It turns out that when you do the work to solve the equation you find that these energy levels tend to cluster together in shells. Several energy levels of about the same energy with wider gaps in energy in between. There's a group of energy levels at the first shell, the second shell, and so on. How many levels are in each shell?

Actually, the lowest shell only has 1 energy level, but the next one up has, actually, 4 energy levels all close together. Then the next one up has more energy levels, but let's just stick to the bottom 2.

These are the energies the electrons can have in the atom. There's something else to remember and that is electrons are spin-1/2 particles. In addition to moving through space they have an intrinsic spin. To specify the state of an electron we need to specify both its Schrödinger wave in the atom and also something about its spin. One of its spin components and usually, just so we have something definite, we'll pick the z direction of the spin component. We have to specify not only what wave pattern it's in. Not only what, therefore, energy level it occupies, but also what its spin is, whether it's spin up or spin down, the 2 possibilities for spin in the z direction.

The Pauli exclusion principle helps us make sense of atoms that contain many electrons, multi-electron atoms. These are atoms, in other words, bigger than hydrogen, which only has one electron. What the Pauli exclusion principle tells us is that no 2 electrons can have the same wave pattern and also the same spin. We can put up to 2 electrons in each energy level. We can have 2 different electrons with the same wave pattern provided they have opposite spins but not more than that. If there are lots and lots of electrons in the atom, some of them are going to have to be living in the higher energy levels. This is very important because if electrons were distinguishable, or if they were bosons, then they wouldn't obey the Pauli exclusion principle and all the electrons could collect in the lowest energy level. The world would be very different.

To see how this works out, let's just work our way along a list of the elements starting with the lightest elements, the elements containing the fewest numbers of protons and electrons and working our way up. We'll start with hydrogen. Hydrogen has one electron and in the energy level diagram for hydrogen, that electron in the lowest energy sits at the lowest level and it has some spin. One electron in the lowest level. Hydrogen is pretty easy. How about helium? Now you have 2 electrons and both of those electrons can sit in the lowest energy level because they can have opposite spins. You could imagine we have an electron with spin up and an electron with spin down in the lowest energy level about the atom—in the lowest energy wave pattern for the Schrödinger wave. This configuration of electrons is especially stable because there's no extra room for another electron to be inhabit that shell and there's a big gap in energy between that shell and the next one. Because there's a big gap, that means that if you want to pry one of the electrons loose or excite one of the electrons in helium, you're going to have to add a considerable amount of energy. Helium holds onto its electrons very nicely. The helium configuration is especially stable.

What's the next element? The next element is lithium. Lithium is an atom with 3 electrons and so we know how a lithium atom's going to behave. We know that there'll be 2 electrons in the lowest shell, the lowest energy level, they will have opposite spins, and then the remaining electron has to be up at the next level, which is the next shell. Lithium has 2 in the lowest shell and one in the next shell up. If you look at it just right, that actually looks a little like hydrogen because those 2 electrons down in the lowest shell are in nice cozy Schrödinger waves that are tightly bound, close to the nucleus. But then there's a single electron in the outer shell just as there is a single electron in hydrogen. Lithium has some affinities to hydrogen.

We can go on. We can talk about beryllium, which has 4 electrons, boron, which has 5. Carbon has 6, nitrogen has 7, oxygen has 8, fluorine has 9, and in all of these, you have 2 electrons in the lowest shell filling up the lowest shell and then some number of electrons—2 or 3 or 4 or 5 or 6 or 7 electrons—in the outer shell of the atom. It's not completely filling that outer shell, but occupying the second shell up. Then we reach neon. Neon has 10 electrons. Now we have enough electrons that when we put them in, in accordance with the Pauli exclusion principle, with just 2 electrons of opposite spin in each energy level. We find that we filled not only the lowest energy level, but the next 5 forming the next shell. You've completely filled both the inner and the next shell out. We have 2 completely filled shells, filled with electrons. We can say neon, like helium, is in an especially stable electron configuration. It should be very stable. There isn't any room to be another electron in one of those shells and the electrons that are there are held in place very tightly because it's a long way, it's a big step, from these shells to the next energy level.

Then we go on after neon, we get to sodium. Sodium has 11 electrons and so you have 2 filled shells, an inner one and the next one and then in the third shell, there's one electron. That sort of looks like lithium. There's some filled shells and one electron. It sort of looks like hydrogen. There should be affinities between sodium, hydrogen, and lithium. What I mean by affinities is they should have some similarity in the electron structure.

What's happened? The chemical properties of an element depend mostly on how the outer shell electrons in the atom are arranged. The electrons that are buried in inner shells, full inner shells, do not participate in ordinary chemical reactions in which electrons are exchanged and shared. It's the outer shell electrons and how many of those there are and what their configuration is. The outer shell electrons determine the chemical properties of an element.

What do we predict? By looking at the patterns of how the electrons fill up the shells, we predict that there will be a numerical pattern in the chemical properties. That numerical pattern will correspond to the shells or energy levels in the atoms. We predict that atoms with similar outer shells will have similar properties. Hydrogen, lithium, and sodium, all have one electron in their outer shell and then some filled inner shells, or no inner shell as hydrogen has. With that one electron in the outer shell participating in chemical reactions, those elements should have some similar chemical properties. We also predict that atoms with filled outer shells, ones that have a completely filled shell, will be especially stable. They're much, much less likely to give away or accept electrons in chemical reactions. Helium would be an example of that. Neon would be the next example.

All of these predictions that I've made are exactly right. In other words, using the Pauli exclusion principle in exploring atomic structure is able to explain the periodic table of the elements. We've all seen the periodic table of the elements in high school and let me just remind you. The periodic table of the elements is a graphical arrangement of the different chemical elements. It was first discovered by the Russian chemist Dmitri Mendeleev over 100 years ago. The elements are listed in the periodic table by atomic number—that is the number of electrons that the neutral atom has. In the periodic table, the elements in the same column generally have similar chemical properties. Hydrogen and lithium and sodium form similar salts, for example. That's something organized, something that is understood by chemists using the periodic table.

Then, the elements all the way over on the right-hand column are the so-called "inert gases." These are elements that do not readily form chemical combinations at all. And what do you have in the right hand column? You have helium. You have neon. You have argon and so on. All of the features of the periodic table can be explained by the way that electrons occupy the energy levels in atoms due to the Pauli exclusion principle. Armed with that principle, Pauli was able to explain the organization of the properties of the chemical elements. It's a tremendous triumph for quantum physics.

The fermion rule, the anti-symmetry of the quantum state, leads to the Pauli exclusion principle. When you apply that principle to the structure of atoms with many electrons, you're able to understand the chemical properties of those elements and why those chemical properties organize themselves in a periodic way as in the periodic table. The quantum physics of identical fermions helps to explain chemistry, and all of the chemical properties of all of the elements depend on the fermion rule. The world would be radically different and probably much, much less varied and interesting if electrons were bosons and they all hung out at the lowest energy level of the atom. Then, all atoms would look about the same.

The fermion rule is not just about electrons and atoms. It also applies to nuclear particles, protons and neutrons, in the nucleus. These things are also fermions. They're also spin-1/2 particles. We can do a similar business about shells, and being occupied by particles or not, for atomic nuclei. The protons obey the Pauli exclusion principle with other protons and the neutrons obey the Pauli exclusion principle with other neutrons. Protons and neutrons are not identical so they don't get in each other's way.

This leads us to what's called "the shell model of the nucleus," which is a very successful theory for explaining the properties of different atomic nuclei with different numbers of protons and neutrons. In the shell model of the nucleus you have separate sets of energy levels for protons and neutrons. They aren't quite exactly the same because protons are not quite exactly the same as neutrons. The energy levels are grouped into shells but not exactly the same way as the electron energy levels are grouped in the atomic structure.

What can we get out of this without working too hard? One example would be suppose you had a nucleus that contained exactly 2 protons and 2 neutrons. All of those would be in their bottom energy levels. They would have opposite spin. You'd have 2 protons of opposite spin and you have 2 neutrons of opposite spin. Something like that should be exceptionally stable. You've sort of filled up the lowest energy levels with protons and neutrons. It turns out that it is exceptionally stable. The helium nucleus is made of 2 protons and 2 neutrons and the helium nucleus is very tightly bound together. It holds together extremely strongly and the reason is because you've filled up the nuclear shells.

You can predict that there should be certain numbers of protons and neutrons that lead you to particularly stable nuclei. The so-called "magic numbers" of nuclear particles and these magic numbers, roughly speaking, correspond to the inert gases on the right hand column of the periodic table. Things work out a little bit differently from the atomic story because the nuclear forces are different. The next magic number instead of being 10 as it is for electrons and neon, it actually happens to be 8. The oxygen nucleus, oxygen 16 which has 8 protons and 8 neutrons for a total of 16, oxygen 16 is an exceptionally stable type of nucleus.

The fermion rule with the Pauli exclusion principle is not simply about nuclear and atomic structure as important as that is. That's a really great thing that you can do with the fermion rule, but there's other stuff that you can apply it to. Not just the structure of atoms and nuclei, but also to things that we see every day. As we see, it's the fermion rule, the Pauli exclusion principle, that tells us why matter occupies space.

To begin with, consider a gas. A gas is relatively easy to compress. It's actually not too hard to compress. It's very compressible. If you want to put twice as many atoms of a gas on the same volume, it's enough to simply double the pressure on the gas and you can squeeze that gas into a smaller volume, put twice as many gas atoms in a given volume. It's relatively speaking easy to compress gas and the reason is that there's lots of empty space between the molecules of a gas. By pushing just a little harder, you can get the molecules to be closer together. A solid or a liquid would be much, much less compressible than a gas. It's almost impossible to push twice as much solid material into the same volume. Let me see if I can give you a specific example. Imagine that you had a piece of ordinary iron. What's the density of ordinary iron? It's about 8 grams per cubic centimeter under ordinary lab conditions, under atmospheric pressure if you will. Eight grams per cubic centimeter, that's the traditional units for density.

Suppose we increase the pressure to 2 atmospheres. It's very difficult to see any change in the volume at all. Let's suppose we increase it a whole bunch. Let's increase the pressure on this piece of iron to 3 million times atmospheric pressure. Why do I pick 3 million times atmospheric pressure? It turns out that that's approximately the pressure at the earth's core, which happens to be mostly made of iron. The iron in the core of the earth is under 3 million times atmospheric pressure because the weight of all the outer layers of the earth pressing down on it.

Here's the question: What's the density of the earth's core? It's a little hard to tell. We can't get to the earth's core, but we can send seismic waves through it and we can do other kinds of measurements. We have a pretty good idea. The central density of the earth's core, which is made of iron mostly, is about 13 grams per cubic centimeter, only 60 or 70 times greater. If you take the pressure on a piece of iron from 1 atmosphere of pressure to 3 million atmospheres of pressure, you only reduce the volume occupied by that piece of iron to about 60% of its original volume. You don't get it down to half the size. You don't get twice as many iron atoms in the same amount of space, even pressing on it millions of times more strongly than atmospheric pressure. The point is that solids and liquids, comparatively speaking, are almost incompressible. There's a related fact. There's the solidity of ordinary matter, of solid matter. I can't put my hand into the same space as the podium. Something resists very strongly. I try to put my hand into the same space as the podium but it won't go. What is it that is resisting so strongly?

One idea you might have is that maybe it's electric repulsion. I've got some negatively charged electrons in my hand and I've got negatively charged electrons in the podium and so maybe they're repelling each other because like charges repel each other. But that can't be the answer because in my hand there are also positively charged nuclei and there are positively charged nuclei in the podium. Shouldn't they be attracting my electrons just as strongly? Just electrostatic forces are not sufficient to explain the fact. Why is it that solid matter is solid? The answer is the Pauli exclusion principle. In the podium, there are lots of electrons, trillions of trillions of electrons, and the low lying energy levels, in this region of space occupied by the podium, are already full of electrons, of all the podium electrons. It's true. I can add more electrons into that region of space but the electrons that I add into that region of space have to have a lot of energy. They have to occupy the higher energy levels that aren't occupied by the podium electrons because the Pauli exclusion principle says those are full. Those low energy levels, they have the no vacancy sign out.

To put my hand into the podium, I would have to put more electrons into that volume because my hand is also full of electrons, trillions of trillions of electrons. I could only get those electrons into that volume if I gave them very high energies since the low lying energy levels in the podium are already occupied by podium electrons. The moral of the story is that to get my hand into the podium, I'd have to push hard, really, really hard. Unimaginable hard. I'd have to do immense amounts of work to get the electrons in my hand to have big enough, high enough energies to find unoccupied energy levels in the space of the podium and that would allow me to force my hand into the podium and to occupy the same space. But that would not be good for the podium and it would not be good for my hand. It's really completely impractical.

When I was back in grade school, they told me that matter was anything that occupies space and has weight. It took me a long time, until I was in graduate school in physics, I think, to realize what a host of mysteries that simple sounding phrase concealed. Let's consider the property that it has weight. Matter has weight. That's related to mass and to gravitation and as Einstein would say, that's related to the energy content and to the curvature of space and time. To say that an object has weight is actually a statement that's full of mysteries.

For our purposes, let's consider the statement that matter occupies space. This is such a familiar property of ordinary matter. We don't really see how strange it is because on the next page of my textbook, they told me that an atom is mostly empty space or almost empty. Almost all of the mass of the atom is concentrated in the nucleus, which occupies less than 1 trillionth of the volume of the atom. The rest of the atom is occupied just by the electrons which have only a few thousandths or one in a few thousand of the mass of the atom. Almost all of the mass of the atom is in this little tiny thing in the middle. Why does the atom take up space? Why is something which is mostly empty, so hard?

The answer is the Pauli exclusion principle applied to electrons. Imagine that we compare this to light. Light does not take up space. You can always add more light to a region of space. If you have a region filled with bright light you don't have to push the photons any harder to get them in. The presence of some photons doesn't exclude others. Quite the contrary, the laser's based on the principle that the more photons the merrier. We see that in the fermion rule, the anti-symmetry of the quantum state, when we SWAP identical particles it has far reaching consequences. It leads us to the Pauli exclusion principle, the fact that no 2 identical fermions can exist in the same quantum state. Fermions are anti-social particles. That explains the electron configuration of many electron atoms, and thus their chemical properties, and the periodic table of elements, and all kinds of things like that. It can be applied to the structure of atomic nuclei. We get the shell model, which explains some of the properties of atomic nuclei, and it tells us why solid matter is solid, why matter occupies space.

Clearly, the properties of bosons and fermions and the distinction between bosons and fermions are of gigantic importance to everything that we see. That distinction boils down to a minus sign and how the SWAP operation works in the quantum state. Where does that come from? Is that just one of those things? God just made it that way and that's the way it is? Or can quantum theory provide us with a deeper insight into the origin of the distinction between bosons and fermions? In fact, there is a deeper insight and that's what we'll do next time. I'll see you then.

The Most Important Minus Sign in the World
Lecture 14

What's the difference between bosons and fermions? At the fundamental level, bosons and fermions differ only in a single minus sign. For a system of identical bosons, $\text{SWAP} \left| state \right\rangle = \left| state \right\rangle$. For a system of identical fermions, $\text{SWAP} \left| state \right\rangle = - \left| state \right\rangle$. Yet the difference between bosons and fermions is extremely important. Bosons are more likely to be found together, fermions less likely. Physicists sometimes say that bosons and fermions have different "statistics"—Bose-Einstein statistics versus Fermi-Dirac statistics. Boson properties are especially important for light and for matter at low temperatures, while fermion properties, especially the Pauli exclusion principle, determine atomic structure, chemical properties, nuclear structure, the solidity of matter, etc. This is undoubtedly the most important minus sign in the universe!

But where does it come from? Nature provides a clue: There is a link between a particle's spin and the swapping rule it obeys. Physicists call this the "spin-statistics connection." Bosons always have spin 0, spin 1, spin 2, etc. Fermions on the other hand always have spin $\frac{1}{2}$, spin $\frac{1}{2}$, etc.

Let's revisit spin and rotation. Richard Feynman created a useful "magic trick" based on an idea of Dirac's. In the trick, two pencils are connected by a flexible ribbon. Start with the ribbon untwisted. Rotate 1 pencil by 360°, which is 1 full turn. Now the ribbon is twisted, and it stays twisted even if we shift it around in space. Now start again with the ribbon untwisted. Rotate 1 pencil by 720°, 2 full turns. The ribbon appears twice as twisted—but this twist is not real, since we can remove it simply by shifting the ribbon around.

The moral of this story is that a 360° rotation is not the same as no rotation—but a 720° rotation is!

What does this have to do with quantum mechanics? Recall the quantum physics of a spin-$\frac{1}{2}$ particle. When we rotated a spin-$\frac{1}{2}$ particle by 360° (4 × 90°), we wound up with an unexpected minus sign in the quantum state:

$$|\uparrow\rangle \;\Rightarrow\; |\rightarrow\rangle \;\Rightarrow\; |\downarrow\rangle \;\Rightarrow\; -|\leftarrow\rangle \;\Rightarrow\; -|\uparrow\rangle.$$

This is part of a general rule about 360° rotation. For spin 0, spin 1, spin 2, etc., ROTATE $|state\rangle = |state\rangle z$. For spin $\frac{1}{2}$, spin $\frac{3}{2}$, etc., ROTATE $|state\rangle = -|state\rangle$.

The effects of this minus sign can be observed in a clever experiment. We can make a Mach-Zehnder interferometer that works with neutrons instead of photons. The neutrons enter in the upper beam and undergo state changes at the beam splitters.

$$|upper\rangle \;\Rightarrow\; s|upper\rangle + s|lower\rangle \;\Rightarrow\; |upper\rangle.$$

The neutrons are always detected by the upper neutron detector.

Neutrons have spin $\frac{1}{2}$. We can rotate the spin of the neutron by using a magnetic field. Suppose we rotate the spins by 360°, but only on the lower beam. This introduces a sign change for the $|lower\rangle$ state but not the $|upper\rangle$ state. Now,

$$
\begin{aligned}
|upper\rangle &\;\Rightarrow\; s|upper\rangle + s|lower\rangle \\
&\;\Rightarrow\; s|upper\rangle - s|lower\rangle \;\Rightarrow\; |lower\rangle.
\end{aligned}
$$

In this case, the neutrons are always detected by the lower neutron detector.

We can make a table relating the amount of rotation and the fraction of neutrons that are detected by the upper detector.

Rotation	0°	180°	360°	540°	720°
Upper beam	100%	50%	0%	50%	100%

To restore the original situation, we must rotate the neutrons by 720°. Electrons, protons, and neutrons see a "720° world." This is very difficult to imagine!

The spin-statistics connection is as follows: Spin-$\frac{1}{2}$ fermions have 2 mysterious minus signs, with 1 for particle swapping and 1 for 360° rotation. In fact, these are the same minus sign!

Electrons, protons, and neutrons see a "720° world." This is very difficult to imagine!

We return to the Feynman magic trick with 2 pencils connected by a flexible ribbon. If we start with the ribbon untwisted and swap the positions of the pencils, the ribbon becomes twisted. To restore an untwisted ribbon, we have to rotate 1 pencil by 360°. The pencils represent 2 identical particles with spin. Swapping the particles involves an easy-to-miss relative rotation by 360°, which is revealed by the twist in the ribbon. This leads to the minus sign in the fermion rule!

We have not exactly "explained" the most important minus sign in the universe. However, we do understand much better what it means and why there is a connection between spin and statistics. ■

Questions to Consider

1. Use a ribbon or a belt to create your own version of the Feynman ribbon trick and try the following experiments. In each case, you should find out whether the belt ends up twisted or not. (Remember that a ribbon might appear to be twisted when in fact it can be straightened out by simply shifting it around.)

   (a) Each end of the ribbon is individually rotated by 180° in the same direction.

(b) The ends are exchanged by rotating the whole setup by 180° around a central point, then unrotating each end individually to restore their original orientation. (In the lecture, we did not rotate the ends as we did the exchange.)

(c) Each end of the ribbon is individually rotated by 360° in the same direction.

2. In the neutron interferometer, suppose the neutrons enter with spin $|\uparrow\rangle$ and then the lower beam spin is rotated by 180°. The upper and lower beams now have distinct spins $|\uparrow\rangle$ and $|\downarrow\rangle$. The spin state thus amounts to a "measurement" of which beam the neutron is in, and thus there should be no interference effects. How does this analysis compare with the results we described?

The Most Important Minus Sign in the World
Lecture 14—Transcript

Welcome to the 14th lecture in our course on quantum mechanics. Every time I start one of these lectures, every time I think about the story I'm about to tell, I say to myself, this is the most amazing story yet. This is the simplest and most mysterious and most profound story I've told so far. Today it might really be true.

I want to tell you the story of a mathematical idea and what that mathematical idea means for the quantum world. What mathematical idea? It's a minus sign. A minus sign seems like a pretty minor piece of mathematical paraphernalia. They don't even stick around; 2 minus signs can annihilate each other. They go away. They become a plus sign and it's hard to keep track of minus signs sometimes. It's hard to avoid making minus sign mistakes in a complicated algebra problem. Paul Dirac, the great physicist, used to joke that the trick was not to avoid minus sign errors all together but to make an even number of them so that they all cancelled out. I wish minus signs were so simple. It turns out, of course, that minus signs can be important. In quantum mechanics, a minus sign can make the difference between constructive and destructive quantum interference and that's not a trivial matter. Let's begin.

For the last several lectures we've been talking about a very important minus sign, the different between symmetric and anti-symmetric states for identical quantum particles. For bosons, if you apply the SWAP operation that exchanges 2 particles to a quantum state, the SWAP acting on the quantum state, you get the state back. But for fermions if you apply the SWAP operation to the state, you get the negative of the state back, minus 1 times the state. The difference is a minus sign and what a huge difference that minus makes. As we saw, bosons are gregarious. They're more likely to be found in the same quantum state. Conversely, fermions are anti-social. They obey the Pauli exclusion principle. They can never be found in the same quantum state. Physicists put it this way: They say bosons follow Bose-Einstein's statistics, which means that boson properties, like bosons being the same quantum state, can be especially important for things like light and for matter at extremely low temperatures, and superfluids, and superconductors, and Bose-Einstein condensates. A physicist would say that fermions follow Fermi-Dirac statistics. Fermion properties determine atomic structure, chemical properties, nuclear structure, the solidity of matter, all kinds of things.

The only difference between bosons and fermions, this minus sign, is arguably the most important minus sign in the world, but where does it come from? What is the essential difference between fermions and bosons? Nature provides a clue. It turns out there is a link between a particle's spin and the SWAP rule that it obeys. It turns out that bosons have spin 0 or spin 1 or spin 2. Their intrinsic angular momentum, their internal angular momentum, is always an integer. Fermions, it turns out, always have spin 1/2 or spin 3/2 and so on. It turns out, for example, electrons, protons, and neutrons are all fermions and they're also all spin-1/2 particles.

Pauli, himself, was the first one to realize this in 1940 and physicists call it "the spin statistics connection." In order to figure out where the boson-fermion minus sign comes from, we're going to have to follow the spin statistics connection. We're going to have to go back and think about the properties of spin. You may recall back in Lecture 10, there was another slightly funny minus sign that arose in Lecture 10 when we discussed the spin-1/2 particles and their physics. That minus sign had to do with rotating a spin state completely around by 360°. What about that? That seemed funny because our intuition is that rotation by 360° is like no rotation at all. I mean suppose I turn around. I rotate myself by 360°. My final relationship to the rest of the world, to the walls, the floor, the podium appears to be restored exactly to my initial relationship. I'm facing the podium, standing on the floor and that's why we say 360° rotation, a turn by 360°, is really the same as not turning at all. It's the same as 0°. The same geometrically intuition holds for any geometrical shape. If you rotate a shape by 360° about any axis you'll wind up with something that seems to sit in the world in just exactly the same way.

The first point I want to make about this is that this is a kind of symmetry. "Symmetry" is a word that I've used a bit, so let me take a moment to give you a definition of symmetry. Symmetry is a transformation of something that returns it to exactly its initial condition. For example, we talk about left-right reflection symmetry. An object is symmetric if it looks just the same after we reflect it, after we exchange left and right. The capital letter "R" doesn't look the same when you reverse it, but the capital letter "T" does look the same. That's why we say that the letter "T" is left-right symmetric, but the letter "R" is not. This is why we called the state of a boson, a system of bosons, symmetric because when we exchange 2 particles, that's a transformation, the quantum state stayed exactly the same. You had a SWAP acting on the state, you applied SWAP to the state, you get the state back.

We can also have rotational symmetry. Any shape is symmetric under a 360° rotation. Any geometric shape is the same if we rotate it by 360°. Some shapes do even better. The letter capital "N", for example, is symmetric under a 180° rotation, a rotation by only half as much. There's a useful exercise here. Write down the capital letters of the Roman alphabet and ask yourself what are their symmetries? Can you reflect them? Can you rotate them? How does that change the shape of the letter? How can you transform the shape of the letter and get back the same letter? Some shapes are more symmetric than others. They have more symmetry but every shape has that 360° symmetry and that's why we think that a 360° rotation is the same as not rotating at all.

The second point I want to make is that when we rotate, we're rotating one thing relative to everything else in the world. Rotation is about the relation between one thing and everything else in the world, the relation of its orientation to everything else. If there was an object that was the only thing in the world, the only thing in the whole universe, how would we know if it was rotating? How we'd know if we'd turned it? There'd be no frame of reference to answer that question.

Rotation is about the relationship between something and the rest of the world and how that relationship changes. There's actually a surprise in the concept of rotation that I want to tell you about now. To show you this, I'm going to borrow a magic trick, a useful magic trick, from the American physicist Richard Feynman, based on an idea of Dirac's to illustrate this surprising thing about rotation. Here is the apparatus for my magic trick. I have 2 pencils and they're connected by a flexible ribbon. For those of you who are playing at home, you can do this experiment yourselves. Instead of a flexible ribbon, you can use your own belt or you can make your own device that looks like this. We're just going to be turning things around and we need something reasonably flexible that we can turn. One pencil, let's suppose it's the pencil on your left, represents an object in the world and the other pencil represents the rest of the world. The ribbon connecting them is flexible and can be moved around however we like. In fact, we're going to allow ourselves to even move it around the pencils if we wish as long as we don't actually detach it from the pencils. The ribbon can go anywhere. All right, so here's the first part of our trick.

Experiment number 1 in our trick. We're going to start with the ribbon untwisted. We're going to rotate this pencil by 360°, one full turn. We see that the ribbon between the pencils is now twisted or is it twisted? Maybe it just looks twisted. Maybe we can shift it around in space. Maybe if we shift it around in space this way, it will look less twisted. No, I just made it worse. Maybe if we shifted it the other way, it would get untwisted? I try all kinds of things. We find out that no matter how I move the ribbon around in space, it stays twisted. It stays twisted no matter how we shift it. When we rotated this pencil by 360° we twisted its relationship with the rest of the world. The pencil looks the same but the ribbon remembers. The ribbon remembers the rotation. So as far as the ribbon is concerned, something has changed. There's been a difference.

That was the first part of the trick and I don't think there are any surprises there. Now we're going to start the trick again. We're going to start with the ribbon untwisted and we're going to rotate this pencil but this time we're going to rotate, not by 360° but by 720°, 2 full turns. Let's do it. We rotate it once and again in the same direction. Voila as we say, well the ribbon looks pretty twisted. It looks twice as twisted, or is it? Let's see if we can shift the ribbon around in space. To be fair, I'm not going to rotate the pencil. Although I might move the pencil a little bit in order to shift the ribbon around it. Let's suppose that I bring the ribbon around. That's not the right way. I bring the ribbon around this way. I'm just moving the ribbon around in space. I'm not turning the pencil. I put it back, but now I find that the ribbon has no twist at all. The doubly twisted ribbon only appears to be twisted. The doubly twisted ribbon is not really twisted at all.

The moral is when we rotated the pencil by 720°, we restored its rotation with the rest of the world. As far as the ribbon was concerned, it was as if no twist had occurred at all. The ribbon remembered a 360° rotation and was definitely twisted but when you did the rotation twice, the ribbon was untwisted. This is an astounding conclusion. A 360° rotation is not quite equivalent to zero rotation but a 720° rotation, twice around, is equivalent to zero.

Let me show you a second version of the demo that you can also do at home. You can use a coffee cup. I suggest that you use an empty coffee cup. I'm going to turn this coffee cup around. I'm going to turn it around in a consistent direction while holding onto it. That's actually going to be quite difficult. I'm going to have to twist my arm around but you'll see how it works out. As I turn it around, it keeps turning the same direction. I have to put my arm way up here and then at the end I've turned the cup around once in a particular direction and now my arm is kind of twisted around but now let's continue the process. Let's keep twisting. Let's keep turning the cup in the same way. The cup is continuing to rotate in the same way. Now it's returned, after 2 full turns, and my arm is untwisted. Try it at home.

What does all this ribbon twisting and coffee cup juggling have to do with quantum mechanics? Recall the spin of a spin-1/2 particle; recall the quantum mechanical rules for that spin. In Lecture 10, we described how a spin-1/2 particle could be rotated in space by using a magnetic field and that acted on the spin like the magnetic field of the earth acts on a compass. It allows you to twist it around. Now when we rotated a spin-1/2 particle by 360°, and we went in 4 90° steps, we wound up with an unexpected minus sign. We begin with the state up and when we rotated that we got the state right. When we rotated that again we got the state down, so far so good, but when we rotated the state down we wound up with the state minus spin to the left. Then when we rotated minus spin to the left we came back to minus spin up.

When we rotated the spin by 360°, we went from spin up to minus spin up, this original state with a -1 amplitude out front. Now it turns out that this fact is part of a general rule about 360° rotation. If you take a spin-0 particle or a spin-1 particle or a spin-2 particle or so on and you rotate by 360°, the state just returns to the original state. If you rotate the state you get the original state. But if you have a spin-1/2 particle or a spin-3/2 particle, then when you rotate the state you wind up the negative of the original state just as we did when we rotated the spin up state by 360°.

At the time, we decided that this didn't really worry us. We argued that this minus sign that shows up did not matter because spin up and the negative of spin up, -1 times spin up, are physical equivalent states. Why is that? It's because of the rule of probability, the Born rule. It says that the probability for any measurement result is just the magnitude of the amplitude squared, but that's the same as the magnitude of the negative of the amplitude squared, and so you always get exactly the same physical results for any measurement with the state, the original state, and the negative of the original state minus the original state. We said that extra minus sign didn't really mean anything physically. We just didn't have to worry about it and I have to confess that I wasn't being strictly truthful. That's almost true but it's not quite true.

There actually is a clever experiment that can show the affects of this minus sign. What I want to describe for you now is the thought experiment version of an experiment that can actually be done. That actually has been done in the laboratory. The idea is to make a Mach-Zehnder interferometer. Here's our Mach-Zehnder interferometer. We promised whenever we were confused to go back to the Mach-Zehnder interferometer. Here it is. We're going to make a Mach-Zehnder interferometer, but we're going to make it to work with neutrons instead of photons. You can actually do this. The interferometer is actually a little bit smaller than this but not much. It's actually made of a big single crystal of silicon and all these parts are just carved out of a single crystal of silicon. Of course, we have neutron detectors instead of photon detectors and we have to introduce a beam of neutrons from a nice well-controlled nuclear reactor. We can make a neutron interferometer.

Let's talk about our simplified version. The neutrons enter in the upper beam. The beam-splitters work just as before. The state upper, that is to say a neutron in the upper state, becomes at the first beam-splitter a superposition s, our favorite number the square root of 1/2, times upper plus s times lower. That's what the beam-splitter does. We imagine that the sign change only happens at the bottom side of the beam-splitter. When that state reaches the second beam-splitter exactly what happens with a photon happens with the neutrons and you get constructive interference in one direction, destructive interference in the other and the final state is upper. The neutrons always come out in the upper beam, they never come out in the lower beam because there's constructive interference in the upper beam, destructive interference in the lower beam. All the neutrons wind up in our green detector.

Neutrons are spin-1/2 particles. Suppose we send them in with a spin up just for simplicity, spin up. We can rotate that spin by using a magnetic field. Suppose we rotate the spin of the neutrons by 360° but now we're only going to do that for one of the beams. We're going to put our magnetic field on the lower beam. There's going to be a little region of magnetic fields. The neutron's going to fly through a little magnetic field. So we start out with the state upper. It goes to the state s upper plus s lower because of the first beam-splitter. Now the lower beam passes through the little magnetic field, which produces a 360° rotation. What do we get? We get s upper, the upper beam's unaffected, minus s lower. We produced a minus sign by the 360° rotation. Now our state is different. Instead of being s upper plus s lower, it's s upper minus s lower. When it reaches the second beam-splitter, the interference works in just the opposite way. The minus sign changes constructive interference to destructive interference and vice versa. You have destructive interference in the upper direction. You have constructive interference in the lower direction. You never get the neutrons in the upper detector. You always get the neutrons in the lower detector.

You can see the effect of this minus sign. In fact, we can make a neat little chart, which is the amount of rotation versus the fraction of neutrons detected in the upper detector.

Rotation	0°	180°	360°	540°	720°
Upper beam	100%	50%	0%	50%	100%

If we rotate the neutrons by 0°, all the neutrons wind up in the upper detector. If we rotate them by 180° just 50% wind up in the upper detector, 50% in the lower. If we rotate them by 360° constructive and destructive interference trade places and 0% of the neutrons wind up in the upper detector. If we rotate them by 540° that 3 times 180, that's one and a half times around, it's 50/50 again. Finally, we only get 100% of the neutrons reaching the detector again when we rotate the neutrons 720°, 2 full turns around.

There's a quick little note I would like to make when we rotate the spin by 180°. That means that the neutrons in the upper beam are spin up and the neutrons in the lower beam have now become spin down. That means that the spin actually carries with it path information. If you looked at the spin of the neutron it would tell you which path it had followed and because the spin then measures, in a certain sense, which the path the neutron went on, the interference between the 2 paths completely disappears and that's why you have a 50/50 probability distribution when you rotate the spin by 180°. That's kind of an interesting comment.

Our main point is that to restore the original situation with the neutrons, we must rotate those neutrons by 720°. That's an astounding fact but it's a fact of experimental physics. I seem to see, seem to experience, a 360° world. When I turn myself around once by 360° I see myself in the same relation to the world as I was before. I say once around, 360°, is just like not going around at all but electrons and protons and neutrons see a 720° world. This is something that's very difficult to imagine. They experience something about the geometry of space that we do not quite see ourselves.

We're almost there. Let's go back to Feynman's magic trick. Now we're going to take these 2 pencils to represent 2 identical fermions. The pencils, if you will, represent the spins of the fermions. We're going to start with them untwisted. Now we're going to SWAP the 2 pencils. We're going to take the pencils and we're going to exchange their position in space without rotating them at all but now, when we look at the ribbon we note that the ribbon has become twisted. To untwist the ribbon we're either going to have to SWAP them again or rotate one of the pencils by 360° and that will take care of the twist in the ribbon. SWAPping the pencils twists the ribbon. SWAPping the pencils actually involves an easy to miss relative rotation by 360°. It's easy to miss it but it's revealed by the twist in the ribbon that connects them and that twist in the ribbon when we exchange to the 2 fermions leads to the minus sign in the fermion exchange rule. What we have is the spin statistics connection, the connection between the intrinsic spin of a particle and whether it's a boson or fermion. Particles like those which have spin 1/2 or spin 3/2, that pick up a minus sign when you rotate them by 360°, also pick up a minus sign when you exchange 2 of them.

We haven't quite explained the most important minus sign in the world but what we have done is we have sort of reduced the mystery of it to its proper size. The universe is in some sense irreducibly mysterious but there are some explanations we can give. We saw that spin-1/2 fermions had 2 weird minus signs. There's the minus sign from what happens when you SWAP 2 of them, the fermion SWAP rule. There's the minus sign you get when you do a 360° rotation of the spin. We've done several valuable things. First using Feynman's ribbon trick, we showed that it was not at all unreasonable. A 360° rotation should be different from zero, but a 720° rotation was the same as zero. That's not at all unreasonable. That's just exactly what the twist in the ribbon tells us. Second, we showed that this minus sign, though not directly observable, could actually affect an interference experiment with neutrons. This is something that's real. Finally, we showed that the 2 minus signs, the minus sign in the SWAP operation and the minus sign in the rotate once around operation, were actually the same minus sign. That's the spin statistics connection. That's the secret behind the most important minus sign in the world.

With that, we're going to conclude our discussion of the quantum physics of identical particles. The next thing we're going to want to do is to look more carefully at quantum systems composed of 2 pieces. This will lead us to the idea of quantum entanglement between systems, and that will lead us straight back to the next act of the Bohr-Einstein debate. Einstein and his collaborators are going to argue that quantum entanglement shows that quantum mechanics cannot be a complete description of the physical world. There are things about physics that are real, but not included in quantum mechanics. The question we're going to ask is, are they right? Interestingly, what will Bohr say in response? That's what we're going to do next time. I'll see you then.

Entanglement
Lecture 15

In this lecture, we're going to talk about the quantum mechanics of composite systems, systems that are composed of 2 or more individual particles. ... We skimmed this topic for our discussion of identical particles. ... [Now] we're going to follow this road to a different destination. It's going to lead us to the idea of quantum entanglement ... a key feature of the quantum world.

As mentioned above, a composite system composed of 2 or more particles can have "quantum entanglement." What states are possible for a pair of particles? Assume that they are distinguishable in some way, so that we can designate them #1 and #2. "Simple states" arise when each particle has a state of its own. If the state of #1 is $|U\rangle$ and the state of #2 is $|V\rangle$, then the state of the composite system is just $|UV\rangle$. (Note that $|U\rangle$ and $|V\rangle$ do not have to be basis states.) Simple states work like multiplication and thus are sometimes called "product states." If particle #1 is in the state $|U\rangle$ and particle #2 is in the state $a|V\rangle + b|W\rangle$, then the composite state is:

$$|U\rangle \text{ "times" } a|V\rangle + b|W\rangle \;=\; a|UV\rangle + b|UW\rangle.$$

This fact is called the "composition rule" and is the last of our basic rules of quantum mechanics.

Not every state of the 2 particles is a simple state. The ones that are not are "entangled states," or states with entanglement. (We may also say that the particles themselves are entangled or have entanglement.)

Entangled particles display some interesting features. First, if 2 particles are in an entangled state, neither particle has a definite quantum state of its own, but the pair does. This is a strange situation. In classical physics, every particle has its own state—its own position and momentum—no matter what. Also, if we measure 1 particle, update rule II applies at once to both particles, even if they are far apart.

A very useful example of entanglement is a pair of spin-$\frac{1}{2}$ particles in a total spin 0 state. The total spin 0 state looks like this: $s|\uparrow\downarrow\rangle - s|\downarrow\uparrow\rangle$. (The minus sign is important.) We can arrange for 2 spins to be in such a state. For example, the spins of the electrons in a helium atom in its ground state are in a total spin 0 state.

The total spin 0 state has 2 key properties. First, for any spin-axis measurement on 1 spin, the probability of either result is always $\frac{1}{2}$. Second, if we measure both spins along the same spin axis, we must always get opposite results, since the total spin is 0.

For example: If we measure the z-axis on spin #1 and get the result $|\uparrow\rangle$, we must immediately assign the state $|\downarrow\rangle$ to spin #2; if we measure the x-axis on #1 and obtain $|\rightarrow\rangle$, we must immediately assign the state $|\leftarrow\rangle$ to #2; and so on.

How do we know when something is real? EPR gave their answer: If we can predict something about a system without interacting with the system in any way, then that something must be real.

Quantum entanglement became the focus of the last stage of the Bohr-Einstein debate. After 1930, Einstein accepted that quantum mechanics is consistent. However, he still did not regard it as a complete description of nature. Einstein thought that there must be things in nature that are real but are not described by quantum mechanics. In 1935, Einstein, Boris Podolsky, and Nathan Rosen (EPR for short) wrote one of the most consequential papers in history: "Can Quantum-Mechanical Description of Physical Reality Be Considered Complete?"

In this paper, EPR called attention to the strange nature of quantum entanglement. Before a measurement on spin #1, spin #2 does not have a definite state. Particle #2 gains a definite state instantly—even if it is far away—when the measurement is made on #1. (Einstein called this "spooky action at a distance.") How do we know when something is real? EPR gave their answer: If we can predict something about a system without interacting with the system in any way, then that something must be real. Quantum mechanics says that no spin can have definite values of x and z at the same time. In quantum physics, the values of x and z cannot simultaneously be real.

The EPR experiment worked like this: 2 spins are created in a total spin 0 state. If we measure x on #1, then we know the value of x on #2. (It must be opposite.) If we measure z on #1, then we know the value of z on #2. (It must be opposite as well.) Without "touching" spin #2 in any way, we can determine either its x value or its z value. By the EPR criterion, both x and z must be real. Therefore, quantum mechanics is not a complete description of nature!

Bohr's reply was rather tricky and hard to understand. He argued that we must regard the 2 entangled particles as a single system, not 2 systems. The x and z measurements on #1 are still complementary. We cannot make both measurements at once, and so we cannot actually know both x and z for particle #2 at the same time. If we measure 1 of the 2, we cannot say what would have happened if we had measured the other. (Recall Peres's motto: "Unperformed experiments have no results!") There is no "action at a distance," as Einstein called it. But there is a sort of "complementarity at a distance" in the entangled system, and this knocks down the EPR argument. Einstein, however, was not convinced.

The final round of the Bohr-Einstein debate seems inconclusive. Among the remaining questions are these: Is the EPR argument correct? That is, does quantum mechanics demonstrate its own incompleteness? Do quantum variables like x and z really have definite (though hidden) values? Can a particle affect another instantaneously at a distance? Or is Bohr's subtle rejoinder correct? ■

Questions to Consider

1. A coin is sliced into 2 thinner pieces, each piece bearing 1 of the coin's faces. The 2 half coins are randomly put in 2 envelopes and mailed to 2 separate locations. Before an envelope is opened, we do not know whether it contains the head or the tail, but afterward we know the contents of both envelopes. What does the EPR argument say about this situation? How are the properties of the total spin 0 state different from the half coin experiment?

2. Write the total spin 0 state $s|\uparrow\downarrow\rangle - s|\downarrow\uparrow\rangle$ in terms of the basis states $|\rightarrow\rangle$ and $|\leftarrow\rangle$. You will need to write $|\uparrow\rangle$ and $|\downarrow\rangle$ in terms of $|\rightarrow\rangle$ and $|\leftarrow\rangle$, then use the composition rule. This calculation involves a bit of work, but the final result is satisfying!

Entanglement
Lecture 15—Transcript

Welcome to the 15th lecture in our course on quantum mechanics. In this lecture, we're going to talk about the quantum mechanics of composite systems, systems that are composed of 2 or more individual particles. Now, we skimmed this topic for our discussion of identical particles, but now we're going to go back and do it more carefully. In particular, we're going to follow this road to a different destination. It's going to lead us to the idea of quantum entanglement, which is a key feature of the quantum world. It's also the subject of the last round of the Bohr-Einstein debate, so we'll return to that story as well.

All right. So, the question is, what states are possible for a pair of particles? And let's assume throughout that they are distinguishable in some way so that I can label them as particle number 1 and particle number 2. Now, there are 2 possible situations for the pair of particles. There's the possibility that we may be in a simple state, or we may be in an entangled state.

Well, what do I mean by a simple state? What I mean by a simple state is that each particle has a quantum state of its own. So, for example, particle number 1 might be in the state U (U), and particle number 2 might be in the state V (V), and then we would just say that the composite system is in the simple state that we'll call UV (UV). The first letter tells me what the state of particle number 1 is, the second letter tells me what the state of particle number 2 is.

Now, these simple states that I'm describing are often called "product states." Now, why are they called product states? The reason is that composition works kind of like multiplication. So let's suppose that particle 1 starts out in the state U, right enough, but particle number 2 is in a superposition state, say a times state V plus b times state W, for amplitudes a and b. What happens when I put these 2 together and I make the simple state, the product state? Well, that simple state is U times, if you will, $WbVa+$. And that works out to be $UWbUVa+$. So, the composition of systems distributes over the sum in the superposition, and it acts like multiplication. So, we call these simple states "product states" because we make them by just taking the product of 2 single-particle states.

Now, this is called "the composition rule," and it's our fifth and final general rule for quantum mechanics. Remember I promised there would be one more? Remember, here's the list of rules we have: There's the rule of superposition, which says that superposition states are okay, they're just as legitimate as basis states. And then there was the second rule, the rule of probability, the Born rule, which says that we compute probabilities by taking the amplitudes, taking their magnitude, and squaring them. Then there were the 2 update rules. Update Rule I told us how the state updates when there are no measurements. It updates according to a definite rule that respects superpositions. And then there was Update Rule II, which tells us how the state updates when there is a measurement, and then the update is random, it's probabilistic, and it depends on the outcome of the measurement. Now we have the composition rule, and the composition rule says the state of 2 or more particles is either a simple product state, or a superposition of simple product states.

Now, not every state is a product state. When we take superpositions of them we can sometimes arrive at a state which is quite different. And the states which are not simple product states are called "entangled states;" states with the quality of entanglement. And we might also say that particles are entangled together, or that a pair of particles has entanglement.

So, what is entanglement? If 2 particles are in an entangled state, then neither of them has a definite quantum state of its own; otherwise we'd have a simple state. If they had their own quantum states, they'd just go together by the composition rule. So neither individual particle actually has a quantum state. That's a very strange idea. In classical physics, each particle always has its own definite state, its own definite position and momentum, no matter what. Quantum physics, however, says that the quantum state might only exist for the pair of particles, or a whole group of particles, not for the particles separately. And in this situation, the particles are said to be inseparable. They cannot be considered independently of each other, in some sense.

Now, this has nothing to do with distance, because particles that are very far apart in space may be entangled, though they typically got that way because they were once close together and they interacted with each other. Nevertheless, the entanglement does not diminish with distance. They could be as far away as we like, as distant from each other as we like, and still be entangled.

And the other thing about entanglement that's kind of funny, is an interesting result: If we measure one of the particles, if we perform a measurement on particle 1, say, then of course we update the state using Update Rule II—but that update rule applies at once to *both* particles, even if the other one is far away. And this is the trouble. This is the trouble. This is what's going to perplex us for this lecture.

So, here's a really useful example of entanglement. Imagine you have 2 spin-1/2 particles, then you can put them together and form a state of a composite system which is a total spin 0 state. The total spin 0 state is just s, our favorite number, the square root of 1/2, $s\left|\uparrow\downarrow\right\rangle - s\left|\downarrow\uparrow\right\rangle$. The minus sign is important. So $s\left|\uparrow\downarrow\right\rangle - s\left|\downarrow\uparrow\right\rangle$, and that is an entangled state. It's not a simple combination, a simple product of one-particle states. And the interesting thing about the total spin 0 state is that it's a state of this composite of 2 spin-1/2 particles that collectively have spin 0. The pair has spin 0. It's a possible state for a couple of spins, that if you combine them together the total spin is 0. For example, the spins of electrons in the helium atom ground state are actually in this state, and there are lots of other examples in nature. So, we can make 2 spins in a total spin-0 state.

So what are the properties of this total spin 0 state? Well, one is that if we make any measurement of any spin component of one of the spins, we could get either result with equal likelihood. The probability of either result is always just 1/2; either result being +1/2 or −1/2, in the basic units of spin. So, neither particle has a definite spin along any direction. Neither particle has a definite spin component along any direction; so that's curious.

The second point about the total spin 0 state is that the total spin component of both particles, along any axis that we choose, is 0. The total spin is 0. So if I make the same spin component measurement on number 1 and number

2, we must always get exactly opposite results. So, for example, prepare a couple of spin-1/2 particles in the total spin 0 state, and let's measure the z component of spin on particle number 1. Now, if we find that particle number 1 is spin up, which will happen with a 50-50 probability, then we know immediately that particle number 2 has to be down, because they have to be opposite; the total spin is 0. Alternately, if we find that particle number 1 is spin down, we know immediately that particle number 2 is spin up, no matter how far apart particle 1 and particle 2 are.

Similarly, we could measure the x component of spin on particle 1, and if we found that particle 1 had x component of spin to the right, then we would know that particle number 2 is spin left. And if we found that particle 1 was spin to the left, we would know that particle number 2 is spin to the right, and so on.

If we make the same measurement on the 2 spins, we always get exactly opposite results. And, you know, when we make a measurement on spin 1 and we find out what its spin is, we make these new spin assignments according to Update Rule II—these new spin assignments, updated spin states on particle number 2 immediately, we make them immediately via Update Rule II—even if particle 2 is very distant from particle number 1. And that's kind of curious.

Quantum entanglement becomes the focus of the last stage of the Bohr-Einstein debate. So let's recall the state of the debate so far. In the late 1920s, Einstein tried to show that quantum mechanics was not quite right by proposing a series of thought-experiments to find an inconsistency; for example, an exception to the uncertainty principle. But Bohr was able to find a flaw in every one of Einstein's proposals. And finally, after the Solvay Conference of 1930, Einstein reluctantly accepted that quantum mechanics was consistent. But at that point he still thinks that quantum mechanics is not complete. Einstein believes that there are things in nature that are real, but are not described by quantum mechanics.

Okay, like what? Well, like the results of measurements. See, quantum mechanics does not predict what measurement results will occur, it only predicts probabilities. It sets the odds, but what actually happens is random.

But when we actually make a measurement, one result or the other does actually occur, we see one result or the other. Quantum mechanics provides no explanation about why one appears rather than another. And so Einstein says every effect should have a cause, that there should be something in our physics, maybe something we do not yet know about, something beyond quantum mechanics, that really causes one result or another. Quantum mechanics does not include this something; quantum mechanics is not complete.

But how could we know that such a something really exists? Or is this just a kind of conversation that we can never come to a conclusion with? How can we know? Well, in 1935, Einstein, together with Boris Podolsky and Nathan Rosen—Einstein, Podolsky, Rosen, EPR for short—together write one of the most consequential quantum mechanics papers in history, entitled "Can Quantum-Mechanical Description of Physical Reality Be Considered Complete?" And in this paper, EPR call attention to the strange nature of quantum entanglement. They're some of the first people to point out the properties of quantum entanglement. They don't actually call it quantum entanglement, that term is actually invented by Schrödinger later in the same year. So, we're going to talk about the argument, the very profound argument, in the EPR paper. And we're going to express this argument in terms of this total spin 0 state for 2 separated spins.

So, imagine you have 2 spin-1/2 particles in a total spin 0 state. Now, before we make any measurement on spin 1, spin 2 does not have a definite state. Spin 2 gains a definite state instantly when we measure spin 1. It's always opposite. Whatever we measure spin 1 to be, spin 2 is opposite. That's total spin 0. Now, this happens even if number 2 is very far away. This is the thing that Einstein called, "spooky action at a distance." The means by which spin 2 acquires its state is kind of mysterious and magical and instantaneous and he thought that was crazy. You do something over here and then something magically happens over here. Suddenly, oh, spin 2 has a state. So, Einstein wants to argue that there must be something we're leaving out, something that is real, but not quantum mechanics.

So, how do we know when something is real? And this is where the EPR paper gets interesting. They put their cards on the table. They give a criterion of reality, a way to decide whether something is real or not, and here's their criterion of reality. If you can predict something about a system without disturbing or interacting with that system in any way, then that something that you can predict must be real, must really exist. And that something must have been real all along, before you predicted it. After all, you didn't touch the system in any way; it hasn't changed. You were able to predict this thing without ever touching the system, so it must be real. That's a common-sense view, and it's very hard to argue with it.

Let's go back to the quantum mechanics of spin. Remember, no spin-1/2 particle can have definite values of both x and z at the same time. In quantum mechanics, x and z are complementary variables. They cannot be simultaneously real. That's what quantum mechanics tells us. So EPR suggest the following experiment.

Create 2 spins in a total spin 0 state. Now, if I measure spin in the x direction on particle number 1, I will know the value of the x component of spin on particle number 2; it must be exactly opposite of what I found over here. And if I measure the z component of spin on particle number 1, then I'll be able to predict the value of z on particle number 2; it must be exactly the opposite. So, without touching 2 in any way, making all my operations on particle 1, I can determine its x value or its z value for certain. So by the EPR criterion of reality, both the x value of spin for particle 2 and the z value of spin must be physically real for particle number 2. They must both be real, because I can predict either one of them without touching particle number 2.

Therefore, there must be physically real things that are not included in quantum mechanics, because quantum mechanics doesn't allow x and z to be real at the same time. And therefore, quantum mechanics is not a complete description of nature.

Or again, let's cast this as a game. Suppose I give you a spin-1/2 particle, and if you wish to make an x measurement I can predict what result you'll get, and if you wish to make a z measurement, I can predict what result you'll get. How do I do it? Well, I made a pair of spins in total spin 0 state, and I kept one of them, number 1 for myself; I gave you the other one. And to predict either x or z, I just make my own measurement and I predict the opposite result for you; but I don't touch your spin in any way. And the common-sense conclusion that you would draw is that your particle must already have had definite x and z, at the same time, to start out with, because I can predict either one.

The EPR paper was published, it arrived in Copenhagen at Bohr's institute, and it produced immediate consternation. One person who was there described it as striking like a thunderbolt. The argument appeared very powerful. And Bohr thought it was wrong somehow, but it was extremely difficult to figure out what was wrong with it. Bohr has immense difficulty in framing his reply to it. He goes over and over the EPR paper, struggling to think clearly about their argument. And eventually, he does frame a reply—a reply that is tricky and hard to understand, but very profound. And he published his reply a few months later in a paper with exactly the same title, "Can Quantum-Mechanical Description of Physical Reality Be Considered Complete?" The same question, but a different answer.

First, Bohr notices that when we play the game, I cannot really predict both x and z for your particle. I mean, here's how we can play the game: I give you a particle, you choose what measurement you're going to do and tell me what you choose, I can do my own measurement and predict the result of your measurement, then you make your measurement and confirm my prediction. Notice the order of the moves. I give you the particle, you decide what to measure, then, knowing that, I make my measurement, then you make your measurement and voilà, I was right.

Here's a way we *can't* play the game. We can't play the game as follows: I give you the particle, and then I predict both x and z and then you choose what to measure and make a prediction. I can't actually predict both x and z because in order to make a prediction, I have to make a measurement, and I have to choose which measurement to make. The key point here is that I must choose whether to make the x or the z measurement on particle number 1, and those are still complementary; and since I cannot make both measurements at once, I can't actually know both x and z for your particle at once. What complementarity means is that I have to choose what thing to predict for you. I can't predict both of them; I can only predict either of them.

Bohr says that the 2 particles, particle number 1 and particle number 2, must be regarded as a single quantum system, not 2 separate systems. Why? It's because the quantum state that we have is only a quantum state of the pair, the total spin 0 state; it's entangled. I can't tell you a quantum state for each particle independently. The whole point about entangled systems is that the individual pieces do not have quantum states all by themselves. Bohr says we cannot actually know both x and z for particle number 2 at the same time. If we were to predict one of those things, we cannot say what would have happened if we had predicted the other, because the prediction means a choice of measurement, and as Asher Peres said, "Unperformed measurements have no results." So Bohr says of course there is no action at a distance, as Einstein called it. Particle number 1 does not exert any instantaneous forces on particle number 2, or exchange any energy instantaneously with particle number 2. But there is complementarity at a distance in the entangled system.

The x and z measurements on particle number 1 are still complementary, still mutually exclusive, even though the 2 particles in the pair are widely separated. What Bohr is saying is that the EPR criterion of reality is ambiguous. It's not adequate for quantum mechanics. It reflects classical thinking. The measurement that I make on particle number 1 in order to make my prediction on your particle, the measurement that I make is of course not a conventional disturbance or interaction with the other particle, but it does affect the circumstances. It does affect the whole set of conditions under which you make measurements on particle 2. This is the way Bohr put it. And so, x and z are not simultaneously real. I can predict one or I can predict the other, but I can't predict them both at the same time. And it is this complementarity at a distance that blocks the EPR argument, that prevents you from drawing the conclusion that Einstein, Podolsky, and Rosen drew, namely that quantum mechanics is not a complete description of the world.

That's Bohr's argument. As I said, it's tricky, it's subtle, it's hard to understand. Einstein was not really convinced, and a lot of other scientists were not so sure, either. Most physicists concluded that Bohr's response was correct as a logical matter, that he'd shown that the EPR argument was not airtight, that it didn't prove that quantum mechanics was incomplete. But, the EPR argument nevertheless retained a lot of intuitive force. It's based on ideas that are very commonsensical ideas. It says if I don't touch it, but

I can predict something about it, the thing I predict must be real, must have reality independent of my prediction. So it's hard to argue against these ideas without sounding as tricky and obscure as Bohr.

And there the matter stood, actually, after 1935. The final round of the Bohr-Einstein debate is inconclusive. There are lots of questions that still remain in the air. Are EPR somehow correct? Is quantum mechanics after all an incomplete description of physical reality? Does entanglement reveal this to us? Do quantum variables like the x and z spin components for a spin really have definite, though hidden, values? Can one particle instantaneously affect another one at a distance? Is Bohr's subtle, obscure-sounding counterargument that you have complementarity at a distance, rather than action at a distance, correct?

The EPR paper detonated in the middle of quantum physics, and the shockwave kept going for decades. And it drew the attention of the physics community to the question of quantum entanglement: quantum entanglement as a central mystery of quantum mechanics. Nevertheless, the issue would not be completely understood for about 30 years after the EPR paper and Bohr's reply. Then, in 1964, the Irish physicist John Bell dropped an even bigger bombshell. Bell turned the EPR argument on its head, and he led the way to a dramatic new understanding of quantum entanglement, something that Einstein, Podolsky, and Rosen, indeed that Bohr, never dreamed of in the 1930s. That story is next time. I'll see you then.

Bell and Beyond
Lecture 16

> **Bohr responded to the EPR argument. … Based on his critique, we concluded that the EPR argument was not airtight. So the matter stood for almost 30 years. Then, in 1964, John Stewart Bell, an Irish particle physicist, reconsidered the EPR argument, and thereby changed the world. … He showed that the physics of quantum entanglement actually leads us to a very different conclusion about the nature of reality.**

In his paper, John Bell carefully analyzed the EPR argument. He noted that it includes 3 identifiable propositions about the world. One proposition is that quantum mechanics correctly predicts the behavior of entangled states—specifically, the total spin 0 state of 2 particles, which we can check by experiment. Another proposition pertains to hidden variables; it says that the results of measurements are actually predetermined. We use probabilities only because we lack detailed information about the hidden variables that determine the results. The third proposition relates to locality. Specifically, the behavior of any particle is locally determined—that is, it is governed only by the particle's own variables and the immediate circumstances, including any measurement apparatus. According to Bell, the EPR argument can be summarized this way:

$$\text{entanglement} + \text{locality} \Rightarrow \text{hidden variables.}$$

Bell decided to try something different: Assume both locality and hidden variables, then study the consequences for entanglement.

Bell derived an inequality that any "local hidden variable theory" must satisfy. We imagine 2 spins: #1 and #2. On #1 we measure spin components A or B, and on #2 we measure spin components C or D. This gives us 4 possible joint measurements: (A,C), (A,D), (B,C), and (B,D). Let $P(A = C)$ be the probability that A and C measurements give the same results (either both $+\frac{1}{2}$ or both $-\frac{1}{2}$). In a similar way, define $P(B = D)$, etc.

Assume that there are hidden variables and that locality holds. A particular example illustrates Bell's argument. A, B, C, and D all have values every time we do the experiment, even though we only find out some of the values. Furthermore, by locality, the value of A on #1 does not depend on whether we are measuring C or D on #2. Assume the following: $P(A = C) = 0.85$, $P(C = B) = 1.00$ and $P(B = D) = 0.85$. What can we say about $P(A = D)$? Our assumptions mean that B and C are always the same, so A agrees with B 85% of the time. (We can conclude this even though we never measure both A and B together.) If B agrees with D 85% of the time, then A must agree with D at least 70% of the time. Therefore, $P(A = D) \geq 0.70$. This is a special case of Bell's inequality.

Quantum systems can violate Bell's inequality. We create our 2 spins in a total spin 0 state. The probability of agreement between 2 spin measurements A and C depends on the angle α between the axes. By applying the quantum rules and what we have already learned about spin, we arrive at the following table:

α	0°	45°	90°	135°	180°
$P(A = C)$	0.00	0.15	0.50	0.85	1.00

We can choose the 4 spin axes so that the AC angle is 135°, the BC angle is 180°, the BD angle is 135° and the AD angle is 45°. This will satisfy our assumptions about $P(A = C)$, $P(C = B)$, and $P(B = D)$. However, quantum mechanics predicts that $P(A = D) = 0.50$, which is less than 0.70. Quantum entanglement violates Bell's inequality!

Bell finds the fatal flaw in EPR. The 3 propositions—entanglement, hidden variables, and locality—cannot all be true at the same time! Therefore, the latter 2 cannot imply

Bell finds the fatal flaw in EPR. The 3 propositions— entanglement, hidden variables, and locality—cannot all be true at the same time!

the first. Experiments confirm quantum mechanics, even when the 2 spins are very far apart. Therefore, we must either give up determinism (hidden variables), or we must imagine that entangled particles can influence each other instantaneously over great distances (faster than the speed of light), or both! Bohr would have said that the hidden-variables assumption is flawed because of complementarity. Bell himself preferred to say that quantum mechanics was "nonlocal."

A postscript: Einstein died in 1955, Bohr in 1962. Neither of them got to see the surprise twist in the debate about EPR. ∎

Questions to Consider

1. In a classroom simulation of the Bell experiment, 2 students are given separate instructions and sent to opposite ends of campus. The students then answer yes or no to questions posed to them. Student 1 is asked either question A or question B, and student 2 is asked either question C or question D. After doing the experiment many times, we find that the answers to A and C agree 85% of the time, as do the answers to B and D, while B and C answers always agree. What can we say about how often A and D agree?

2. Now suppose the 2 students are provided with radios so that they can coordinate their answers "instantaneously" at a distance. Can we draw the same conclusion? Is this a fair representation of the Bell experiment?

Bell and Beyond

Lecture 16—Transcript

Welcome to the 16th lecture in our course on quantum mechanics. In the previous lecture, we began our look at quantum entanglement. We saw that a composite quantum system, a system made up of 2 or more particles, can be in an entangled state. In an entangled state, the pieces of the system do not have definite quantum states of their own. Only the whole system has a quantum state.

Now, the properties of entangled systems led Einstein, Podolsky, and Rosen, EPR, to argue that quantum mechanics could not be a complete description of nature. EPR said there must be things that are real, but are not part of the quantum description. In the example that we studied, we could either predict x or z of one spin, just by looking at the components of the other spin. And according to EPR, this meant that both x and z values must already be real for the spin we're predicting. Now, Bohr responded to the EPR argument. We described his counterargument as complementarity at a distance, and based on his critique, we concluded that the EPR argument was not airtight.

So the matter stood for almost 30 years. Then, in 1964, John Stewart Bell, an Irish particle physicist, reconsidered the EPR argument, and thereby changed the world. Bell showed that the EPR argument is not merely weak, it is exactly wrong. He showed that the physics of quantum entanglement actually leads us to a very different conclusion about the nature of reality. Bell's result is so astonishing, its implication so far reaching for our view of the world, that we will spend this entire lecture following his reasoning for ourselves. So, pay close attention, something truly amazing is in the works. Let's begin.

How does Bell proceed? First, he boils down the EPR argument to its essentials. He identifies 3 propositions about the world; each proposition may be true or not, but 3 propositions about the world. And the first one is entanglement. That proposition states that quantum mechanics correctly describes the behavior of entangled systems, and in particular, correctly describes the behavior of a pair of spins in a total spin 0 state, like we analyzed last time. And notice that this proposition is something we can check. We can check it by doing experiments on pairs of spins, and when we do those experiments, the predictions of quantum mechanics are confirmed. So that's the proposition of entanglement.

The second proposition is the proposition of hidden variables. This says that the results of our measurements are actually predetermined; that we use probabilities to describe them only because we lack detailed information about the hidden variables that determine the results. If we only knew those hidden variables, we would be able to tell what the results would be for sure. And this is Einstein's view of the probabilities in quantum mechanics.

Then there's the third proposition, the proposition of locality. This states that the behavior of any particle is locally determined. That is, it's governed by the particle's own variables and the immediate circumstances, including any measuring apparatuses and so on. What happens here is determined by things which are here. There's no magical influence from far away. Note that if I am getting my instructions by radio, my actions are still locally determined, because my radio receiver picks up local radio waves, the radio waves in my vicinity, which of course may have originated somewhere else and traveled here. So, even if I'm getting my instructions by radio, my behavior is locally determined.

Bell says that the EPR criterion of reality is really based on this idea of locality. Remember, we had 2 particles, number 1 and number 2, which were far apart, and we made measurements and so forth on number 1. And locality says that these actions that I perform on number 1 cannot have any immediate effect on number 2, because they happen far way. I mean, remember Einstein's theory of relativity. One of the consequences of that theory is that nothing can travel faster than light. So, it will take some time for any physical influence, like the radio instructions in my example, any physical influence, to reach all the way from number 1, where we're doing the manipulation, to number 2. So according to the EPR criterion of reality, what we do on particle number 1 does not count as a disturbance of particle number 2, and that's why according to EPR, what we find out from particle number 1 that allows us to predict particle number 2 must reflect something that is already real about particle number 2. That was the EPR argument.

So there are 3 propositions. There's entanglement, hidden variables, and locality. And only the first one, entanglement, is directly checkable by experiment, but the other 2 represent common-sense assumptions about the world. They certainly represent the view of the world advocated by EPR.

So here's the EPR argument according to Bell: Entanglement, the behavior of entangled quantum particles, together with locality, which encompasses the EPR criterion of reality, means we have to accept hidden variables. Entanglement plus locality means hidden variables. We have to accept that things are really predetermined. So given the behavior of 2 spins in a total spin 0 state, and assuming that the particle behavior is locally determined, then, according to EPR, the results of quantum measurements must be real before we measure them. There must be hidden variables that are not included in quantum mechanics. That's the EPR argument.

Now Bell does something very clever indeed. He does not start out with quantum mechanics; instead, he imagines a world of his own, a world in which there really are hidden variables that function in a local way. And this is easy to do. It's easy to imagine a world like this, because this is the world of our common sense. Bell thinks carefully about what that world would have to be like, and he proves that this imagined world cannot be the quantum world. It cannot be the world as it really is.

So let's take a look at the "common-sense" picture of the world—this is the cartoon version. We have particles flying all over the place, obeying the laws of physics. So, the question is, how do the particles know what to do? Well, we imagine each particle carries along with it a book of instructions. The instructions say things like if you fly through an electric field do this, if your spin is measured do that, and so on. This book of instructions of course is just a metaphor for the real physical properties of the particle that will determine its behavior.

And the instructions might or might not be deterministic. They might say do this or do that with such and such probabilities. And so if we like, we can equip our particles also with dice, and whenever they need to generate some randomness they just throw the dice and figure out what to do. The key point is that each particle throws its own dice. The behavior of a particle here is not determined by the throw of the dice of a particle over there.

And so, in the general kind of experiment we're going to consider, we have 2 particles that interact with each other, and they fly off in opposite directions, and then we observe that the behavior of the particles is correlated in some way. So, the common-sense view is that the particles are cooperating based on a previous agreement that they struck, so to speak, that the correlations of the particles are all explained because they've coordinated the instructions that they're carrying. They agreed on things like you have spin up and I'll have spin down, and these agreements are written down in their instruction books, and once the common instructions are agreed to, the particles carry them away, and then they act independently on the instructions they have. That's the common-sense view of how correlations between particles can arise.

And so, Bell's imagined world, the world of our common sense, obeys 2 assumptions: hidden variables and locality. All the correlations between particles are explained by hidden factors, namely the secret instructions carried by each particle, the secret instructions which may have been devised in agreement with other particles. And if there's any randomness, it is purely local randomness; each particle has its own dice. And so, based on these assumptions about his imagined world, Bell derives a relation, a mathematical inequality that must hold true in any world governed by these local hidden variables. This inequality is called Bell's inequality, and there are many different versions of this inequality, and we'll take an especially simple one.

Now, Bell's imagined world actually looks a lot like quantum mechanics. There are spin-1/2 particles, and if you measure any spin component of a spin-1/2 particle, you only get the values +1/2 or −1/2, just like in quantum mechanics. And each particle has more than one spin component that might be measured. That's something like complementarity. We can measure spin in the x direction, we can measure spin in the z direction, we can measure some other component of the spin in between.

So we suppose that we have a pair of spin-1/2 particles, call them number 1 and number 2, and on spin number 1 we can measure either spin component *A* or we can measure spin component *B*. And on particle number 2 we can either measure spin component *C* or spin component *D*. And later, we'll choose what directions these are; for now they could be anything. So there's *A* or *B* on particle 1, *C* or *D* on particle 2, so that means there are 4 possible combinations of measurements. We could measure *A* and *C* together, we could measure *A* and *D* together, we could measure *B* and *C* together, or we could measure *B* and *D* together.

So in each of those combinations of measurements, we have a particular question that we're going to ask: How likely is it for the measurement results of the 2 particles to actually agree? How likely is it that the measurements are both +1/2 or both −1/2? And we could write down something like: The probability that *A* equals *C* is the probability that *A* and *C* measurements yield the same results. The probability that *B* equals *D* is the same thing for *B* and *D* measurements, and so on. There's one such probability for each combination of measurements; the probability that that combination of measurements yields agreeing results.

Now, remember, we are in Bell's imagined world. In this world there are hidden variables, and locality holds; which means—hidden variables means—that the values of *A*, *B*, *C*, and *D*, are all definite. They all have definite values. In any given experiment we only find out 2 of them, but in every particular run of the experiment, all 4 of them actually have a value. And locality means that the choice of which measurement we make on particle 1 does not affect the result that we get for particle 2, and vice versa. These are the 2 assumptions.

Now, in our imaginary world, let's suppose we find the following experimental data. Let's suppose we find that the probability that *A* and *C* agree is 0.85. That is to say, *A* and *C* agree about 85% of the time. And let's also suppose that *B* and *C* agree all the time. The probability that *B* equals *C* is 1.00; they always agree. And also, let's suppose that the probability that a measurement of *B* agrees with a measurement of *D* is also 0.85, that *B* and *D* measurements agree 85% of the time. We're just going to assume that these are observed facts about the system.

What can we say, then, about the probability that a measurement of A agrees with a measurement of D? Well, let's think about it intuitively for a minute. We know that A and C agree a lot, 85% of the time. And we know that C always agrees with B, and we know that B agrees a lot—85% of the time— with D. And so, A and D will have to agree pretty often. Let's take that intuitive argument and make it mathematical. Let's make a diagram, a chain, A and C and B and D, in that order, and all of these have definite values because of hidden variables.

So, how likely is it that A agrees with D? Or, to turn it around, how likely is it that A disagrees with D? For A to disagree with D, then somewhere along this line there has to be a disagreement somewhere. Now, the disagreement can't happen in the middle, B being next to C, because B and C always agree with each other. And A disagrees with C only 15% of the time, B disagrees with D only 15% of the time. So you conclude that A and D disagree no more than 30% of the time, and maybe less. They disagree no more than 30% of the time, so they agree at least 70% of the time. The moral of the story, the probability of agreement between A and D is at least 0.70. It might be more, A and D could be in more agreement, but it can't be less. And this is a particular example of Bell's inequality. Given our assumptions about the imaginary world, this inequality must hold, that is, it must hold in any world governed by local hidden variables, particles that operate according to separate instruction books. And that's pretty cool. We've made a definite prediction. And we can ask, is it true?

Let's leave Bell's imagined world behind and go back to the world of quantum mechanics. And we're going to set up an experiment that looks just exactly like the one in Bell's imagined world, and then we'll see whether the results of the laws of quantum mechanics lead to the same conclusion that the other assumptions led to in Bell's world. So here's the experiment, the Bell experiment. We start out with 2 spins in a total spin 0 state. And to figure out what happens, we're going to do a little background analysis here to get it figured out.

Let's just imagine we measure spin components along 2 axes, A and C—A for particle 1, C for particle 2—and what's the probability that the results will be equal in quantum mechanics? Well, that depends on the angle α

between the 2 spin axes, the *A* and *C* axes. And so, think about it, if we have a total spin 0 state and we measure *A* on number 1, then whatever result we get, we know that the state of number 2 is exactly the opposite. So we can use our previous analysis, our analysis from Lecture 10 about spin, to figure out—if we know the state of particle number 2—we can figure out the probabilities for a measurement of some spin component of it. And it needs a little thought, but we actually have everything we need to do this in Lectures 10 and 15, so we can review the material there if we have any difficulty, but it's actually not too hard. If we let α be the angle between the *A* and *C* measurements, we can actually just make a chart of probabilities. In the first column we have various angles between the 2 spin axes, and in the other column we have the probability that the 2 measurements will agree in outcome—will either be both + ½ or both − 1/2.

So if the angle between the 2 is 0°, the probability of agreement is 0.00. If the angle is 45°, the probability is 0.15; they only agree 15% of the time. If the angle is 90°, it's 0.50. If the angle is 135°, it's 0.85. And if the angle is 180°, the probability that the 2 measurements agree is 1.00.

Now, some of those entries are really easy to understand. If the angle between the 2 axes is 0, that means that *A* and *C* are really the same spin component. *A* and *C* are really the same axis. And for a total spin 0 state, the results of measuring the same spin component on both particles is "disagree." *A* will never be the same is *C* and so there's probability of 0.00. In the same way, if the axes *A* and *C* are opposite to each other, then, because it's a total spin 0 state, the spins must be opposite, and therefore the probability that *A* and *C* agree is actually 100%, 1.00. So we have a chart of probabilities that will let us calculate the likelihood that 2 spin components agree with each other if we measure them on a total spin 0 state.

Now let's describe the experiment. We're going to have 2 particles in a total spin 0 state. We're going to measure either *A* or *B* on spin 1, just like we did in the imaginary world. We're going to measure *C* or *D* on spin 2, just like in our imagined experiment in Bell's imaginary world. And now we're going to choose exactly the axes that we're going to use. And I'll describe it in this way: *A*, spin component *A*, points north, let us say, and spin component *B* points northwest. And over on particle number 2, spin component C points southeast, and spin component D points east.

So we have a set of 4 directions, 2 of them for particle number 1, 2 of them for particle number 2. We'll choose these directions for our experiments. And now we can calculate the probabilities that the measurement results will agree with each other.

For the combination A and C, spin component A and spin component C, the angle between those 2 directions is 135°, that's 90° plus 45°, and so, consulting our chart, the probability that A and C agree with other is 0.85. They agree with each other 85% of the time. Spin components B and C are along directions that are exactly opposite to each other, at a 180° angle from each other, and so the probability that the results agree for a total spin 0 state is 1.00, 100% of the time. They always must agree, because they're in opposite directions. And for the combination B and D, these are at an angle of 135° from each other, and so the probability that their results agree is 0.85. Again, this is just like the imagined experiment. Remember what we're doing, we're finding out what the predictions of quantum mechanics are for an experiment done on a pair of particles in a total spin 0 state.

Now, if we were in that world that was governed by local hidden variables, the imagined world of John Bell, then Bell's inequality would have to apply. All of these results that I've said so far are just like that experiment, so what follows must follow that the probability that A agrees with D has to be at least 0.70. So what does quantum mechanics tell us? What does quantum mechanics of a total spin 0 state say? Well, the A axis and the D axis are 90° apart, so the probability that the results of measurements on the A and D axis agree with other is 0.50, and this violates Bell's inequality.

We've come such a long way that it's easy to miss how stunning this conclusion is. We need trumpets to play and fireworks to explode. Here's what we did. Following Bell's own argument, we imagined a world governed by local hidden variables, that is to say, the hidden variable proposition and the locality proposition hold good in this imagined world. And based on that set of assumptions, we derived a conclusion about the probabilities for joint measurements of 2 spins, and that conclusion was called Bell's inequality.

And then we compared all this to a real quantum mechanics experiment done on the entangled state total spin 0, and we found that Bell's inequality was violated, was not true. Therefore, the imagined world of John Bell cannot be our world.

Remember, the EPR argument is that entanglement, together with locality, implies hidden variables. Bell tells us that this is 100% wrong because entanglement, locality, and hidden variables are actually inconsistent with each other. If you pick any 2 of them, the third one must be false. And by the way, we contest one of them; we contest the entanglement proposition. We can do lots of experiments to see whether quantum mechanical entangled particles have the predicted behavior, and we do that and we find that quantum mechanics is confirmed, even when the particles are very far apart—kilometers apart. Bell's inequality has been decisively violated again and again, and so the entanglement proposition is very secure. We can rely on it. Therefore, we must either give up determinism, give up the idea of hidden variables; or we must suppose that entangled particles can somehow influence each other instantaneously over great distances, we must give up locality. Or, we must give up both.

Now, Niels Bohr might have said that the hidden-variables assumption is flawed at the outset because of complementarity. John Bell himself preferred to say that quantum mechanics is non-local; that widely separated particles do exert some kind of influence on each other. And either response is reasonable. But notice that either is an earthshaking conclusion. One physicist, a Nobel Prize winner no less, has called John Bell's discovery, which is known as Bell's theorem, the most important discovery in the history of physics. This is probably an exaggeration, but it is a pardonable exaggeration. No discovery brings with it more startling philosophical implications. Think about our common-sense view: Our view that what happens here depends only on the physical circumstances here; that particles effectively carry instructions, and if dice must be thrown to make randomness, the dice are thrown locally; that correlations between particles are due to shared instructions. This common-sense view of the world is wrong.

A final remark: Einstein died in 1955, Bohr died in 1962, so neither of them had a chance to hear about Bell's astounding discovery. Neither of them got to see the surprise twist at the end of the debate about EPR. And it's interesting to speculate about what their reaction might have been. Whatever else, though, I believe that both of them would have been flabbergasted by Bell's theory.

We're going to learn more about quantum entanglement later, especially in Lecture 21, but meanwhile, we're going to continue on to some other stops on our tour of the quantum world. Our next stop is a weird and novel way of looking at quantum mechanics developed in the 1940s by Richard Feynman. The Feynman approach will help us understand more about electrons and photons, and this approach forms the basis of the most precise physics theory ever invented, the theory of QED, quantum electrodynamics. QED is the basis and the model for elementary particle theories right through to the present day. So next time: QED. I'll see you then.

All the Myriad Ways
Lecture 17

Now [we're] going to turn our attention to another important part of quantum theory. We're going to talk about a new way of looking at the theory. It's a way that has proved to be terribly important in making detailed theories about elementary particles in the present day.

In the 1940s, Richard Feynman devised a startling new way to look at quantum mechanics. The new perspective that he provided stemmed from his answer to the question of how an electron travels from point A to point B. Specifically, he looked at the question of what determined the probability $P(A \rightarrow B)$ that an electron makes the trip. According to Schrödinger, who also had looked at this question, the electron's quantum wave travels through space, and the intensity of the quantum wave determines the probability of finding the particle there. Must we imagine that the electron somehow "solves" Schrödinger's wave equation? That would be a pretty smart electron!

Feynman says this is how it works:

- Write down all of the possible ways (paths) to get from A to B.

- Assign an amplitude to each path according to a simple rule. (We will skip the details.)

- Add up all of the amplitudes for all paths to get a total amplitude $A(A \rightarrow B)$. This adding of amplitudes may involve a lot of constructive or destructive interference.

- The total probability is just $P(A \rightarrow B) = \left| A(A \rightarrow B) \right|^2$.

In this scenario, the electron does not have to be smart; it simply tries everything, and the amplitudes add up. This is called the "sum-over-histories" approach to quantum mechanics. The general idea of the sum-over-histories approach can be illustrated by our favorite example, the photon in a Mach-Zehnder interferometer.

Feynman's idea turned out to be extremely useful for working out the quantum interactions between electrons and light—the field of quantum electrodynamics (QED). He drew little cartoons to represent possible histories of electrons and photons. These are called Feynman diagrams. In these cartoons, time points upward—the future is at the top, the past at the bottom. Solid lines pointing up represent electrons. Solid lines going down represent "positrons," which are antiparticles to electrons. Positrons and electrons have the same mass and spin but opposite electric charge. In QED, a positron is an electron going "backward in time." Wavy lines represent photons. These are either "real photons" (wavy lines that come out of the diagram), which can be detected, or "virtual photons" (wavy lines that begin and end within the diagram), which are not directly detectable. A "vertex" represents an event where a photon is created or destroyed by an electron or a positron. Feynman gave a mathematical rule for assigning amplitudes to each diagram. More complex diagrams (with more vertices) make smaller contributions, so we can often just consider the simplest ones.

He drew little cartoons to represent possible histories of electrons and photons. These are called Feynman diagrams.

QED gives a quantum description of the electrical repulsion between electrons. The simplest diagram involves an exchange of a virtual photon. Where does the energy for this photon come from? A usable though imperfect answer is that we can "borrow" energy ΔE for a time Δt without violating any laws, provided we stay below the "uncertainty limit." Thus $\Delta E \Delta t < h$. Virtual photons can be exchanged even over long distances because photon energy can be as small as we like. However, the resulting force will be weaker at large distances.

QED also describes the collision of a photon and electron, called "Compton scattering." There are several possible diagrams for this process, and all contribute to the quantum amplitude for it. The most important ones have 2 vertices. In these diagrams, the electron may absorb the incoming photon, then emit the outgoing photon. It may also emit the outgoing photon first, then absorb the incoming one. Alternatively, the incoming photon may create an electron-positron pair, and then the positron annihilates the incoming electron.

To get more precise results in QED, we must simply include more and more complicated diagrams in the calculation. There might be a lot of these. Electrons continually emit and absorb virtual photons. This changes their observed properties. Mathematically, the process can lead to an apparently infinite result. However, in the not-quite-magic procedure called "renormalization," the infinities can be persuaded to cancel out, leaving only the finite answer.

QED is the most accurate physical theory ever developed. It predicts certain phenomena, like the magnetic properties of the electron, to about 1 part in 1 trillion (1 in 10^{12}). QED is also the prototype for modern theories of fundamental forces. All forces are carried by the exchange of virtual bosons of one sort or another. For nuclear forces, the exchanged particles have mass, which means there is a lower limit to the energy ΔE that must be "borrowed" to make them. These forces act only over very short ranges. ∎

Questions to Consider

1. Feynman regarded his sum-over-histories way of thinking as simply an extension of the quantum 2-slit experiment. Give an explanation of that experiment in Feynman's terms.

2. Consider the Compton scattering process, in which a photon "bounces off" an electron. Draw several Feynman diagrams for this process. How many different diagrams can you find with exactly 3 vertices? Four vertices?

3. Japanese physicist Hideki Yukawa proposed in the 1930s that the nuclear force between protons and neutrons is carried by particles. From the observed short range of the nuclear force, he deduced that these particles had to have about 200 times the mass of an electron. Explain how such a deduction was possible. (Yukawa was proved correct a decade later with the discovery of the pi meson, or "pion.")

All the Myriad Ways
Lecture 17—Transcript

Welcome to the 17th lecture in our course on quantum mechanics. Now we've just finished, for now, our look at the phenomenon of quantum entanglement, culminating with a discussion of Bell's theorem. Bell showed that quantum mechanics, and the observed behavior of the quantum world, cannot be squared with any theory in which the world is governed by hidden variables that act locally, and that was an amazing result. But we're now going to turn our attention to another important part of quantum theory. We're going to talk about a new way of looking at the theory. It's a way that has proved to be terribly important in making detailed theories about elementary particles in the present day. And so it's always useful to find a new way of looking at something that you already understand, because sometimes it can you show you the way ahead.

By the 1940s, quantum mechanics was already invented. The mathematical ideas were very well developed, there were lots of new challenges and applications of it all the time. And then along came Richard Feynman. Now in 1942, Richard Feynman is a doctoral student at Princeton under John Wheeler; we've already met John Wheeler in connection with the delayed-choice version of the interferometer experiment. This is the start of World War II, and both Feynman and Wheeler, and many other physicists, would soon be joining the Manhattan Project to develop the atomic bomb. But meanwhile, Feynman is doing his doctoral research on quantum theory.

Now, Feynman is a brilliant and original physicist. His physics work throughout his career is amazingly distinctive; it somehow expresses his own personality. You can understand how an artist or a writer could do that, but how could a mathematical physicist do that? Nevertheless, he's able to look at the world in a very distinctive way. And a lot of his physics have many of the characteristics of a good joke: simplicity, surprise, and a kind of screwball inevitability. And Feynman, I have to tell, you is the hero of a great many physicists.

All right, so what's Feynman working on? What's his Ph.D. thesis about? Basically it's a new way of looking at quantum mechanics. Feynman starts with a deceptively simple question. He says, how does an electron get from point *a* to point *b*? Or, since quantum mechanics is not determinate, he says, what determines the probability that the electron will make the trip from point *a* to point *b*?

Well, Schrödinger would have said the electron's quantum wave travels through space—here's the equation describing the quantum wave—and the intensity of the quantum wave determines the probability of finding the particle there. So must we imagine that the electron somehow solves the Schrödinger wave equation to figure out where to go? That's a pretty smart electron. And Feynman said, no, it's much simpler than that.

To calculate the probability of going from *a* to *b*, here's what you do: You write down all the possible ways, all of the possible trajectories, all the possible paths of going from *a* to *b*. There's one that goes straight, there's one that goes over here, there's one that goes and circles Saturn and then comes back … all of the paths, no matter how ridiculous, you write them all down. And you can assign an amplitude to each path according to a simple rule. I'm going to skip the details of the rule, but there's a very simple rule for ascribing an amplitude to each path. And then, Feynman says, you just add up all of the amplitudes, add up the amplitude for this path, and this path and this path, to get the total amplitude, quantum mechanical amplitude to go from *a* to *b*. Now notice that adding up these amplitudes may involve a lot of constructive and destructive interference.

Now that you have the amplitude, what do you do? You use the Born rule. The probability of going from *a* to *b* is just the amplitude for going from *a* to *b*, the absolute value squared. So for Feynman, the electron does not have to be smart at all, it didn't have to solve any equations, it simply tries everything and the amplitudes add up altogether.

Think about it, when we talked about what a classical particle was, we said that a classical particle had a definite trajectory through space. Feynman says a quantum particle not only doesn't have a definite trajectory, it tries all the trajectories. And this came to be called "the sum-over-histories" approach to quantum mechanics. How could a particle get from *a* to *b*? Well, tell every possible history of the particle that starts from here and goes to there, add up the amplitudes, find the probability.

Now this idea can be illustrated in the Mach-Zehnder interferometer, our old friend; I have it over here to remind us. There's a simple rule for calculating amplitudes as the photon wanders through the interferometer. When you encounter a half-silvered mirror, if you're transmitted, multiply your amplitude by s—our old friend s, our favorite number, the square root of 1/2. If you're transmitted by the mirror, multiply by s. If you're reflected from the unsilvered side, the top side, multiply your amplitude by s. If you're reflected from the bottom side, the silvered side, multiply your amplitude by $-s$. Those are the rules.

So our photon starts out over here in this upper beam, and if we want to see how it can go to the upper detector, there are actually 2 ways. The first way is that it's transmitted twice. It's transmitted by the first half-silvered mirror and then comes around and is transmitted again at this mirror, and so you transmit it twice, 2 factors of s; total amplitude for that is s^2. Or you might be reflected twice: You might be reflected at the first half-silvered mirror and reflected again at the second half-silvered mirror, both times from the unsilvered side, and so the total amplitude for that is $s \times s$, s^2. The 2 ways to get to this detector. The total amplitude is $s^2 + s^2$, just $2 \times s^2$; s^2 of course is 1/2, and so $2s^2$ is 1. The probability of getting to this detector is 1.

Or what about the other way? Well, let's see … It can either be transmitted and then reflected or reflected and then transmitted. Let's suppose you consider this the reflected then transmitted; if I'm reflected here I get a probability amplitude factor of s, because I'm reflected off the top part of the mirror; I'm transmitted here, I'm not a factor of s, that's s^2. How about the other way, or I'm transmitted through the first one but I'm reflected off the second one and now I'm being reflected off the silvered side, so I'm multiplied by $-s$; $s \times -s$ is $-s^2$. I add the amplitudes, there's s^2, there's $-s^2$, they add up to 0. Total probability: 0. You can't get to this detector, and that's exactly what we saw in the interferometer. Now, we've actually simplified the discussion from what Feynman talked about, because we've assumed that the photons stay in the beam, but Feynman would be happy to consider the possibility if the photon wanders all over the place; and he's actually able to figure out how to analyze that. Feynman figures out mathematical ways to include all possible paths, including weird ones that do quite bizarre and unreasonable things. In fact, Feynman is actually able to derive the Schrödinger wave equation from his theory as a kind of quick shortcut for figuring out how the amplitudes behave.

So in fact, his idea, as strange as it sounds, is really quantum mechanics in different form. Okay, so what good is this? Well, it got him his Ph.D., that was very good; but it turns out it's even better. It turns out this idea leads somewhere. After the Second World War, in the late 1940s, Feynman's idea turns out to be extremely useful for working out the quantum interactions between electrons and light; something that had been pondered for 20 years by then. It turns out to be crucial for understanding quantum electrodynamics, or QED. Now, lots of people contribute to QED—Sin-Itiro Tomonaga, Julian Schwinger, Freeman Dyson—but Feynman's work is decisive. Because Feynman provides not only tools for solving problems in QED, he also provides concepts for thinking about those problems, and providing concepts is a tremendous advantage in proposing a theory. It's not just mathematics, it's also meaning.

So what's Feynman's approach to QED? Well, Feynman draws little cartoons to represent the possible histories for the electrons and the photons in the problem; and these little cartoons are called Feynman diagrams. So I'm going to show you how to draw Feynman diagrams for quantum electrodynamics. In the diagrams, these diagrams are actually diagrams of both space and time, and time points upward. So the future in the diagram is at the top and the past is at the bottom; and as you go from the past to the future you should read the diagram from bottom to top. Now, in the diagrams, you might have solid lines going up, and we'll put little arrows on them; those solid lines going up represent electrons. And we also actually will sometimes have solid lines going down. What are those? Well, they represent positrons.

Now, what are positrons? Positrons are the antiparticles of electrons, the antimatter counterpart of electrons. They have the same mass, the same spin; but they have opposite charge to electrons, and if you put a positron and an electron together, they'll annihilate in a flash of high-energy radiation. So, there are positrons in the world, they were discovered in 1930, and they're represented in quantum electrodynamics by lines that look just like electron lines but they point from the future to the past. In other words, in quantum electrodynamics, a positron is, roughly speaking, an electron that's going back in time. Now, we probably should not take that phrase too literally, but that's the picture in quantum electrodynamics.

And finally, in our Feynman diagrams, we need to represent photons; and we represent photons by little wavy lines. Those are our photons. Now in a Feynman diagram, the particles are either real particles—that is to say, photons, real electrons, and so on—these are lines in the diagram that come out of the diagram. They either go into the diagram at the bottom, in which case they're particles that were around at the beginning of the process or they come out of the diagram at the end, they're particles that are around at the end of the process. And real particles are the particles you can actually see; they are the particles that might be detected by an experimental apparatus. But in addition to the real particles there are also virtual particles: virtual photons, virtual electrons.

What are virtual particles? Well, virtual particles are lines in the diagram that begin and end in the diagram. These are lines that are never seen by the outside world. They're part of the process, they come and go as part of the process. They're called virtual particles.

And finally, there's one more thing in the diagram, and it is how do these lines meet up? It turns out that there is just one kind of way for the lines to meet up; it's called "a vertex." A vertex is an event, it's a point in our diagram, where a photon is either created or destroyed by an electron or a positron. So you've got a solid line and then there's a point on the solid line, and a photon either is going away from or coming into that point. That is a vertex. There's only one kind of way to put the lines together, and that's the way.

What Feynman did was he found a mathematical rule. Each diagram, each little cartoon that you draw, represents a quantum amplitude for a process. And it turns out that more complex diagrams, ones with more vertices, make smaller contributions. Each vertex involves a mathematical factor that's considerably less than 1, and so if you have many vertices that makes the factor very small.

So let's see how this Feynman picture, this Feynman cartoon version of physics, describes the electrical repulsion between 2 electrons. Electrons are both negatively charged, the 2 electrodes are negatively charged, and so they push against each other, they repel each other. The simplest diagram describing this process contains 2 electron lines coming in from the past and then a virtual photon travels from one electron to the other with a vertex at each end, and then the electrons go out, perhaps with different energies and momentum.

Okay, so the electrons come in and a virtual photon is emitted by one and absorbed by the other, and then the particles go out. Of course, that raises a question: Where did the energy for this photon come from? A particle just sitting in space, one of these electrons just sitting in space, does not just emit a photon for no reason. An electron has no extra store of internal energy to use to emit a photon. An electron in an atom can emit a photon, but that's only because it jumps into a closer orbit in the nucleus. An electron just flying through space doesn't have any extra energy to emit a photon. Where does the energy for the photon come from?

The mathematics gives an answer; I'm going to try to translate that answer into English and my translation is going to be a little bit imperfect, but it's a useable answer and it gives you pretty much the right picture. The answer is: Where does the energy come from for the virtual photon? Well, we borrowed it for a while.

You see, energy is conserved—yes, energy is neither created nor destroyed, that is a great principle of physics—but remember the time-energy uncertainty principle. Remember that we had Δe, the uncertainty of the energy of some process; the energy was not necessarily completely fixed. And we had Δt, the duration of that process, our uncertainty about exactly when the process takes place. Because of the time-energy uncertainty principle, we can only observe things if the product Δe and Δt is greater than or equal to h, Planck's constant. That's the criterion for being able to have a certain kind of knowledge about the process. So if a virtual photon carries an energy Δe and only exists for a time Δt and the product of Δe and Δt are less than Planck's constant, then we would never actually see any breaking of the law of conservation of energy; it would be hidden by the time-energy uncertainty principle.

See, the law of energy conservation is still obeyed in any experiment where we measure the energy, because any experiment where we measure the energy necessarily is restricted by the time-energy uncertainty principle. Meanwhile, virtual particles can come and go quickly using energy borrowed from the universe, the whole transaction taking place sort of underneath, beneath the uncertainty principle.

It sounds dishonest, but it is a legitimate consequence of the time-energy uncertainty principle. And so as a result the electric force between 2 charges is carried by an exchange of virtual photons. And we can draw a couple of conclusions. Electrons can exchange one or more virtual photons and they can do that even over long distances, they can do that over a distance that would take a large Δt to exchange, provided that the Δe for the photon is small enough. And so that means that because they can exchange virtual particles over a very long range, the force is a long-range force. On the other hand, the electric force between the electrons is weaker at large distances when they're very widely separated, because only virtual photons of less energy and momentum can be exchanged at that long distance and still stay comfortably inside the time-energy uncertainty principle. And the electric force is long range, but diminishes with distance.

Let's explain another phenomenon. Let's explain the phenomenon of Compton scattering. In Compton scattering, an electron and a photon bounce off each other, they exchange some energy and momentum but otherwise it's like 2 billiard balls colliding. And this was first measured and described by Arthur Compton in 1923. It was a very important early illustration of wave-particle duality; photons are so much like particles that they can actually have collisions with electrons.

So how does QED describe Compton scattering? Well, there are several possible diagrams, there are several ways this could happen, and all of the diagrams make a contribution. So what diagrams are they? Well, all the diagrams have the same input, there's an electron and a photon coming into each diagram. And all of the diagrams have the same output, there's an electron and a photon leaving the diagram. But the internal stuff in the diagrams, those will be different. Now the most important diagrams, the simplest diagrams for the phenomenon, those diagrams will have 2 vertices. And so let's take a look at the diagrams that have 2 vertices.

First of all, you can have one where the electron and photon come along and the electron absorbs the incoming photon. And then a little bit later the electron emits an outgoing photon. Now wait a second, you might say, that new photon isn't the same one that we had before. But of course all photons are identical; you can't tell if the one coming out is a different photon from the one that went in. You can't tell whether it got absorbed and recreated later on. Photons are all identical. So that's a diagram that made sense.

Here's another diagram. First the electron emits an outgoing photon, then it absorbs the incoming photon. You might say, well, that doesn't make sense, why would it emit an outgoing photon before it absorbed the incoming photon? Well, it's because you can borrow energy for a short period of time—everything that's happening inside the diagram is happening sort of underneath the time-energy uncertainty principle—and so that can happen. And really what we see in nature is what goes in and what comes out. This diagram's weird but it's consistent.

See, the crucial fact is we do not see exactly how the process we're talking about takes place. And this is exactly why the different detailed histories that we're drawing in the diagrams all contribute to the quantum amplitude. It's just like the interferometer. We don't see which path the photon took; all paths contribute. We don't see exactly how the electron and the photon interact; every story we tell about that makes a contribution. And afterwards it's impossible to say exactly how the process took place. The process, the particular diagram, leaves no footprints behind to tell you exactly what really happened.

Finally, here's the third, and for my money the strangest, diagram that contributes: The incoming photon may suddenly turn itself into an electron-positron pair, and then the positron part annihilates with the electron and produces an outgoing photon. You might say, wait a second, this electron that's going out is not the same as the … oh, of course, you can't tell whether it's a new electron or not, electrons are all identical; it doesn't really matter. Notice that in between the 2 vertices there's a virtual positron. A virtual positron. In fact, this pair creation/annihilation vertex, this vertex where a photon turns itself into an electron and positron together or an electron and positron turn itself into a photon, that vertex is the same kind of vertex we've been drawing before, it's just sort of turned on its side in time. There's still only one kind of vertex. In fact, if you think about it, this diagram is really just like the second kind of diagram we talked about, except that in between the 2 vertices this electron happened to go backwards in time, acting like a positron.

Now, all of these diagrams are important in calculating the probability of a Compton collision between an electron and a photon. And if you include all 3 of them and you do the math, you get approximately the right answer. And if you want to get a more precise answer you must include more and more complicated diagrams. You must include diagrams that have 4 indices of lots of virtual photons and positrons and electrons in the diagram. Or 6 indices, and there are a whole bunch of those, and you have to include them all, each one of which corresponds to a mathematical expression. And so on. To calculate the amplitude you include more and more complicated diagrams until you get tired, or you achieve the requisite accuracy, and then you can calculate the total amplitude, the total probability, and you'll get a better and better answer. And that's the general way that quantum electrodynamics works.

This gets pretty strange. This gets really pretty strange, but in fact it works beautifully. I mean, just consider an electron moving through space. Now, actually, that electron in quantum electrodynamics may emit and reabsorb virtual photons over and over again. It continuously emits and absorbs virtual photons; the charge is surrounded by a kind of a cloud of virtual photons. And this process, this continuing process, changes the observed properties of the electrons, like their mass and their electric charge. In fact, when you sit down and try to calculate those changes, this process can lead you to apparently infinite results. You say, oh, the mass must be infinite or the charge must be infinite.

That sounds bad, but what Feynman and the rest figured out was that there's a not quite magical mathematical procedure which is called "renormalization;" and in this mathematical procedure the unpleasant infinities can be persuaded to cancel out and you're left with only the finite answer. And if you think that seems pretty fishy, you're right, it is pretty fishy; but it works like anything. And it is based in part on a physical insight. The insight is that we've never actually seen a naked electron. We never could—any electron that exists is always clothed in a swarm of virtual photons being emitted and reabsorbed around it. Those are always present around the electron; and so all of the properties we've ever measured about the electron always already include the effects of the virtual photons. So if we wanted to say something like the electron mass or charge would be infinite without the virtual photons around it, that assertion is actually physically meaningless, because we can never have an electron without its retinue of virtual photons continually emitted or absorbed.

Now as an aside, in some experiments particles get very close together—you can get 2 electrons very close together, a little bit inside their surrounding cloud of virtual photons—and at extremely short distances the electron properties do appear to be slightly different, just as predicted by quantum electrodynamics.

Okay, where does that leave us? Quantum electrodynamics is the most accurate physical theory ever developed. It predicts certain things like the magnetic properties of an electron to 1 part in a trillion—1 part in 10^{12}. That's like being able to predict the number of grains in a truckload of sand and getting it right to the nearest grain.

And quantum electrodynamics is also the prototype for all modern theories of fundamental forces between particles. All the forces are carried by the exchange of virtual particles. So, for example, nuclear forces, the forces between nuclear particles like protons and neutrons, the particles that are exchanged there actually have mass, and because they have mass this means that we must borrow a bigger amount of energy from the universe in order to make them; we have to borrow at least mc^2, as Einstein reminds us. And that means that those particles, those virtual particles, can only exist for a very short period of time and can only travel a very short distance. And that means that the nuclear forces which are carried by massive virtual particles can only act over very short ranges, less than 1 100-trillionth of a meter, 10^{-14} meters. The size of a nucleus, but peanuts compared to the size of an atom.

So to recap, Feynman introduced his sum-over-histories view of quantum mechanics, and the view is this: What you do is you think of all possible ways for something to happen, including quite ridiculous ways that it could happen, and you realize that every possible history contributes an amplitude. All the amplitudes are added together—there's lots of interference that happens there—and the total probability is just the square of the magnitude of the total amplitude. This is the concept of quantum interference, raised to a very high degree; everything is just quantum interference. And Feynman always drew inspiration from the old 2-slit experiment. He said that the 2-slit experiment contained all the mysteries of quantum mechanics. His view of quantum mechanics was just the 2-slit experiment, constructive and destructive interference, raised to the highest degree.

Now applied to quantum electrodynamics, the Feynman idea leads to the most precise physical theory ever, a theory with some odd aspects. It tells us that there are virtual particles that can come and go so long as they stay beneath the radar of the time-energy uncertainty principle; so long as the energy that they carry times their lifetime is less than Planck's constant. It also tells us that electric forces, for example, are carried by the exchange of these virtual particles, virtual photons. It tells us that electrons just moving through space are surrounded by swarms of virtual photons, virtual electron-positron pairs—all kinds of stuff happening around even one particle flying through space.

So even when nothing is happening, a lot is happening; even though we cannot, even in principle, say exactly what. And all of it contributes to the total quantum amplitude and thus to the probability of a process they can place. There are some apparent infinities, infinite mathematical results, but they can be canceled out by this kind of interesting voodoo of renormalization. The net result is that all of the forces between elementary particles have the same general picture; they all have to do with exchanging virtual particles, and if the particles that are exchanged have mass, the force is a short-range force only.

It's a curious picture, it's a remarkable picture, but it is the modern picture of how things work. This business about virtual photons is so strange that next time, we're just going to forget all the real particles and only think about virtual particles. How are we supposed to think about empty space? Is it a simple void or is it filled with virtual particles? Next time: the quantum vacuum. I'll see you then.

Much Ado about Nothing
Lecture 18

Swarms of virtual particles are present in these [Feynman] diagrams. They come and go unobservably, underneath the limit set by the time-energy uncertainty principle. ... This time we're going to analyze what is going on in so-called "empty space," and we'll find that the quantum mechanical answer is quite a lot is going on; and that this fact, that there's a lot going on where nothing appears to exist, has enormous consequences.

At its absolute minimum energy, a quantum system still has some energy in it. This is called "zero-point energy." One way to think about this idea is to consider both classical and quantum pendulums. A classical pendulum has energy both in its motion (kinetic energy) and by virtue of its displacement from the bottom (potential energy). If it is exactly at rest at the bottom point, its energy is zero. This cannot be true for a quantum pendulum. To be exactly at rest at the bottom point, we would need both Δx and Δp to be 0. The uncertainty principle forbids this. Even in its ground state, the lowest energy level, the quantum pendulum has a zero-point energy of $hf/2$, where f is the pendulum's frequency. This is half of a "quantum of energy" for the oscillating system.

Zero-point energy can make a real difference. One example is the strange difficulty of freezing helium. Almost any substance will freeze if it is made cold enough. Molecules are slightly "sticky" due to the van der Waals force, so if they are moving slowly enough they will stick together and be "frozen" in place. Helium condenses into a liquid near absolute zero. But helium atoms have a very low mass and the van der Waals force between them is extremely weak. This means that, even at absolute zero, helium atoms have enough zero-point energy to prevent freezing. It is possible to freeze helium, but only by imposing very high pressures to make up for the lack of "stickiness" between the atoms.

Even "empty space"—the vacuum—has quantum zero-point energy. In the electromagnetic field, energy comes in the form of photons. Even with zero photons—the vacuum state—the electromagnetic field has zero-point energy. The vacuum is filled with electromagnetic fluctuations at all frequencies. Spontaneous emission of a photon from an atom can be viewed as "stimulated emission" by the quantum fluctuations of the vacuum.

In 1948, Hendrik Casimir discovered a way to observe vacuum energy directly. The presence of metal objects slightly reduces the number of ways that the vacuum can fluctuate. The vacuum state is distorted to "fit around" the objects. Between 2 parallel metal plates, the vacuum fluctuations are reduced. Therefore, there is less vacuum energy (less "nothing") between the 2 plates than there is outside of them. This leads to a tiny attractive force between the plates called "the Casimir effect." This effect was soon detected experimentally, but the first really accurate measurements had to wait for the 1990s.

One leading hypothesis is that the dark energy is quantum vacuum energy, the energy of empty space. As space expands, more dark energy appears, driving the expansion faster.

Vacuum energy may have cosmic implications. In 1998, cosmologists learned that the expansion of the universe is actually getting faster over time. Not only are galaxies getting further apart—an aftereffect of the Big Bang—they are doing so at an increasing rate. This was a surprise—simple gravity would suggest that the expansion should be slowing down, not accelerating. The physical cause of the acceleration is called "dark energy"—"dark" because we do not see it directly; "energy" to distinguish it from "dark matter," which is matter of an unknown type that is also present but has a different effect.

One leading hypothesis is that the dark energy is quantum vacuum energy, the energy of empty space. As space expands, more dark energy appears, driving the expansion faster. One major difficulty with this idea is that, if we plug in some obvious numbers, there should be a lot of vacuum energy—an amount that is much, much, *much* too large to account for the dark energy. We have to assume that the vacuum energy is almost, but not exactly, irrelevant to the cosmic expansion. On the other hand, cosmologists believe that, immediately after the Big Bang, the universe experienced a short period of superfast expansion called "cosmic inflation." Vacuum energy could well account for this. ∎

Questions to Consider

1. As we saw in Lecture 5, a stretched wire can vibrate in standing wave patterns at many different frequencies. Explain why such a wire can never be absolutely still, even at its minimum possible energy.

2. In some highly speculative cosmological theories, the entire visible universe had its origin as a quantum "fluctuation" in a primordial quantum vacuum. Does this really count as "making the universe out of nothing?" (Does a quantum vacuum really count as "nothing?")

Much Ado about Nothing
Lecture 18—Transcript

Welcome to the 18th lecture of our course on quantum mechanics. Last time we looked at Feynman's sum-over-histories approach to quantum mechanics. We saw it applied to quantum electrodynamics, the theory of how electrons and photons interact. And we saw that in QED, quantum electrodynamics, each physical process is represented by a set of Feynman diagrams, and each diagram represents a possible internal history for that process. All the diagrams contribute to the quantum amplitude for the process to occur.

We found last time that swarms of virtual particles are present in these diagrams. They come and go unobservably, underneath the limit set by the time-energy uncertainty principle. This means there's kind of creative energy accounting in quantum mechanics, but the energy accounting always passes any audit, any experimental test of the law of conservation of energy. Now this time we're going to analyze what is going on in so-called "empty space," and we'll find that the quantum mechanical answer is quite a lot is going on; and that this fact, that there's a lot going on where nothing appears to exist, has enormous consequences.

So let's start out by supposing we have a simple pendulum, a mass that swings back and forth at the end of a string. Now, the simple pendulum has 2 kinds of energy: there's kinetic energy, its energy due to its motion, and also potential energy due to its height above the bottom. And as the pendulum swings, it exchanges kinetic and potential energy. At the bottom, when its potential energy is least, its kinetic energy is greatest; up at the top of its swing, when its potential energy is greatest, its kinetic energy is zero.

Now, for a classical pendulum as I've described, if the pendulum were exactly at rest, exactly at the bottom, then its energy would be zero. But a quantum pendulum can't do this. For a quantum pendulum to have zero energy it would have to have its uncertainty in position, Δx, and its uncertainty in momentum, Δp, both equal to 0, and the uncertainty principle forbids this. This means that even in the ground state, even in the state of minimum possible energy, the quantum pendulum has zero-point energy.

What is zero-point energy? Well, for a quantum pendulum, the zero-point energy—the energy it must have even in its lowest energy state—happens to be Planck's constant times the frequency of the pendulum divided by 2. And of course that's just half the size of 1 quantum of vibrational motion, as Einstein posited it back in his explanation of the heat capacity of solids. So even when the quantum pendulum has its least possible energy, it still has what we might call half of the ghost of 1 quantum of energy. That's the zero-point energy: the energy it has even when it's as close to zero energy as a quantum system can be.

Could this possibly make any difference? I mean, usually we just measure how the energy changes in a system. We don't really know exactly how much energy is in the system, just how the energy is changed, and this is always present. It's like having a minimum balance of $100 in your bank account; that minimum balance is not something that makes any difference, you can just ignore it and you deal with the amounts that are above $100.

And yet it does have effects. Consider, for example, the strange difficulty we have in freezing helium. Now, almost any substance will freeze, will become a solid, if we make it cold enough. What do we mean by cold? Low temperature, a temperature close to absolute zero, means that the molecules in the substance have very little heat energy. And heat energy is just disorderly energy of motion, it's an ordinary sort of energy; there's very little of it in something at low temperatures.

Now, molecules have something called a "van der Waals force." And a way of thinking about the van der Waals force is that molecules are very slightly sticky; they like to stick together. And so if the molecules are moving slowly enough, if the temperature is low enough, then the molecules will stick together and they'll freeze in place. Now, helium atoms have very low mass, they're the next-to-lightest kind of atom, and they have very weak van der Waals force. And so helium is actually very difficult to condense. It condenses to a liquid close to absolute zero, only 4° above absolute zero, it just barely condenses into a liquid. But even at absolute zero, helium atoms have enough quantum zero-point energy to prevent freezing, to prevent them sticking in place. So instead of a solid, helium forms a superfluid, a state of matter that's at very low temperature but can flow.

Now, it is possible to freeze helium by imposing very high pressures, and those high pressures sort of make up for the lack of stickiness in the atoms; but at ordinary pressures, no, it's impossible to freeze helium, and zero-point energy is to blame. You see, in quantum mechanics, the ground state is not the state with no energy. The lowest rung on the energy level ladder, to call to mind a picture we use to describe atomic structure, the lowest rung on the energy level ladder may still involve kinetic and potential energy, a kind of irreducible quantum motion, and that's going to have physical effects.

All right, so now we're going to turn to a related subject, and that is the physics of empty space. By empty space I mean it has no particles in it at all; certainly that has to be the lowest possible energy. Sure, if there are particles they'll have to have at least zero-point energy; but if you have no particles, surely that is really empty, that is really no energy at all. Empty space, in short, sounds very boring. And in classical physics, empty space *is* boring; there is nothing in empty space. But in quantum mechanics, so-called empty space, the vacuum state, has quantum zero-point energy of its own.

Let's think about the electromagnetic field. In the electromagnetic field the energy comes in the form of photons. So if you consider one particular type of light, one particular frequency and one particular direction, you can have 1 photon with that direction and frequency, 2 photons, 3 photons; each photon has an energy which is equal to Planck's constant times the frequency. And so you have lots of different amounts of energy in that particular type of light.

But even with zero photons, there's still a little leftover electromagnetic energy, a little zero-point energy, that has this frequency and direction in the electromagnetic field. How much zero-point energy? Well, once again the zero-point energy is equal to Planck's constant times the frequency of the light divided by 2. Even when we take out all the photons we can, even in the vacuum state, there's still half of the ghost of a photon left. So the moral of the story is that the vacuum, the quantum state of no particles at all, is filled with quantum electromagnetic "fluctuations," they're called, and they occur at all frequencies. Every frequency and direction has half of a ghost of a photon, even at the lowest energy state.

Does all this quantum vacuum energy make a difference? And the answer is yes, it does. Remember when we talked how about atoms can interact with light we said that an atom all by itself with no light around it that was in an excited state could emit a photon. This is called "spontaneous emission": spontaneous emission of a photon. But when you really explore where that spontaneous emission comes from you find that you can actually regard it as a kind of stimulated emission; but the emission is stimulated by the zero-point fluctuations of the electromagnetic field—it's the energy of the vacuum. There's always some energy around at a given frequency, and that energy kind of tickles the atom until it emits the photon. Spontaneous emission is actually due to the zero-point energy in the electromagnetic field.

That seems a bit iffy, though, kind of an interpretational impression. Is there anything more concrete, anything more definite that tells us that there really is energy in empty space? And the answer is yes. And the person who gave us the answer was a physicist named Hendrik Casimir. Casimir was a Dutch physicist. He worked for both Bohr in Copenhagen and Pauli in Zurich, and then he went to work for industry, he became the director of the Philips Research Laboratories in the Netherlands. But nevertheless he continued to do research into quantum theory.

In 1948, Casimir, who was already the director of the laboratories, found a way to observe quantum vacuum energy directly. And here's how he reasoned: He said the presence of metal objects actually slightly reduces the way that the electromagnetic field can vibrate. The electromagnetic waves have to fit around the object in some way. If you imagine a metal wall, the electromagnetic waves must vanish at the surface because they can't exist inside the metal. Now, that's only true for low frequencies; extremely high frequency electromagnetic waves, X-rays and so on, they can pass right through. But at low frequencies, radio waves or even light, the waves can't exist in the metal and so they have to be zero at the wall. And so we simply do not have electromagnetic waves that fit right up against the wall, that don't go to zero at the wall. There are some waves that would otherwise be possible that aren't possible because of the presence of the metal surface. And so the vacuum state is also affected; we don't have half of the ghost of a photon in waves that cannot actually exist. So Casimir showed that the vacuum itself is slightly distorted to fit around a conducting metal object.

This sounds pretty weird, but in fact you can propose a definite experiment. Imagine you have 2 parallel metal plates. Now between the plates we can only have waves that fit exactly between the plates. This is like the standing waves on a stretched piano wire that we discussed way back in Lecture 5; only certain wavelengths, only certain frequencies, could fit between the 2 fixed ends of the piano wire. In a similar way, only waves that exactly fit between the 2 parallel metal plates are allowed; all the rest of them simply don't exist. And so that means that between the metal plates, even if there are no photons at all, the kinds of vacuum fluctuations that there might be between the plates is a little bit less than it would be if the plates were not there.

So, what does that mean? That means that there will be less vacuum energy; there'll actually be less "nothing" between the 2 plates than there would be outside them. The vacuum energy, if you think of it as zero, it's actually a little less than zero between the 2 plates, because there are fewer ways to put waves between the plates and therefore fewer waves that have half of the ghost of a photon in the vacuum. And so if there's a little bit less energy between the plates, that leads to a kind of negative pressure between the plates, a tiny attractive force between the plates. So Casimir predicted that due to the quantum vacuum, these fluctuating electromagnetic fields, these ghostly half photons that are present as zero-point energy even when no real photons are present—there's an attraction between parallel metal plates. That's called the Casimir effect.

And the Casimir effect was soon detected—not long after he worked it out— it was soon detected experimentally. Accurate measurements of the Casimir effect had to wait for the 1990s, though, and that is kind of an interesting story. Why the wait? Well, this force that they were talking about is really, really tiny unless the plates are extremely close together. And if the plates are this close together, it's really hard to make the plates exactly parallel. No matter what you do, one end of the plate will be a little closer than the other end of the plate, and it's really hard to predict and to measure. And so because you can't make the plates parallel enough, then it's hard to get a good quantitative measurement of the effect.

The better experiments that they've done more recently involve a flat plate and a sphere; and it doesn't matter what angle the sphere is at, you don't have to arrange it very precisely. The theory of the Casimir effect between a flat plate and a sphere is a little bit more complex, but the experiment is much easier to do. And so now we have very accurate measurements of the Casimir effect, and it is just as Casimir proposed back in 1948.

So, moral of the story: The Casimir effect is real. It's a force between objects that is entirely due to the properties of empty space, to the energy that's present in the quantum vacuum. Well, that's kind of neat. There's a force due to the energy of empty space. Could we use this force as a source of power? Could we extract useful energy from the vacuum and solve all of our industrial energy problems? This is an idea that sometimes comes up, because getting something from nothing sounds pretty good.

So let's imagine the Casimir engine. In the Casimir engine we bring 2 metal plates really close to each other, and there's an attractive force between them, and so we let this attractive force between them pull, lift weights, or do some useful work or generate electricity. As we allow the plates to come together we allow that force to do some useful work. Now, the force is pretty weak, but in fact we can actually get energy out of it until the plates actually come together and touch.

Well, so we'd like to use the Casimir engine again, but to pry the plates apart would amount to rebuilding the vacuum in between, and we'll have to put back in just as much energy as we extracted. So the moral of the story is we can get a little something out of nothing, but only up to a point. The Casimir engine actually uses up the available vacuum energy as we draw the plates together. So the Casimir engine will not solve all our energy needs. Too bad. But that doesn't mean that the vacuum energy is not important. In fact, it's tremendously important. It may be cosmically important.

As you may know, the universe is expanding. All of the galaxies in the universe are moving apart from each other. It's as if space itself is expanding, that's really the right way to think about it. And this is all an aftereffect of the big bang. The big bang was a time when the universe was very small, whatever that means, very dense and hot, the matter in the universe was very close together; and then the universe expanded rapidly. The big bang happened about 13 billion years ago.

Now, the ordinary gravity between the galaxies tells us that the expansion of the universe should slow down over time because the galaxies are pulling on each other; the expansion slows as the universe expands. That has lead, over the decades, to an interesting question. The question is whether the universe will expand forever—its expansion will outrun gravity—or whether the gravity will be enough to cause the universe to come to a stop and maybe collapse back in on itself at some distant future date.

So that's a question that cosmologists have been pondering and making observations to answer for some time. Then in 1998, the cosmologists announced a totally astounding discovery. When you look out into distant space billions of light years away, you're also looking back in time, because it takes light time to travel to you. When you look very far out in space you are looking at how the universe was at an earlier phase of the universe's history. So when you do measurements very precisely, you find that not only is the cosmos expanding, it's actually expanding at an increasing rate; it's expanding faster and faster. The expansion of the universe is accelerating. So it certainly looks like it's going to expand forever because it's not only not slowing down enough, it's not slowing down at all; it's actually speeding up.

Why? Why is the universe speeding up as it expands? The short answer is that cosmologists don't know; but they have a name for the cause of this, a name for what they don't know, and that name is "dark energy." Now, it's called "dark energy" for a very good reason. It's called "dark" because we actually do not see it directly; whatever it is it is not emitting light, we don't see it in our ordinary telescopes, so it's dark. And it's called dark "energy" to distinguish it from dark matter, which is a kind of matter of an unknown type which is also present; we can see its gravitational effects, but it has a different effect on the universe. There's something called "dark matter," but this is dark energy.

And this dark energy is really important. In fact, if you want to make a rough inventory of the contents of the universe, no more than 5% of the stuff in the universe is ordinary matter, the stuff that's made of atoms. This no more than

5% includes all the stars, all the planets, all the gas clouds, all of that stuff that we're familiar with; that's less than 5% of the stuff in the universe.

About 25% of the stuff in the universe is dark matter, whatever that is. And there are some interesting proposals about what that is, but nobody knows for sure. 25% of the stuff in the universe is this dark matter and we're not quite sure what it is.

But that leaves 70% of the stuff in the universe which is dark energy. And it's the dark energy that causes cosmic acceleration, and it's the dark energy that dominates. Most of everything is dark energy. That's actually a very astounding result of modern cosmology: at least 95% of the universe is stuff that is unknown to us. We don't know what it is, what its nature is, which means of course, from the point of view of a scientist, these are great days for cosmology because there are some of the most important discoveries yet to be made.

Now, interestingly, Einstein himself suggested something like dark energy in his early work on relativity and cosmology. You see, Einstein thought that the universe was static over time, that it neither expanded nor contracted over time; sort of a common-sense view in his day. And so to make his model of the universe work out he needed an outward push to counter the effect of gravity, which would cause the universe to collapse. He found that if there wasn't such a push then the universe would have to either be expanding or contracting; it couldn't be static. Later on it was discovered that the universe was actually expanding and Einstein said, this extra stuff that I put into the universe, this kind of dark energy that I included in the universe, that was my greatest mistake. But nowadays Einstein's greatest mistake is coming back into fashion.

Einstein's dark energy, what he called his "cosmological constant," is a kind of energy that is present even in otherwise empty space. As the universe expands there's actually more of it. Now that may make us worry, say, well, if there is more of it, where does it come from? Where does all this energy come from? And with your permission I'm going to duck the question; the law of conservation of energy is extremely tricky to apply to the universe as a whole. Suffice it to say it does make sense mathematically, although it is very strange to express it in English.

So, what's the dark energy? What is this energy of empty space? And our leading hypothesis is that dark energy is the same as the quantum vacuum energy, as the zero-point energy that the electromagnetic field and other quantum fields have even when there are no quanta, even when there are no photons. The quantum vacuum energy is the dark energy. And as space expands more dark energy appears and that drives the expansion faster; and that's why the expansion of the universe is accelerating. In other words, quantum vacuum energy may have cosmic implications.

Now, I have to confess there is a major difficulty with this theory. If you plug in the obvious numbers, if you do the calculations, then you find that there should be a lot of vacuum energy, a *lot* of vacuum energy. I mean, there's half of a ghost of a photon of every frequency and direction no matter how high the frequency. Talk about your ultraviolet catastrophe. There are huge amounts of vacuum energy in empty space at these extremely high frequencies because there are lots and lots of ways that the light waves could be going, and every one of the waves has half of a ghost of a photon in it.

So the amount of vacuum energy that you calculate is much, much, much too large to be the dark energy, which is after all pretty sparsely distributed in the universe. It's only a couple of dozen times more prevalent than matter, and the universe is mostly empty space. Mostly space is between the atoms; atoms are very sparse in the universe as a whole. So there is way too much quantum vacuum energy to account for the dark energy.

Now, most people would say that it does make sense for the vacuum energy to have no effect at all. The vacuum energy somehow doesn't count when you're considering how the universe behaves, like considering gravity, that it's kind of renormalized away like we talked about last time, where you have something that appears to be infinite but there are other infinities that cancel it and it doesn't really make any contributions. But that's very difficult to make it work out. It's easy to imagine that the vacuum energy has a huge effect. It's easy to imagine that the vacuum energy has zero effect. Both of those make mathematical sense. It's very hard to imagine that the vacuum energy has only a small, non-zero effect, which is what the dark energy in the cosmos is.

So the dark energy might not be quantum vacuum energy after all, it's hard to say; we just don't know right now. However, cosmologists believe that immediately after the big bang there was a short period in the universe's history, a small fraction of a second, where there was a super fast expansion of the universe called "cosmic inflation." This cosmic inflation hypothesis explains a lot about the distribution of matter and energy in the universe. And this period of cosmic inflation may well have been driven by quantum vacuum energy in the early universe; and that would have been very, very important indeed in the formation of the universe we see.

We've gone pretty far—to the origins of the universe and the reason why it's expanding—and what we've been telling is a very fascinating and complex story. It's a story that is still unfinished. It's the story of how nothing at all in the quantum sense can lead to stupendous implications for the physics of the world. Fascinating story, but I'm afraid we're going to have to leave it there.

With the physics of the quantum vacuum we've completed our so-called sightseeing tour of the quantum world. We've completed Section Three of this course, and looking back on it with the eyes of a quantum physicist, I have to tell you we have skipped almost everything. But at least we saw bosons and fermions and the distinction between them, the most important minus sign in the world. And we've seen quantum entanglement; we've seen the EPR argument and Bell's theorem that told us such a startling story about the nature of physical reality. We saw Feynman's quantum mechanics; we saw quantum electrodynamics and this whole strange business of virtual particles. And we saw the physics of the vacuum, the very strange and important quantum physics of so-called empty space.

Next we're going to spend a few lectures discussing a contemporary topic in quantum research. This will be Section Four of our course, on quantum information and quantum computing. We're going to be asking how we can use quantum physics to store and transmit and process information. We're going to ask, what does quantum mechanics tell us about the physical nature of information, and what does information tell us about the nature of quantum mechanics? I'm very fascinated by this; this is my own field of research and this subject, which is a very new one, has disclosed a lot of amazing things about the quantum world. So there are some good stories to tell. We begin quantum information next time. I'll see you then.

Quantum Cloning
Lecture 19

> With this lecture we're starting Section 4 of our course, in which we will explore a contemporary topic in quantum mechanics research: quantum information and quantum computing—my own field of research specialty. ...Our question is how can we use quantum systems to store, retrieve, transmit, and process data?

W e can use single photons, atoms, and electrons to perform our tasks. In this part of the course, we will think about and understand the limitations imposed by quantum physics as well as the opportunities it affords. This is not really a question about futuristic technology. It is mostly a deep question about nature. Rolf Landauer said, "Information is physical." All information is related to physical states and physical processes of physical systems. We will consider what quantum physics can tell us about the basic concept of information.

Classical and quantum information are alike in many ways. Classical information is the type of information that can be stored in classical (macroscopic) systems. This is the sort of information that we are familiar with in everyday life. It can be changed from one physical form to another. If we consider just the classical information generated by and corresponding to this lecture, we see the diverse range of forms it can take. For this lecture, classical information includes light and sound in the studio, electrical signals in the camera, magnetic patterns on a videotape, tiny dimples on a DVD, reflected laser light in a DVD player, more electrical signals, and finally light and sound again. Yet the information remains the same throughout.

The basic unit of classical information is the "bit." A bit is a binary digit, which can be either 0 or 1. This can stand for "yes" or "no," "on" or "off," etc. We can use different physical systems to represent bits, and any sort of information can be encoded into a series of bits. We can use bits to measure "how much information" something contains. How many bits do we need to store a novel? A nice photograph? A minute of music on my digital player? All of these have an information content of about 1 megabyte (8 million bits).

On the other hand, quantum information is the type of information that can be stored in quantum systems. Like classical information, we can transform the physical form of quantum information. The basic unit of quantum information is the "qubit." A qubit is a quantum system with just 2 basis states. (We have seen a couple of examples already: a single photon in an interferometer and a spin-$\frac{1}{2}$ particle.) We can call the basis states $|0\rangle$ and $|1\rangle$. In addition to the basis states, a qubit may be in any superposition state $a|0\rangle + b|1\rangle$. If we have more than 1 qubit, they can be entangled with each other. Qubits have lots of possibilities!

The fundamental difference between classical and quantum information is that, while quantum information cannot be exactly copied, we can always in principle copy classical information.

Qubits can be used to send classical information, if we wish. For example, Alice wishes to send Bob a 1bit message (0 or 1). She prepares a spin-$\frac{1}{2}$ particle in the state $|\uparrow\rangle$ for 0, $|\downarrow\rangle$ for 1. The spin is sent to Bob, who makes a z measurement and reads the message. But there are more spin states available. Can Alice send more than 1 bit in a single qubit? Suppose she wants to send a 2bit message. She encodes 00 by $|\uparrow\rangle$, 01 by $|\downarrow\rangle$, 10 by $|\rightarrow\rangle$ and 11 by $|\leftarrow\rangle$. All of these available states of a single spin. This message will not get through, because Bob cannot read it. He can correctly tell $|\uparrow\rangle$ from $|\downarrow\rangle$ using z, or $|\rightarrow\rangle$ from $|\leftarrow\rangle$ using x, but no measurement will let him distinguish all 4 spin states. The capacity of a qubit for sending classical information is 1 bit.

It is not so straightforward to send qubits via bits. This depends on exact definitions. At worst, it is impossible. At best, it will take very many bits to describe the exact superposition state $a|0\rangle + b|1\rangle$ of a single qubit.

The fundamental difference between classical and quantum information is that, while quantum information cannot be exactly copied, we can always in principle copy classical information. In classical physics, observing a system need have no effect on it. By carefully measuring our bits, we can duplicate them exactly. The ability to copy classical information is a huge problem of copyright law, intellectual property, and privacy!

To consider how we would copy, or try to copy, quantum information, we imagine a "quantum cloning machine" that would take as input a single qubit and produce as output 2 qubits with exactly the original state: $|state\rangle \Rightarrow |state\ state\rangle$. Imagine that the cloning machine works for the states $|\uparrow\rangle$ and $|\downarrow\rangle$ of a spin-$\frac{1}{2}$ particle. That is, $|\uparrow\rangle \Rightarrow |\uparrow\uparrow\rangle$ and $|\downarrow\rangle \Rightarrow |\downarrow\downarrow\rangle$. For simplicity, assume there are no measurements, so that only update rule I applies. How does the cloning machine work for $|\rightarrow\rangle = s|\uparrow\rangle + s|\downarrow\rangle$?

$$|\rightarrow\rangle = s|\uparrow\rangle + s|\downarrow\rangle \Rightarrow s|\uparrow\uparrow\rangle + s|\downarrow\downarrow\rangle.$$

But this result is an entangled state of 2 spins, not the product state $|\rightarrow\rightarrow\rangle$ we wished for. The quantum cloning machine therefore has to fail for some input states!

In 1982, the "quantum no-cloning theorem" was proved in this way by William Wootters and Wojciech Zurek, and in a different way by Dennis Dieks. A perfect quantum cloning machine is impossible. Quantum information cannot be exactly copied.

We now move on to a science fiction story to illustrate the fact that if we *did* have a perfect cloning machine, then we could send 2 bits in 1 qubit. In our story, Alice sends Bob the 4 states $|\uparrow\rangle$, $|\downarrow\rangle$, $|\rightarrow\rangle$, $|\leftarrow\rangle$ as before. Bob uses a cloning machine to make 2000 copies. He now has: $|\uparrow\uparrow\uparrow\cdots\rangle$, $|\downarrow\downarrow\downarrow\cdots\rangle$, $|\rightarrow\rightarrow\rightarrow...\rangle$, $|\leftarrow\leftarrow\leftarrow\cdots\rangle$.

Bob measures z on the first 1000 spins.

If he has $|\uparrow\uparrow\uparrow\cdots\rangle$, he will obtain $+\frac{1}{2}$ all 1000 times.

If he has $|\downarrow\downarrow\downarrow\cdots\rangle$, he will obtain $-\frac{1}{2}$ all 1000 times.

If he has $\left|\rightarrow\rightarrow\rightarrow\cdots\right\rangle$ or $\left|\leftarrow\leftarrow\leftarrow\cdots\right\rangle$, he will obtain $+\frac{1}{2}$ and $-\frac{1}{2}$ about 500 times each. Bob also measures x on the next 1000 spins. Combining his results, Bob can determine which of the 4 original states Alice sent and read her 2bit message.

Why can a qubit only convey 1 bit of classical information? Part of the answer lies in the quantum no-cloning theorem. ∎

Questions to Consider

1. Write a paragraph that clearly explains to your Aunt Mary the essential difference between bits and qubits. (If your own Aunt Mary happens to be a quantum physicist, pick someone else's Aunt Mary.)

2. Think of some technical and legal methods by which we try to make it hard to copy certain kinds of classical information. (This is done for privacy, copyright, and other reasons.) Are any of them foolproof?

Quantum Cloning
Lecture 19—Transcript

Welcome to the 19th lecture in our course on quantum mechanics. With this lecture we're starting Section Four of our course, in which we will explore a contemporary topic in quantum mechanics research: quantum information and quantum computing—my own field of research specialty. Our question is how can we use quantum systems to store, retrieve, transmit, and process data? How can we use single photons, electrons, and atoms to perform our tasks? We're going to ask what are the limitations imposed by quantum mechanics? And we'll also ask what are the opportunities that quantum mechanics affords? However, this is not really a question about futuristic technology. It might be fun, it might even be useful, to build a quantum communications system or a quantum computer; but we are interested in another aspect of the subject, a deep question about nature.

Rolf Landauer, who was a physicist at IBM, said it best; he said, "Information is physical." There's no such thing as disembodied information. Information is always represented by the state of a physical system—by ink on paper or electrons or photons and so on. Similarly, there's no magical information processing. The computation in a real computer is always a physical process; it always follows the laws of physics. So that leads us to 2 profound questions about the nature of quantum physics and information. And the first one is: What does quantum physics tell us about the concept of information? And the second is: What does the concept of information tell us about quantum physics?

Now, the concept of information is somewhat familiar to us these days; we live in the information age. We're familiar with telecommunications and optical and electronic storage media and computers and so on. And so basically we already have a concept of information, although we'll need to discuss that concept. That concept is basically what we'll call "classical information." That's the information that can be stored in macroscopic systems. It's our familiar idea of information; it's the information that could be in a book, the information that could be in a movie, the information that could be in a musical recording.

The amazing thing is that information can be changed from one physical form to another. Let's take as an example this lecture. There's light and sound here in our classroom, but then we have that information turned into electrical signals in the camera and the microphone. Those are recorded as magnetic patterns on a videotape. You may have received this lecture in the form of tiny microscopic dimples on a DVD. That DVD is read by reflected laser light in a DVD player—it's turned into electrical signals again. And finally, right now it's light and sound again. All of these are transformations of physical form, yet the same information through all of the transformations; a remarkable fact, a remarkable property of information.

Now, the basic unit of information is the bit. One bit is a binary digit, a 0 or a 1; and that 0 or 1 can stand for yes or no, it could stand for on or off, it could stand for left or right, etc. So how do we understand bits? Well, let's take for example the game of 20 Questions. In the game of 20 Questions you're supposed to guess a word by asking 20 yes/no questions. In other words, in the course of the game you get to learn 20 bits of information, 20 yes/no answers. So is 20 bits of information enough to guess the word? Well, how many different combinations of yes/no answers could you get in the course of the game? You get 2 different answers for the first question, 2 different answers for the second question, and so on; so the total number of possible combinations of answers is $2 \times 2 \times 2 \times 2 \ldots 2^{20}$, which is about 1 million. So you ought to be able to identify any of a million different words with 20 yes/no questions if you're clever. It turns out that this is not far from the actual number of distinct words in English, especially if you leave out some of the very unusual words like "syzygy" or something. If you play 20 Questions with somebody who picks syzygy, you're in trouble! So you could hope to win at 20 Questions, but it isn't easy, and that's exactly why it's a fun game. And it's helpful to remember the result of this calculation; an English word needs about 20 bits of information to represent.

Okay, we can use different physical systems to represent bits; we mentioned some of the physical manifestations of the information in this lecture, for example. And any sort of information can be recorded, encoded, in a series of binary digits, a series of bits. And we can use bits to measure how much information something contains by asking how many binary digits, how many 0s and 1s, do we need to represent that information? So how many bits do we need to store a novel? How many bits do we need to store a nice photograph? How many bits do we need to store a minute of music on a digital music player? And it turns out that all of these are about the same. All of them are about 8 million bits, or 1 megabyte, and that's the amount of information that those different kinds of information contain.

Okay, so much for classical information. What about quantum information? Quantum information is the type of information that can be stored in a quantum system. We can transform the physical form of quantum information just as we can transform classical information, using our rules for quantum mechanics, following our Update Rules I and II, depending on whether or not there is a measurement or not.

The basic unit of quantum information is called the "qubit." Now, a qubit is a quantum system that has 2 basis states; and we've seen a couple of examples already. The photon in an interferometer was a qubit; it had 2 basis states, upper-beam or lower-beam states. The spin $-1/2$ particle is another example of a qubit. If we measure the z component of spin we've got basis states up and down, spin $+1/2$ or $-1/2$. So a qubit is just any one of these, any quantum system with just 2 basis states. We can call those qubit basis states 0 and 1 if we like, the $|0\rangle$ (ket 0) and the $|1\rangle$ (ket 1). But if the only thing there were to qubits were basis states, then this would just be a bit, it would just be another kind of a bit, a classical bit. So there's actually more to a qubit, because of course in a qubit you can have superpositions of the basis states. You can have a funny combination of 0 and 1; you would represent that by a state $a|0\rangle + b|1\rangle$, where a and b are amplitudes. You can have a superposition of 0 and 1. You can't have that for a classical bit.

Similarly, if you have more than 1 qubit they might be entangled together; that's another possibility. So qubits are much richer, qubits are much more complicated and subtle and interesting than ordinary bits. But of course we could use qubits to send classical information, to send bits, if we like. To explain this I'm going to introduce you to our 2 protagonists: Alice and Bob. By tradition, Alice and Bob are the heroes of quantum information theory thought-experiments. Alice and Bob are the characters that carry out our thought-experiments. And so we'll just mention Alice and Bob, and they'll show up quite often. Sometimes there will be other cast members, but the stars of the show are Alice and Bob.

And so in this thought-experiment, Alice wishes to send Bob a 1-bit message, 0 or 1. It might stand for a very important piece of information, yes or no, on or off, left or right. She wants to send it by using a qubit, say, a spin-1/2 particle. So what does she do? She prepares the spin of the particle. If she wants to send 0, she prepares it spin up; if she wants to send 1, she prepares spin down; so, 0 or 1, up or down, yes or no. The particle then is sent to Bob, and what does Bob do? Bob measures the z component of the spin, and that allows him to read the message, because he can tell whether the spin is up or down. If Bob were foolish enough to do something else, like read the x component of the spin, he'd lose the message; but he can read the message by reading the right variable.

But you know, Alice notices that there are more than just 2 quantum states available. In addition to the 0 and 1 basis states, the up state and the down state, there are lots of other states. So she gets the idea that maybe she could send 2 bits of information. If there are 2 bits of information there are 4 possible messages: that's 00, 01, 10, and 11; those are the 4 possible 2-bit messages. So Alice tries to encode, let's see, she encodes 00 is up and 01 is down; but 10 is encoded as spin to the right and 11 is encoded as spin to the left. That's great, she has a quantum state for each of her messages and so she prepares the spin in the quantum state and she sends the spin to Bob. Bob doesn't know what her message is, but he's going to try to figure it out.

Can he read her message correctly? And the answer is no, he can't. I mean, Bob can tell up from down with a z measurement, he can tell right from left with an x measurement; but no measurement will allow him to distinguish all 4 of these spin states. So Bob can't read the message that Alice sends. The moral of the story is that the capacity of a qubit for sending classical information is just 1 bit. You can put a bit in a qubit, but you can't put more than a bit in a qubit.

Can we do the reverse? Can we send qubits using bits? Well, that's a complex question. I'll just tell you that it depends on what you mean by that question exactly; you have to be very careful. And at worst the answer is no, you can't send qubits by bits no matter how many bits you use, and at best it requires a lot of bits to send 1 qubit. I mean, after all, to describe the superposition state, $a|0\rangle + b|1\rangle$, you've got to describe the amplitude numbers a and b. To describe 2 numbers to sufficient accuracy it may take you many, many bits. So just in general there's no easy way to send a qubit using only bits.

Let me tell you a little story, a personal aside: I can tell you the origin of the term qubit. I can tell you because I was there at the exact moment. This happened during a conversation with the quantum physicist William Wootters from Williams College. He and I were in a car driving on our way to the airport in May of 1992, and we were discussing some problems we'd been working on about information and quantum physics; and as a joke we proposed that maybe we need a new unit for specifically quantum types of information. We said, oh yes, we could measure things in qubits; and we thought this was amazingly funny, because of course a cubit is a unit of length in the ancient Near East. Noah's Ark in the Bible is 300 qubits long and 50 qubits wide and 30 qubits high and we thought it was just a hilarious thing to measure something in physics in "qubits." But then over that summer I thought a lot about qubits, and I decided that qubits was a good idea; so in the fall I introduced the term in a talk at a conference and it's now a standard scientific term. But just between you and me, it started as a pun.

Okay, what is the fundamental difference between classical and quantum information? Physically, what's the essential distinction between them? And the answer is really interesting. The answer is copying. We can always, in principle, copy classical information. We can always in principle make a duplicate of it. And the reason is that observing a classical system, like a DVD for example, observing a classical system need have no effect on it, need make no damage to the DVD. And if we measure our bits very carefully we can duplicate them exactly, we can make a copy of a DVD— and that's a serious issue because the copyability of classical information is a problem for copyright law, it's a problem for intellectual property law, it's a problem for privacy. How do we prevent unauthorized people from copying information that they shouldn't? It's a terrible problem. But in fact, we cannot always copy quantum information. Quantum information is different. Quantum information is not copyable.

Let's see if we can understand this a little better. And I want to understand it by imagining a device, we're going to call this device a "quantum cloning machine." It takes a single qubit as its input and it produces 2 qubits as output, and the output is such that both qubits are exactly in the same state as the original qubit input. That's how a quantum cloning machine would work. Mathematically we would represent that the ket state goes to a ket which is state state ($|state\rangle \Rightarrow |state\ state\rangle$); it is a product composite state of 2 systems, 2 qubits, in exactly the original state. And our requirement is that the cloning machine should work on any input state. That's the process of quantum cloning. The question I want to ask is can such a machine really exist? Is such a machine consistent with the laws of quantum mechanics? A super quantum copying machine, a quantum cloner.

So suppose we have such a machine that actually works for the up and down states of a spin-1/2 particle. So up becomes up up ($|\uparrow\rangle \Rightarrow |\uparrow\uparrow\rangle$), or down becomes down down ($|\downarrow\rangle \Rightarrow |\downarrow\downarrow\rangle$). All right, let's suppose it works for those. Well, how does the machine work? Does the machine work by Update Rule I or Update Rule II? Are there measurements involved in the machine or not? Well, we don't want randomness in our machine operation, we want a definite result; so let's assume for the sake of argument that it has to operate according to Update Rule I. In general, we'll have to consider more complicated combinations of the rules, but this is good enough for now. Let's assume that it operates according to Update Rule I. Update Rule I preserves superpositions.

Now, suppose we wanted to duplicate the state right, the state right which is s up plus s down; s is our favorite number, the square root of 1/2. So, if we wanted to duplicate right we would have to wind up with right right. And what is right right? Well, it's the composition rule in action, it's s up plus s down times s up plus s down. And if you work it out it's s^2 times up up plus s^2 times up down times s^2 plus down up plus s^2 times down down. If you want to simplify that a little bit you can just remember that s^2 is 1/2, but it's basically a sum of 4 different basis kets. That's the state we want.

But what state do we actually get out of the quantum cloning machine? Remember the quantum cloning machine applies Update Rule I and it takes up to up up and down to down down; so it's going to take a superposition *s* up plus *s* down to *s* up up plus *s* down down ... that's not what we want at all. The 2 output spins are entangled; this is not the product of right and right, it's something else. So the moral of the story is that the quantum cloning machine has to fail for some inputs, it has to work wrong for some inputs, and that means that no machine that operates according to the laws of quantum mechanics can possibly duplicate a qubit.

It's an amazing fact that quantum mechanics was over 50 years old before this basic elementary and vastly important fact was even noticed. And it was noticed in 1982 when the quantum no-cloning theorem was proved, the theorem we just mentioned, by William Wootters, our old friend from the term "qubit," and Wojciech Zurek of Los Alamos National Laboratory. They proved it in much the way that we've shown, and about the same time Dennis Dieks from the University of Utrecht proved it a completely different way. They proved that a perfect quantum cloning machine is impossible. They proved that quantum information cannot be exactly copied.

Let's tell a science fiction story; really, it's a fantasy story. What if we did have a perfect cloning machine? What if somehow we were provided with a machine that got around this proof somehow and we could actually make perfect copies of quantum information? What could we do with a machine like that? It's sometimes useful to imagine the impossible and see what follows.

Well, one of the things we could do is we could send 2 bits in 1 qubit. Remember our previous attempt, Alice's previous attempt. She sent up, down, right, and left to Bob, each one representing a different message, and Bob had to figure out which one of those he got and he couldn't do it. There was no quantum measurement that allowed him to do it. But now let's suppose Bob has a quantum cloning machine, so what does he do? He takes the spin that Alice sends to him and he runs off 2000 exact copies of it with his quantum cloning machine.

So what does he have? He now has one of the following things: He has 2000 qubits whose state is up up up up up up 2000 times; or down down down down down 2000 times; or right right right right right 2000 times; or left left left left left 2000 times. He has 1 of those 4 situations.

So what does he do with his 2000 qubits? Well, the first thing he does is he measures z on the first 1000 of them. Now, if the state is up up up up up that means that when he measures z on those qubits he'll get $+1/2$ every time, all 1000 times. And if it's down down down down down, he'll get $-1/2$ for his measurement all 1000 times. What about the other 2? What if it's right right right right right or left left left left left? Well, each one of those has a 50-50 shot, so probably he'll get about 500 $+1/2$ and 500 $-1/2$. So he can tell whether it was up or down, or 1 of the other 2.

So how does he figure out what the other 2 are, whether it's 1 or the other 2? Well, he measures x on the next 1000 qubits and he can sort them out. He'll either get all $+1/2$ or all $-1/2$ or a mixture; and by combining the results of these 2000 measurements he can determine which of the 4 qubit states was sent by Alice, so he can read her message. He can send 2 qubits in 1 qubit and that's impossible. Why can a qubit only convey 1 bit of classical information? Part of the answer lies in the no-cloning theorem.

Now let me tell you an even better science fiction story about what you could do with a quantum cloning machine. I mean, after all, sending 2 bits in 1 qubit is not that exciting. Sure, it violates some principle that we had previously found, but it doesn't seem very dangerous. Now I'm going to tell you that if they have a quantum cloning machine, Alice can send a message to Bob faster than the speed of light.

So how does it work? Well, let's imagine that Alice and Bob share a pair of spins that are in a total spin 0 state; in other words. They made a pair of spins like this yesterday or sometime in the past and they now just possess them, they've held on to them and the spins are still in a total spin 0 state.

Now, if Alice measures z on her spin, then we know that Bob's spin is either going to wind up in the up state or the down state, because his spin state has to be exactly opposite to Alice's measurement result because it's a total spin 0 state; that's entanglement, and it's happened sort of at once. Now, it's also true that if Alice measures x on her spin, then Bob's spin is either going to wind up being right or left, because it would have to be exactly opposite to Alice's measurement result because it's a total spin 0 state. And this happens at once.

Now, ordinarily, Bob would not be able to figure out exactly what he has because there's no measurement that he can do that can tell whether he has up, down, left, or right that distinguishes those 4 states that would allow him to sort them out. And anyway, Alice can only control her choice of measurement, she can't control the result of the measurement; that result is random. So she can't really control the exact outcome and therefore couldn't use the outcome of the measurement to send a message. So it looks like there's no hope for sending information using an entangled pair of particles faster than light.

But suppose Bob had a magic cloning machine. Then Bob could do what we previously described, could make a couple of thousand copies and make some x and z measurements, and he could tell exactly what he has. He can tell whether it was a spin up or a spin down, or a spin right or a spin left. And that means that he can determine Alice's choice of measurement instantly. If Alice chose a z measurement, he'd either be getting spin up or spin down. If Alice chose an x measurement, he'd either be getting spin to the right or spin to the left. And he can find out at once, right away, even if Alice is a billion kilometers away. So what does Alice do? Alice represents the message 0 as a z measurement; if she wants to send 0, she makes a z measurement. If she wants to send 1, she sends an x measurement. Bob, on his side, makes thousands of copies of the qubit, performs a lot of measurements on them, and receives Alice's message immediately. He can tell immediately which measurement she made.

It was exactly this idea, the idea that a perfect quantum cloning machine would let you communicate faster than light, that led Wootters and Zurek and Dieks to prove the quantum no-cloning theorem in the first place, that led them to prove that no quantum cloning machine could exist. And so information could not be sent faster than light, because this particular way, using a quantum cloning machine, is impossible.

We've established that there are 2 distinct ideas of information—at least. There's classical information, which is measured in bits and can always be represented by bits, and there's quantum information, which is measured in qubits, can be represented by qubits, which are quantum states with 2 basis states but also lots of other superposition and entangled states. We found that classical information can always be copied in principle. Quantum information, though, cannot always be copied; quantum information is uncopyable. This is the quantum no-cloning theorem.

So that raises an interesting question. The question is can we use the uncopyability of quantum information to do something useful? Because we said that the fact that classical information is so easy to copy is a big problem. Could we solve that problem, maybe, by using quantum information? And the answer is yes. Next time, we're going to talk about the subject of quantum cryptography, which is using quantum uncertainty in the service of privacy. That's next time. I'll see you then.

Quantum Cryptography
Lecture 20

Now, this time, we're going to see how quantum information and the no-cloning theorem play out in action. We're going to see how the laws of quantum physics will help us to keep secrets. We're going to talk about the subject of quantum cryptography. So, let's begin.

The science of cryptography is about keeping certain information private. To think about cryptography, we begin with an example involving Alice and Bob, two characters we met in our last lecture (and whose names also appear frequently in examples in journals of mathematical cryptography). In our example here, Alice wishes to send a message to Bob that cannot be read by any eavesdropper, whom we'll call Eve. They do this by agreeing on a secret code for their messages. Many codes can be "broken" by cryptanalysis. However, there is a type of secret code that cannot be broken, called a "1time pad." A 1time pad uses secret "key" information to encode the message. If Eve lacks the key, she cannot read the message. We can describe the 1time pad using strings of bits. There is a "plaintext string," a "key string," and a "ciphertext string." If Eve intercepts the ciphertext but lacks the key, she cannot read it. Bob, with the key, can decrypt the message and read the plaintext.

The big problem with this involves key distribution. If Alice and Bob use the same key over and over, it becomes insecure, and a clever Eve can begin to read their messages. They must only use the key once! (This is why it is called a 1time pad.) How can Alice send Bob a new key without Eve reading it? Alice might send the key in a tamper-proof box. Bob could check it for Eve's fingerprints, etc. But Eve might be able to make a copy of the key without leaving any traces, so that Alice and Bob

In 1984, Charles Bennett and Gilles Brassard showed how to use quantum mechanics to solve the problem of key distribution. Their idea, known as "BB84," marks the birth of "quantum cryptography."

would be fooled and think their key is still secret. No classical method of key distribution can be 100% safe from Eve.

In 1984, Charles Bennett and Gilles Brassard showed how to use quantum mechanics to solve the problem of key distribution. Their idea, known as "BB84," marks the birth of "quantum cryptography." We will use another example, with our stock characters, to describe the BB84 method.

In our example, Alice sends to Bob a series of spins, their states chosen randomly from the set $|\uparrow\rangle$, $|\downarrow\rangle$, $|\rightarrow\rangle$, $|\leftarrow\rangle$. Bob measures each spin, randomly choosing z or x for each. Then Alice and Bob talk on the phone. (Eve may be listening.) They do not say which states were sent, but they do discuss the measurements Bob made. Alice tells him which spins were measured using the "right" axis. They use the good ones for their secret key and throw out the others.

In our example, why can't Eve intervene and learn the secret key? She cannot do so because she cannot simply make exact copies of the spins as they go from Alice to Bob. The no-cloning theorem prevents this. If she makes measurements on the spins, she is bound to choose the "wrong" axis a lot of the time. This will necessarily introduce errors at Bob's end. If Alice and Bob compare a few hundred of their key bits over the phone, they can detect this. Eve must leave "quantum fingerprints." BB84 works because of complementarity of x and z, plus the no-cloning theorem. ∎

Questions to Consider

1. To use the BB84 scheme, Alice and Bob must individually generate some random sequences of zeros and 1s. Otherwise, if Eve can guess what sequences they are using, she can also guess their key. Make some suggestions for generating these random bits. (Extra points for using quantum physics to do it!)

2. Imagine that Eve possesses a quantum cloning machine that can perfectly duplicate qubit states. How can she use this magical device to "break" the BB84 quantum key distribution?

Quantum Cryptography
Lecture 20—Transcript

Welcome to the 20th lecture in our course on quantum mechanics. We have been discussing the connections between quantum physics and the idea of information. Last time we said that there were 2 distinct kinds of information, classical and quantum information. Classical information is the more familiar type to us. It's the kind of information that can be recorded and stored using ordinary macroscopic physical objects. It's the sort of information that might appear in a book.

Quantum information is something new. Quantum information is represented in microscopic quantum particles. Now, because of the laws of quantum physics, because the laws of quantum physics are a bit strange, the laws of quantum information are also a bit unexpected. And the great example that we saw last time was the quantum no-cloning theorem. We saw that it was impossible, even in principle, to create a device that exactly duplicates the quantum state of a qubit; and indeed this applies to any quantum system, qubits are just the simplest type of quantum system. And so if the device works for some quantum states, it certainly must fail for others; it can't duplicate perfectly an arbitrary quantum state. So that means that quantum information cannot be accurately copied.

Now, it's remarkable to me that so basic and simple a principle of quantum theory was not discovered until the early 1980s. It's a far-reaching idea. If someone were to ask me, "What is the secret of the universe?" I would have to admit that I don't know the secret of the universe. But the quantum no-cloning theorem would be 1 of the 3 or 4 things that would pass through my mind.

Why? Well, consider how we come to know about the quantum world. Let's do an experiment; we set up apparatus, we make a measurement, we get a result. What is a measurement on a quantum particle? Well, it's nothing but an attempt to turn quantum information into classical information. It's an attempt to take some aspect of the quantum world and make copies in our data records, in our brains, where we can communicate it to everyone. And that process is necessarily imperfect. The information in a quantum particle is unique, it's necessarily uncopyable, and so we have only imperfect access to the quantum world.

Now, this time, we're going to see how quantum information and the no-cloning theorem play out in action. We're going to see how the laws of quantum physics will help us to keep secrets. We're going to talk about the subject of quantum cryptography. So, let's begin.

Cryptography is the science of keeping certain information private, keeping it away from unauthorized access. And the science of cryptography has been around for a couple of thousand years, and it's been on solid mathematical footing since about the mid-19th century. Over time it's become a subject of huge importance. So let's reintroduce Alice and Bob, the protagonists who performed our thought-experiments last time. Indeed, Alice and Bob are also the protagonists of cryptography thought-experiments as well as quantum information thought-experiments. In fact Alice and Bob originated in cryptography—if you go to read journals of mathematical cryptography you'll be amazed at how often the main characters of the scientific papers are Alice and Bob.

Our situation is that Alice wishes to send Bob a private message. Now, in cryptography, we introduce a villain to our story, the eavesdropper, whom we'll call "Eve." Now, Alice and Bob don't want the eavesdropper to learn the message. Eve, on the other hand, does want to learn the message. And to do that Eve might tap their phone lines, Eve might make copies of their emails, Eve might open their letters. So what are Alice and Bob to do? How are they to maintain their privacy?

Of course, the way they go about it is to use encryption. Alice and Bob are going to represent the information in their message in an unfamiliar form. So, for example, they might use what is called a simple substitution cipher, where each letter in their message is represented by a letter—so A becomes *x* and B becomes Q and so on; that goes back at least to Roman times. And so when you write out the message "attack at once" or "buy tech stocks" or something like that, in our simple substitution cipher it would appear at first glance to be a meaningless jumble of letters.

The problem with a simple substitution cipher is that it's too simple. This is the sort of code that can be broken, and here's how Eve can do it. In English, some letters are more common than others; the letters E and T and A are more common than J and *x* and Q. And the same is true for letter combinations; the letter combination TH is very common. It's also true for whole words; the words "the" and "and" are quite common. And so Eve, by investigating the coded message, can recognize these patterns in the message. With a little work, she can deduce the code. Indeed there are newspaper puzzles of this type that typically appear next to the comic page in the newspaper, and with a little practice you can learn to crack those codes in just a few minutes. And this process of breaking the code, of penetrating the secret, is called "cryptanalysis." Cryptanalysis is the dark side of cryptography—unless, of course, you are Eve.

Now, the history of cryptography has been an arms race. More and more complex and sophisticated ciphers have been invented, and to try to break them, more and more sophisticated mathematical attacks have been developed to attack. So it has gone back and forth for centuries.

One famous episode in the history of cryptography happened during World War II. The Germans used a complex machine to encrypt their military information. The code continually changed and was different every day. This was called "the Enigma system"; the Enigma machine was the German machine. It was such a powerful system for doing this, such a sophisticated code, that they used it everywhere. All the branches of their armed services used it and it was very important to them. But as it turned out, a group of brilliant Polish and British mathematicians, using some of the earliest electronic computers, were actually able to break the Enigma system. So the Allies—playing Eve in this case—were able to read a great deal of the German military secret information. And this triumph of cryptanalysis, the breaking of the Enigma code, helped the Allies to win the war.

So, the history of cryptography has been an arms race between more and more powerful means of concealing a secret, more and more powerful means of penetrating secret codes. So who wins the arms race? Well, in fact, Alice and Bob do; it turns out that there is a perfect, unbreakable means of encryption. There's a way to encode information so that Eve could not possibly read it; and this has actually been known for some time. It's called "the 1-time pad," and I'll have to explain that name in a few minutes. But let's explain how it works, I'll give you an example of how the 1-time pad works.

We're going to represent our messages by strings of bits, zeros and 1s. And as we saw last time, any sort of information can be represented by zeros and 1s—text, sound, video can all be represented by a string of binary digits.

We're going to be considering 3 particular strings of binary digits. One of them is called "the plaintext." This is the message that Alice wants to send to Bob. The plaintext is the message that they very much want Eve not to be able to read. The plaintext is the secret. Now, in addition to the plaintext, there's also another string of bits, string of zeros and 1s, called "the key." It's a string of bits meaningless in itself, it might be completely random, and the key is known to Alice and Bob, but is not known to Eve initially. So Alice and Bob already share a secret, but it may be a meaningless secret. And finally, there's something called "the ciphertext," and this is the actual transmission, the actual string of bits that Alice sends to Bob. This is the thing that Eve might intercept; Eve might see the ciphertext.

So how does Alice produce the ciphertext from the plaintext, the message, and the secret key? Well, what she does is she simply adds them together. The ciphertext is the plaintext plus the key. Now, what do I mean by plus? Well, the easiest way to do this is to use bit arithmetic, and bit arithmetic is a little different. If you add 0 and 0 you get 0; 0 and 1 you get 1; 1 and 0 you get 1—that's all very sensible. But then, the other rule of bit arithmetic is that $1 + 1$ is equal to 0. So in fact, in bit arithmetic anything plus anything is 0; $0 + 0$ is the same as $1 + 1$, it all equals 0.

We have an example here, we have a string of plaintext bits, and I just picked 0 1 0 1 0 1; that's our secret. Then there is the key, the secret meaningless string of binary digits that's known to Alice and Bob but not to Eve; and I wrote down 0 1 1 0 0 0. And then we have the ciphertext, and I just take each bit of the plaintext with the corresponding bit of the key, I add them together, so $0 + 0$ gives me 0, $1 + 1$ gives me 0, $0 + 1$ gives me 1, and so on.

So Bob receives the ciphertext. What does he do? Well, he can decipher the message. All he needs to do is add the key again. If he takes the ciphertext and adds the key—that's the plaintext plus the key (which is the ciphertext) plus the key—well, if I add the key twice, anything added to itself is 0, and so I just get the plaintext back. And if you like, you can take our example and you can decipher it by simply taking the ciphertext, adding the key, and using bit arithmetic.

I'm giving you the details simply so you can play with your own examples. The point is that with the key, anybody can read the message. But without the key, Eve can learn nothing about the message at all; she knows nothing about the plaintext. The message could be anything. And so if Alice and Bob have a secret key, they win. They can send their secret message without Eve knowing. So this seems great. The 1-time pad means that Alice and Bob have won the war in cryptography. There are just 2 problems.

The first problem is that Alice and Bob cannot keep using the same key over and over again, because if they do, it makes them vulnerable to a particular mathematical attack by Eve. I won't go into the details; suffice it to say that if Eve suspects that they're using the same key over and over again, she can rather quickly extract information about their message. So every time they communicate, Alice and Bob will have to use a new random key. Once Alice and Bob have a key that is secret from Eve they are safe, but they have to do that, which brings up a second problem, the big one: the problem of key distribution. How could Alice send Bob a new key without Eve reading it? Because if Eve gets a copy of the key she can read the message; anybody with the key can read the message. Well, they're going to have to take special steps.

One thing they might try to do is Alice puts the key in a lock box, a special lock box, and she sends it to Bob, and then Bob examines the box very carefully for Eve's fingerprints to make sure that she didn't tamper with the box and open it up. And if they find signs of tampering then they just don't use the key and that's okay, Eve would still lose then, because the key is not interesting, the key doesn't mean anything. If Alice and Bob don't use the key, then even if Eve knows it, it doesn't help her read the message.

But you know, maybe Eve was able to break into the box and make a copy of the key without leaving any traces; that's always possible in principle, because classical information, which the key is, is always copyable. So Alice and Bob might be fooled and think that their key is secret. And if Alice and Bob think the key is secret, they might use it, and then Eve wins. Eve would be able to read their messages.

So there's a disturbing fact, a fact that's really kind of upsetting, and that is that no classical method of key distribution can be 100% secure from Eve. Alice and Bob might take all kinds of precautions so that when Alice sends the secret key to Bob by special courier or some other means, that Eve won't read it; but it's a mathematical fact, there's nothing they can do to be 100% sure that Eve doesn't intercept the key and make a copy. And the history of cryptography is full of examples where the key is compromised in this way.

All right, so much for the history of cryptography. What does all of this have to do with quantum mechanics? Well, in 1984, Charles Bennett of IBM Research and Gilles Brassard of the University of Montreal showed how to use quantum mechanics to solve the problem of key distribution. They invented quantum key distribution. The particular scheme for doing this that they invented is called "BB84," Bennett Brassard 1984; and BB84 marks the birth of quantum cryptography.

So to really get a feel for how this works, we're going to give you an overview of how the BB84 scheme works. There are some details we're leaving out, because as good cryptographers, Bennett and Brassard tried to anticipate all possible things that Eve could do to attack; but here's the basic scheme. And you have to imagine the scheme proceeding in a set of rounds; it's like a game: first one moves, then the other, then the other.

So the first round, the first move, is that Alice sends Bob a series of spins, a series of qubits. And what states does she send the qubits in? Well, she chooses them randomly from up, down, right, or left; she sends any of those with equal likelihood. Now, notice—and we discussed this last time—notice that no measurement can exactly identify all of these states. Nobody can come and do an experiment on these spins and determine exactly which of these states Alice is sending in a particular spin. So Alice sends these—she, of course, keeps a record of which ones she sent—she sends these and then Bob receives them.

Now we're ready for round 2. What does Bob do with them? He makes measurements. But what measurement does Bob make? Bob doesn't know what measurement to make, so he just measures at random. He either measures z or he measures x; he chooses randomly. Then he measures z, then he measures x, and then he measures x, and so on; and he gets the results.

All right, now sometimes the measurement that he makes is appropriate; in other words, the spin is either up or down and he measures the z component of the spin, and the result tells him which one it is. But sometimes the measurement he makes is inappropriate; maybe he measured the z component of the spin but the spin was either right or left. Then his measurement didn't tell him anything about what Alice prepared.

Now we move to round 3, the third move of the game. Alice and Bob now talk on the telephone. Now, Eve might be listening in, so the conversation that Alice and Bob have is a public conversation essentially. They are going to permit anybody who wants to listen in on this conversation. Now, Alice doesn't say which states she sent, and Bob doesn't say what the measurement results he obtained were. They keep those things secret. But in the conversation Bob does say which measurements he made—he says, oh, I made a z measurement, and then I made an x measurement, or whatever—and Alice does tell him whether he made a good measurement or a bad measurement.

What does it mean to make a good measurement? Well, a good measurement is one in which Alice sends up or down and Bob measured z, so his measurement result actually could tell which state it was. Or another good measurement would be if Alice had either sent right or left and Bob measured the x component of spin; then his measurement result, plus or minus 1/2, would tell him whether the spin was right or left. So Alice tells him which measurements he made were good, and she also tells him which measurements he made were bad. For instance, if Alice sent either up or down and Bob measured the x component of spin, he wouldn't find out anything; that measurement result wouldn't tell him anything about which spin it had been. Similarly, if Alice had sent left or right and Bob had measured z, that would be a bad measurement, also. And about half the time Bob's measurement is bad.

Now what do they do? They agree to just discard the bad measurements; they don't use them. They only keep the good measurements, and in the good measurements the result of Bob's measurement tells him which state Alice sent. So if he gets a $+1/2$ or a $-1/2$, that will determine whether they're going to make that key bit 0 or 1. They can use just the good measurements to establish the secret key, so both Alice and Bob will know the results of those measurements.

Now, this public conversation that Alice and Bob had seemed to say a lot. They say, oh, I made this measurement, I made that measurement, oh, that was a good measurement, and so on. But actually it tells Eve nothing, because it tells Eve nothing about the results of the measurements. Afterwards Alice and Bob know the key because they both know enough to figure out what the results of the measurements were, but Eve finds out nothing about the secret key. The public conversation is full of information that tells her nothing about the secret key. But, you know, I have sort of left out one thing that Eve might do: Eve might catch the spins on the way from Alice to Bob and just look at them.

Well, what would she do with a spin? Well, she can't make a copy; she can't make her own copy of the spins because of the no-cloning theorem. So what might she do? Well, she might make her own measurement on the spins. But she can't make any measurement that will completely determine whether the spin is up, down, left, or right. There's no measurement that will determine which 1 of those 4 states it is. So whatever measurement she makes, she'll sometimes make the wrong measurement; just like Bob, she'll sometimes measure the wrong spin component. And if Eve measures the wrong spin component, that will randomly disturb the state because of Update Rule II— remember our original rules—that says that when you make a measurement, that produces a random effect on the state.

So suppose she had done that, and then passes the spins on to Bob? What would be the net effect of that? Well, it turns out the net effect of that is that it introduces errors at Bob's end. Sometimes he should get spin up but because Eve has interfered he actually winds up with spin down. And so what Alice and Bob do is they take a whole bunch of bits from their supposedly secret key and they just announce them publicly and they look for errors. And if there aren't any errors, they can be pretty sure that nobody monkeyed with the spins between one end and the other, but if there are errors they can say, ah-ha, maybe an eavesdropper has been accessing our spins and trying to read them. They can detect Eve's intervention. In other words, Eve, in attempting to figure out what Alice's spins are, must leave "quantum fingerprints" behind. She must necessarily disturb the system in a way that Alice and Bob will be able to detect. And of course if Alice and Bob detect Eve at work, they won't use that key, and Eve loses, because Eve doesn't care about the key so much as its use later on in sending the secret message, the real secret.

So as a result, there are 2 possibilities. Either Alice and Bob wind up with a key that doesn't have any errors—they did some sampling and checked that—and they're sure, therefore, that Eve cannot have been intervening in the spins, Eve cannot know what the key is, it's a secret key for sure. Or Alice and Bob might detect Eve's activity and then they agree not to use the key that they generate. And either way, Eve loses; Eve only wins if she finds out the key but Alice and Bob think it's a secret. The key, of course, is not the important secret message; that comes later.

That is BB84. That is quantum key distribution. It seems a little complicated, but in fact it's actually practical. This is not just a thought-experiment. It's actually commercial. There are several companies in the United States and Europe that will sell you a quantum key distribution system. The system would work using single photons sent over a system of optical fibers, and soon they may be actually using orbiting satellites to distribute their photons.

What kind of customers do they have? Well, large financial institutions, banks, the military, maybe other government agencies. This is a very specialized need we're talking about. This is the kind of system that you might invest in when things absolutely, positively have to be private; that the privacy is guaranteed by the laws of quantum physics. Then it might make sense to use quantum key distribution.

What is it that makes BB84, the Bennett Brussard 1984 scheme, work? Well, let's list a couple of things. One is the complementarity of x and z measurements. Bob must choose x or z; similarly, Eve must choose either x or z, and sometimes she'll choose wrongly. And from that comes the inevitability of disturbance in a measurement, the fact that the interaction between a quantum system and the measuring apparatus is not just one way; there's always a disturbance in the quantum system.

And the central fact, the real important thing that makes it work, is the quantum no-cloning theorem. If Eve had a magic cloning machine, then the game is up, she'll just make copies of the spins as they go by and then she just does whatever Bob does. And remember, Bob is going to announce later on exactly which measurements he made, and she will get exactly the same results for the good measurements and she'll be able to have exactly the same key. And Alice and Bob will never find out what she's done. So a magic quantum cloning machine would mean that quantum key distribution was not secure.

But here's a slightly different question, that's how it works, but what makes BB84 interesting? Why should we care about it? It's kind of an amusing game, but why is it important? Well, it's a place where quantum mechanics lets us do something that we cannot do classically. If the world were really classical, if we lived in a classical world, it would be impossible; but in the quantum world we can actually do it. And in this case the task is 100% secure distribution of a secret key. What BB84 is, is a quantum solution to an unsolvable classical problem. You've actually seen such a thing before. You'll recall back in Lecture 8 we talked about the Elitzur-Vaidman bomb-testing problem, the problem of determining whether these bombs will explode without actually exploding them. But that example may have seemed contrived. The example of key distribution is not contrived at all; it's a very important real example.

The most important thing to me about Bennett and Brassard's work is that it inspired a real change in attitude among quantum physicists. The question before BB84 that was asked by researchers in my field, investigating quantum mechanics and information, the question before 1984 was how does quantum physics limit our ability to communicate? What insurmountable barriers do the laws of quantum physics put in our way? But after BB84 the questions were different. The questions became what useful things might quantum physics allow us to do? What new opportunities does quantum mechanics provide? Quantum mechanics is not a problem, it's an opportunity. When you change your questions you can learn some new things.

Next time we'll have a quick survey of a few new things that we have learned lately in quantum information and quantum computing. We're going to ask questions about what we can do with quantum physics. What tasks do we want to perform? What resources might we use to perform them? We're going to investigate what the basic laws of quantum information are. There are some surprises in store, including some new insights into quantum entanglement. The concept of information is going to teach us things about the quantum world that we never imagined. That's next time. I'll see you then.

Bits, Qubits, and Ebits
Lecture 21

Every age in history has a basic metaphor ... a way of organizing our thinking about the world around us. ... And today ... we sort of inevitably think of the world as a huge network, a vast system of information exchange. ... What we want to do is we want to discover the fundamental rules of that information network. ... All of this is based on something called "information theory."

"Information theory" is the mathematical theory of communication and related subjects, invented by Claude Shannon in 1948. The concepts of information theory include bits, codes, errors, and so on. The study has been vital to the development of telecommunications, computing, and many other fields. Information theory is all about information "resources" and information "tasks." It focuses on which resources are required to perform a given task. These resources may include time, storage space, power, etc. Tasks may include storage of data, overcoming noise, and keeping a message private.

Shannon's information theory does not take quantum mechanics into account. A "quantum information theory" would include quantum resources and tasks. We can identify 3 types of quantum resources: bits (Alice sends 1 bit of classical data to Bob), qubits (Alice sends 1 qubit of quantum data to Bob), and ebits (Alice and Bob share an entangled pair of qubits—like 2 spins in a total spin 0 state—which amounts to "1 bit of entanglement"). Bits and qubits are "directed resources" (Alice to Bob or Bob to Alice), but ebits are "undirected." Together we will work to answer the question of how these different resources are related to each other.

Charles Bennett put together some simple principles about quantum information resources. We'll call these "Bennett's laws." Each law is of the form $X \succeq Y$, which is read, "X can do the job of Y." This means that the resources labeled X can perform the same task as the resources labeled Y.

Bennett's first law says that 1 qubit $\succeq$ 1 bit. We have already seen this in our example in which Alice can use a qubit to send a 1bit message to Bob. However, notice that 1 qubit $\npreceq$ 2 bits because Alice cannot transmit 2 bits in 1 qubit.

Bennett's second law is that 1 qubit $\succeq$ 1 ebit. This is also easy to understand. Alice can make a pair of spins in a total spin 0 state, then send 1 of the 2 entangled qubits to Bob. Qubits are the most capable of the 3 resources. We can use them for anything. We cannot send messages using only an ebit. This is because entanglement by itself cannot be used to send either classical or quantum messages, although it can assist in sending messages.

Qubits are the most capable of the 3 resources. We can use them for anything.

Bennett's third law says that 1 ebit + 1 qubit $\succeq$ 2bits. This was discovered by Bennett and Stephen Wiesner in 1992 and is sometimes called "dense coding." We return to Alice and Bob to consider this law. Alice and Bob initially share an ebit (say, 2 spins in a total spin 0 state). Alice makes 1 of 4 possible rotations on her spin. These are either no rotation or a 180° rotation about the x, y, or z axes. Her choice of rotation represents a 2bit message: 00, 01, 10, or 11. Alice sends her qubit to Bob. Bob now makes a special measurement called the "Bell measurement" on the pair of qubits. From this, he is able to deduce which rotation Alice made—and thus he can read the 2bit message.

Dense coding appears to be very strange, because it seems that the 2 bits are carried by 1 qubit. However, there are 2 qubits involved, though 1 of them stays in Bob's possession the whole time. If we make a diagram of the process, it appears that some information has traveled "backward in time"!

Bennett's fourth law says that 1 ebit + 2 bits $\succeq$ 1 qubit. Here is how this law plays out in another Alice-and-Bob example. The two initially share an ebit. In addition, Alice has a qubit that she'd like to transfer to Bob. Alice makes a Bell measurement on the 2 qubits she has. She sends the result to Bob as a 2bit classical message. Bob can use this information to choose a rotation for his qubit (either no rotation or a 180° rotation about the x, y, or z axis).

Afterward, his qubit is in exactly the same state as Alice's original was! This process, discovered in 1993 by Bennett and several co-workers, is called quantum teleportation.

It's important to note here that teleportation is about information transfer, not transportation. It is barely possible to do teleportation of 1 qubit in the lab. Teleporting the quantum information in a human being is at least 10^{27} times harder—and we would need a *lot* of entangled matter. Because of the no-cloning theorem, the original qubit is necessarily wiped out. Suppose Alice can send qubits to Bob only occasionally, but she can send classical bits at any time. They may store up ebits when quantum communication is possible, then send their qubits whenever they like using teleportation.

How much are different resources worth? If classical bits cost nothing, then qubits and ebits are worth an equal amount. We turn one resource into the other for free. If ebits cost nothing (an odd assumption), then the value of a qubit is exactly 2 bits. ∎

Questions to Consider

1. It is impossible to send more than 1 bit of classical information using just 1 qubit. Why doesn't Bennett and Wiesner's dense coding disprove this rule?

2. Suppose we consider a situation with 3 protagonists: Alice, Bob, and Charles. At the outset, Alice and Bob share 1 ebit, as do Bob and Charles, but Alice and Charles do not share any entanglement. If the 3 can send only classical bits to each other, how can Alice and Charles end up with a shared ebit? Can this be done even if Charles is unable to communicate at all? (It is interesting to try to work out some basic rules of 3-party quantum information theory.)

Bits, Qubits, and Ebits
Lecture 21—Transcript

Welcome to the 21st lecture in our course on quantum mechanics. Last time we took a look at quantum cryptography. We saw that by using the rules of quantum mechanics, Charles Bennett and Gilles Brassard solved a previously unsolvable problem: the problem of distributing a secret key for encrypting messages. Their scheme, called "BB84," relied on the no-cloning theorem of quantum mechanics, the fact that quantum information cannot be perfectly copied.

This time we will talk a little about quantum information theory, the basic rules that govern information in the quantum world. Why would we do such a thing? Well, every age in history has a basic metaphor for the world, a way of organizing our thinking about the world around us. And in antiquity, a common metaphor was that the world is a huge organism with the different parts working together toward harmonious ends. Later on, in the Enlightenment, after the work of Isaac Newton, the basic metaphor was that the world is a huge clockwork, a machine obeying perfect mathematical laws. And today, in the information age, we sort of inevitably think of the world as a huge network, a vast system of information exchange. The particles in the world do not just exert forces on each other and transfer energy from one to another; they send messages to each other. What we want to do is we want to discover the fundamental rules of that information network; that's our business today.

Now, all of this is based on something called "information theory." There's a mathematical discipline called information theory, and it was developed around 1948, mostly by Claude Shannon of Bell Labs. Information theory was vital to the development of modern telecommunications, of computing, and so on; and in fact Shannon's ideas have been among the most influential ideas of the 20th century. The world is permeated by the concepts of information theory, the idea of bits, the idea of codes, the idea of information errors, and so on.

Shannon's information theory is all about information resources and information tasks. And the basic question is, what resources are required to perform a given task? Now, the resources might include time or storage space or electrical power and so on; those are the resources we could bring to bear on performing a task. The tasks may include data storage or overcoming noise or maintaining privacy and so on. So we're asking what resources are necessary to perform what task.

Now, Shannon's information theory, as important and powerful as it is, does not take quantum mechanics into account. It's a theory of classical information. The resources and the tasks it employs in the theory can be completely described in classical terms. And this works pretty well; even today we still use millions of electrons or millions of photons to represent each bit of data that we store or transmit. Nevertheless, Shannon's information theory has left something important out: the quantum nature of the world.

Quantum information theory would include not only classical information but also quantum information resources and quantum tasks. So in quantum information theory, we are going to identify 3 types of quantum resources. The first type is the bit—bits—that's a resource. And what do I mean by bits? I mean that Alice can send to Bob—remember Alice and Bob, our protagonists—Alice can send to Bob a 1-bit classical message, 1 bit of classical data. And if she can do that, she can use that ability as a resource; that's a classical resource. But then there are 2 quantum resources. The first one we've seen: qubits. We say that Alice can send 1 qubit of quantum data to Bob; if she's able to do that, she can use that in order to perform tasks that she may wish to do. The second one, though, is something that we haven't really talked about: the second one is ebits. Ebits are bits of entanglement. The ebit resource is what you have if Alice and Bob share an entangled pair of qubits—say, 2 spins in a total spin 0 state. This is 1 bit of entanglement.

Now, these different resources sort of have different characters. Bits are a classical resource, qubits and ebits are quantum resources. Bits and qubits are directed resources—either Alice sends one to Bob or Bob sends one to Alice; and that matters, it's different. If Alice sends a 1-bit message to Bob, it's a different resource than if Bob sends a 1-bit message to Alice. Ebits, on the other hand, are undirected. They're merely shared. It doesn't matter how Alice and Bob came to share the parts of an entangled pair of ebits, they just share them; that's the resource that they can bring to bear on solving information tasks.

Nobody has done more to sort out this question, the question of what resources are important and what you can do with various resources, than Charles Bennett. Charles Bennett is an IBM physicist, as you recall he helped to event quantum cryptography, and also, as we will see today, he's helped to invent many other fascinating ideas in quantum information. And Bennett has tried to summarize some of the basic principles about quantum information into a set of rules. In fact, he is the origin of the term "ebit"; so when ebits appear in the rules, he was a part of the invention.

We're going to call these rules that Bennett has tried to put together "Bennett's laws." And every one of Bennett's laws looks like this: You have X and you have a funny little symbol and you have Y ($Y \succeq X$). So what's the funny little symbol? The symbol between X and Y means "can do the job of," and that means that the resource labeled X is able to perform the same task as the resource labeled Y. It may be able to perform others as well, but X can do the same job as Y.

So let me give you a homemade example so you know how to do this. Suppose I have 2 different kinds of resources: I have dollars and I have bottles of drinking water. Now, it turns out there's a grocery store nearby and at the grocery store, bottles of water cost a dollar. That means if I have a dollar I can go to the grocery store, buy a bottle of water, and drink it. It's just as good to have a bottle of water or to have a dollar when I can buy a bottle of water; I can get a drink either way. So one dollar can do the job of one bottle of water. We can use a dollar to buy a bottle of water. However, the store is not buying back bottles of water; and that means that if I have a bottle of water, I cannot use it to obtain a dollar. So it isn't true that one bottle of water can do the job of one dollar. The dollar is a stronger resource, a more powerful resource, than a bottle of water in our example.

Let's go through Bennett's 4 laws of quantum information. The first law is actually something that we've already seen. Bennett's first law says that 1 qubit can do the job of 1 bit. What does that mean? It means that we can send 1 qubit from Alice to Bob and use this qubit to send a 1-bit classical message;

and we already saw this. Alice can use the qubit to send a 1-bit message. She can encode her message in the *z* component of a spin state, for example; 0 is spin up, 1 is spin down, and then when the qubit reaches Bob he can measure the *z* component of the spin and figure out what the 1-bit message is. It's not true that 1 qubit can do the job of 2 bits. We found that we could not put 2 bits of classical information into a 1-qubit quantum message; so 1 qubit's not more powerful than 2 bits. Alice can't send 2 bits to Bob with 1 qubit. So 1 qubit can do the job of 1 bit whenever we want.

The second of Bennett's laws, Bennett's second law, is just as easy to understand. It tells us that 1 qubit can do the job of 1 ebit. In this we can imagine that Alice makes a pair of spins in her own laboratory in a total spin 0 state—she can do this, nothing can prevent her from doing this—and now Alice uses her ability to send a qubit to send one of the spins to Bob. And afterward, Alice and Bob share an ebit. So if Alice is able to send qubits to Bob, then they can use that to come to share ebits. They can use qubits to buy ebits.

They could also do it the other way, of course. If Bob can send a qubit to Alice, he could make a pair of entangled spins in his laboratory, send one of them to Alice, and then they would share an ebit. A qubit either direction is enough; a qubit in either direction can do the job of an ebit. What this means is that qubits are the most capable of our 3 kinds of resources. We can turn a qubit into a bit by using it to send a classical piece of information. We can turn a qubit into an ebit by using it to distribute some entanglement that we made locally. Qubits are the strongest.

All right, what other connections might we have? For example, can we send messages? Can we send bits using ebits? Can we send 1 bit using 1 ebit? Can we send classical information using only entanglement? And the answer is no. Entanglement by itself cannot be used to send either classical or quantum messages. Entanglement by itself doesn't let you do anything like that. Now, back a few lectures ago, when we were talking about the no-cloning theorem, we did tell a science fiction story about using ebits to send messages faster than light; but in order to do that we needed to use a magic quantum cloning machine, and that was what enabled us to use an ebit to send a bit. Such machines don't exist; an ebit does not allow us to send a bit.

However, even though entanglement by itself will not allow us to send messages, it will turn out that entanglement can actually *assist* us in sending messages. And that's the subject of Bennett's third law. This one looks a little more interesting. It says that 1 ebit plus 1 qubit can do the job of 2 bits. This is a weird one, and it was discovered by Bennett and Stephen Wiesner in 1992. This is sometimes called "dense coding"; it's not a very good term, dense coding, but it's called that because somehow even though 1 qubit is used, 2 bits get sent. It's like there's twice as much information as you might expect. And here's how it works:

We imagine that Alice and Bob initially share 1 ebit; say, 2 spins in the total spin 0 state. And then Alice takes her qubit and she rotates it, perhaps using a magnetic field, and she chooses 1 of 4 possible rotations. I'll just tell you what those rotations are, actually. She could do no rotation at all, that counts, or she could make a 180° rotation around the x-axis or around the y-axis or around the z-axis; that's 4 possible rotations. And because there are 4 possible rotations, she could use her choice of rotation to represent 2 classical bits of information; the 2-bit message is 00, 01, 10, or 11. So, Alice and Bob started out with a total spin 0 state, Alice rotated her qubit 1 of 4 different ways, and now she sends her rotated spin, her 1 qubit, to Bob; 1 qubit from Alice to Bob. Now Bob has both qubits.

Well, it turns out that Bob can make a measurement on his pair of spins, a joint measurement on the pair of spins, and this measurement is called "the Bell measurement." I'll skip the details; the point about the Bell measurement is it measures the type of entanglement of the spins. Because one of the spins may have been rotated, the type of entanglement has changed. In fact, by making the Bell measurement Bob can actually tell exactly which rotation Alice made. Therefore, he knows exactly which 2 bits of information she wanted to send; he can read Alice's 2-bit message.

Now, this is weird and unexpected, because by itself 1 ebit cannot send any information; 1 ebit is worth no bits. By itself 1 qubit can send only 1 bit of information. But together, they can send 2 bits of information. Now, there are 2 qubits involved, but Bob has been holding on to one the whole time. So let's take a look at this process by making a kind of Feynman diagram of the process. In the diagram, time goes up, we read the diagram from bottom to top, and so at the very beginning our ebit is created somehow and shared so that Alice on the left-hand side and Bob on the right-hand side each have one part of the ebit. And then Alice makes her rotation on her ebit, and this rotation is determined by the 2 bits of her input message. And then Alice sends her qubit over to Bob. Bob now possesses both qubits. He makes the Bell measurement, he reads the output, the Bell measurement gives 2 bits of output and tells him exactly what Alice's message is.

I remember the first time I saw this picture. Charles Bennett was showing me this at a conference we were both at, drawing the picture on a piece of paper in his hotel room, and I remember my feeling of absolute astonishment at this, because I knew that a qubit can only carry 1 bit. I knew that mathematically, I could prove it. But here, somehow, even though Alice only sent 1 qubit to Bob, she could send 2 bits of information to him. Of course there are 2 qubits involved, so I looked at the diagram and I made a joke. I said, oh, of course, 1 bit of information goes across with the qubit and the other bit of information goes back in time to the formation of the ebit and then forward in time on Bob's side; so half of the information goes back in time and gets to Bob that way.

Well, does information really go back in time here? Maybe not quite. But even if that's not the way to describe it, even if that's not the right language to use, there's certainly something very peculiar going on in Bennett's third law.

Amazingly, dense coding was not the biggest surprise in store. The biggest surprise, I think, was quantum teleportation. Quantum teleportation is the subject of Bennett's fourth law. Here's the teleportation law: 1 ebit plus 2 bits can do the job of 1 qubit. So the idea is that Alice and Bob initially share 1 ebit, 1 bit of entanglement. And Alice also has a qubit that's in some quantum state that she doesn't know, but she'd like to transfer that qubit to Bob. Now, if she could just send the qubit to Bob, that would be easy, but for some reason we're not going to do it that way. What Alice does is she takes her half of the ebit and her input qubit and she makes a Bell measurement on her 2 qubits. Now, at first, that seems completely destructive. First of all, this measurement completely wipes out her original; that unknown state that she had is completely destroyed. Furthermore, the result of her measurement tells her nothing about what that state was; it looks like she's just done something destructive. But she got 2 bits of classical information out of the process. So she transmits that any way she pleases—U.S. Mail would be fine—she transmits that to Bob. So what does Bob do? Bob gets 2 bits of information from Alice, so he uses that 2-bit message as instructions for how to rotate his qubit. And once again he does exactly the same rotations that were used in dense coding. He either does no rotation at all or he rotates by $180°$ about the x-axis, the y-axis, or the z-axis. And which rotation he chooses is based on the 2 bits of information, 1 of 4 possible messages that he gets from Alice.

What's the result? Afterward, almost magically, Bob's own qubit, which used to be half of an ebit, is in the original state, the original quantum state that was destroyed by Alice's measurement. Somehow that state has just appeared over at Bob's side. "How did that get there?" is your reaction to this amazing fact. And the, "How did that get there?" question is exactly why they called it "quantum teleportation."

The quantum teleportation process was actually discovered in 1993 by 6 physicists meeting in a workshop in Montreal. And this is a great example of the power of collaboration and discussion to sort of break new ground and find out new surprising things. The list of people who are responsible for quantum teleportation includes many people that we've met before in these lectures, and many that we'll meet again. It included Charles Bennett from IBM, no surprise. It included Gilles Brassard, the other half of BB84, from the University of Montreal. It included Claude Crépeau from McGill University, a cryptographer. It included Richard Jozsa, who's now at the University of Bristol, who was a pioneer in quantum computing, and we'll meet his work in the next lecture. It included Asher Peres—we've been quoting Asher Peres, saying, "Unperformed experiments have no results"—a deep thinker about quantum theory. And it included William Wootters of the no-cloning theorem. So the group of people that invented quantum teleportation is a wonderful nucleus of some of the great thinkers about quantum mechanics and information.

Now, before I leave off talking about quantum teleportation, I should clear up some misconceptions. The first one is that teleportation is about information transfer, not transportation. The teleportation process sends 1 qubit of quantum information from Alice to Bob. In the laboratory it is barely possible to do the quantum teleportation to send 1 qubit from one side of the table to the other, in an optics lab, for example. Teleporting the quantum information in a human being would be, I estimate, 10^{27} times harder; that's a one followed by 27 zeros. That's a thousand, trillion, trillion times harder than teleporting 1 qubit. We'd need lots of ebits to do it, huge amounts of entangled matter. We can make ebits, but making them in those numbers is a bit daunting. So it's not about transportation in any sense.

Teleportation is also limited by the speed of light. Until Bob gets his 2 bits from Alice, he does not know how to adjust his qubit so that it will be in the original state. Until the 2 bits arrive, his state is essentially random. Now, also, because of the no-cloning theorem, we should remember that the original qubit, Alice's input qubit, must be wiped out. This is not like an ordinary communication channel for classical information, because in classical information the fact that I send you a message doesn't necessarily mean that I have to destroy the message on my end. But because of the quantum no-cloning theorem, if Alice sends a qubit to Bob she must destroy her qubit in the process, she must no longer have it.

Finally, I want to just point out one more thing about teleportation. What Alice actually sends to Bob are just bits, bits of information. Can you send a qubit using bits? Now, we previously said that it would take many, many bits to send a qubit, if we could do it at all, which is doubtful, because it would take many, many bits to describe the amplitude numbers in the superposition state of a qubit, and so it would just take many, many, many bits. In teleportation, therefore, since you only send 2 classical bits, most of the work must be done by the ebit. Once again, if you look at the diagram we drew for the teleportation process, most of the quantum information must actually somehow flow along the ebit, it must go back in time, so to speak, to the formation of the ebit and forward to Bob's end. And we just need the 2 bits of classical information to finish the job. A very strange way of looking at it.

What's quantum teleportation good for? Why would you want to do quantum teleportation? Why would you want to send quantum information in this way? Well, just for the sake of argument, suppose Alice can send qubits to Bob only occasionally, only on Thursdays, say, and other days of the week there are too many cosmic rays or something like that; but she can only send qubits to Bob on Thursdays. She can send classical bits any time; they're easy. So what Alice and Bob do is that on Thursday, Alice and Bob use their ability to send qubits to make a lot of ebits. Now they can do teleportation any time they wish. They can store up, in other words, the quantum communication part for use later. And this is not at all like classical communication; we can't use signals that we transmitted yesterday to send today's news. But you can almost do that in quantum mechanics.

Also, they could make the ebits by sending qubits, not from Alice to Bob but from Bob to Alice, and this is a little weird. So sending a quantum message from Bob to Alice, 1 qubit allows you to make an ebit, by Bennett's second law. Sending a classical message from Alice to Bob, 2 bits together let us send a quantum message from Alice to Bob. It lets us do quantum teleportation. This is also not classical. We can't use a signal I sent to you yesterday to get today's news from you to me. Something very strange is going on in quantum information theory.

So here are Bennett's 4 laws. The first law: A qubit can do a job of a bit. We can send classical messages using quantum signals. Bennett's second law: A qubit can do the job of an ebit. We can use quantum signals to set up entanglement between Alice and Bob. Bennett's third law, dense coding: An ebit together with a qubit can do the job of a 2-bit classical message. And Bennett's fourth law, quantum teleportation: An ebit plus 2 classical bits can do the job of a qubit.

Once you have Bennett's laws you can play lots of interesting games with them. For example, if classical bits cost nothing—and as a practical matter they are a lot cheaper than qubits these days—if classical bits cost nothing, then qubits and ebits are worth just the same, because I can always use a qubit to make an ebit and, with some classical information that's free, I can use an ebit to send a qubit in quantum teleportation. So if classical information is free, qubits and ebits are worth exactly the same, and also sending a qubit from A to B is just the same as sending a qubit from B to A, because either way I can set up ebits and then use it for teleportation, because classical signaling is free.

Here's a stranger game you can play: Suppose ebits cost nothing. It's a very strange idea, ebits are not cheap and we really don't know how to keep them around very long; but suppose we could. If ebits are free, then 1 qubit is worth exactly 2 bits. If you have one, you can make the other.

Okay, what have we found out? Some of the rules for the quantum information network have been sort of outlined in the course of our lecture. These rules, Bennett's 4 laws, are sort of clues to how nature itself moves information around. There's something funny going on with entanglement. We can't use entanglement all by itself to send messages at all, but if we have some entanglement, we can do some surprising stuff. We can send messages more easily, or it can help us send messages that we wouldn't otherwise be able to send. And when we try to analyze how that works, we're tempted to say that some signals actually go backward in time.

Now, there are no time travel paradoxes involved here. This backwards in time signaling only happens, if you will, where you can't see it, as usual in quantum mechanics. It only happens if you don't actually find out what the message is. And anyway, this idea of sending information backwards in time might not be the right language for talking about what's going on. But whatever's going on, it does make difference in dense coding and teleportation, Bennett's third and fourth laws.

So, what's next? Next, we're going to investigate other opportunities. We're going to investigate quantum computing. In quantum computing, we're going to harness the power of quantum mechanics to solve math problems. It turns out that just as qubits can exist in superpositions of basis states—they can be not just 0 or 1 but also weird combinations of 0 and 1—so quantum computers can have superpositions of different memories, and they can run superpositions of different programs.

Could such devices really exist? And if they did exist, what would they mean? That's next time. I'll see you then.

Quantum Computers
Lecture 22

> Our everyday language struggles to cope with the nature of quantum information. [In] this lecture we're going to explore the full power of quantum information. ... We will imagine a quantum computer, and we'll see what we can do with it.

Is quantum computing the future of computers? According to Moore's law, computer power is increasing exponentially over time. Roughly speaking, computer capabilities double every 2 years. Basic units of computers are growing smaller at about the same rate. They operate faster, using less energy. If Moore's law continues to hold, in a couple of decades we will be trying to use individual quantum particles for basic computer components. We will need to design quantum computers.

In a quantum computer, the memory elements are qubits. These can be in superposition states (not just $|0\rangle$ and $|1\rangle$), and huge numbers of qubits may be entangled together. While performing computations, a quantum computer operates without any measurements of any kind, even inadvertent ones. Its state therefore changes according to update rule I. (At the end of the computation, of course, we must make a measurement to read the output.) A quantum computer cannot merely do ordinary computations faster or with smaller components. It can do computations in fundamentally new ways, completely unlike any classical computer.

A quantum computer could solve some mathematical problems much more efficiently than a classical computer. In 1992, Richard Jozsa and David Deutsch proposed the Deutsch-Jozsa problem, which first showed that quantum computers could be more powerful than classical ones. The computer can evaluate a function $f(n)$, where n ranges from 1 to N. The value of the function is always either 0 or 1. We happen to know that the function is either constant (always 0 or always 1) or balanced (0 or 1 equally often). How many times must we evaluate f to determine which one it is? On a classical computer, we might have to evaluate f more than N/2 times to be certain. If the function is really hard to compute, this might take a while.

However, on a quantum computer, we can answer the question by evaluating *f* only once, on a superposition of all possible inputs.

In 1996, Lov Grover showed that a quantum computer could help solve the "inverse phonebook problem." A phonebook is an alphabetical list of names, together with phone numbers. But suppose we only have the phone number and want to find the name. How many names do we have to look up to find it? Suppose there are 1 million entries. A classical computer would have to look up about 500,000 names on average, and 999,999 names in the worst-case scenario. A quantum computer could do the same job by consulting the phone book only 1000 times, each time looking up a superposition of all the names.

The most exciting application is "quantum factoring," discovered by Peter Shor in 1994. In this application, we are given a very large number, perhaps with hundreds of digits. This number is the product of 2 smaller numbers. Can we find the factors? On a classical computer, this is a very hard problem. A 200-digit number was recently factored by hundreds of computers working together for over a year. A 500-digit number is so much harder that no imaginable computer could ever do the job. Shor proved that a quantum computer could factor integers very efficiently. A 500-digit number is only about 16 times harder than a 200-digit one. Because much modern cryptography is based on factoring, if someone invents a quantum computer, a lot of secret data will no longer be secret!

Can a quantum computer actually be built? Many scientists are working very hard to build one. Design ideas include atoms suspended in laser beams, nuclear spins in magnetic fields, superconducting loops near absolute zero, and single electrons in semiconductors. Even the best efforts so far involve just a few qubits working for a few seconds.

Many scientists are working very hard to build [a quantum computer]. Design ideas include atoms suspended in laser beams, nuclear spins in magnetic fields, superconducting loops near absolute zero, and single electrons in semiconductors.

The would-be builder of a quantum computer faces a fundamental dilemma. On the one hand, the computer must be extremely well isolated from the outside. Otherwise, stray molecules and photons would make inadvertent measurements of the computer's state, interrupting the magic of update rule I. On the other hand, the different parts of the computer must interact extremely rapidly with each other, so that the computation can be done. The good news is that we need not be perfect. By using "quantum error correction," the computer can tolerate a little outside interference. However, the bad news is that nobody knows how to resolve the fundamental dilemma.

In the mid-19th century, Charles Babbage designed mechanical equivalents of modern computers. His computing ideas were never put into real practice until the development of electronics. Our present ideas about how to do quantum computing may the modern equivalent of Babbage's gears and wheels. ∎

Questions to Consider

1. Your lecturer has a bet with a colleague about whether or not quantum computers will become practical within 20 years. Which way would you bet?

2. Suppose a working quantum computer became available tomorrow. What would be its main practical impact?

3. We said that the builder of a quantum computer faces a fundamental dilemma. Why does this same dilemma not apply to an ordinary "classical" computer?

Quantum Computers
Lecture 22—Transcript

Welcome to the 22nd lecture in our course on quantum mechanics. We've been talking about quantum information—that's the type of information that is carried by quantum particles. And quantum information follows a different set of laws from the familiar classical kind of information. One example was the no-cloning theorem: Quantum information cannot be perfectly copied. We also talked about quantum cryptography. We talked about the BB84 method for quantum key distribution; we use quantum physics to keep our secret messages secret.

In the last lecture we talked about Charles Bennett's 4 laws for quantum information. These were laws about information resources—bits, qubits, ebits—all of which are related. We found, for example, that if bits are freely available, if we can have them for free without paying for them, then a qubit is worth the same as an ebit; they're basically the same thing. And a qubit, if entanglement is free, if ebits can be had for nothing, then a qubit is worth about the same as 2 bits.

Now, entanglement has some strange implications in these laws. We saw this in dense coding and quantum teleportation. In each of these, we were tempted to say that some of the information actually goes backwards in time somewhere in the process. In other words, our everyday language struggles to cope with the nature of quantum information.

This lecture we're going to explore the full power of quantum information. In this lecture we will imagine a quantum computer, and we'll see what we can do with it.

Now, computer technology has advanced with breathtaking speed over the last few decades. Gordon Moore, one of the inventors of the microprocessor, proposed something called Moore's Law, which roughly speaking says that computer power is increasing exponentially. Computer capabilities double about every 2 years. And this has been going on since the 1960s when Moore first made this observation; if you double your power every 2 years and you do it for 40 years, something amazing has happened. And it's also the case that the basic circuits used in computers are getting smaller and smaller at about the same rate. The circuits operate faster; they use less energy in the course of the computation.

So for the future, let's suppose that Moore's Law continues to hold true. Let's extrapolate. Well, then, in about 20 years, maybe sooner, we'll be trying to use individual quantum particles for our basic computer components. We will need to be designing quantum computers.

Now, quantum computers do not just do the same thing on a small scale that an ordinary computer does on a large scale. The microscopic realm is not just a miniature version of a macroscopic realm. And it would not make sense to try to force quantum computers to operate in exactly the same way as present-day computers do on the larger scale. Furthermore, quantum mechanics may afford some other possibilities, some novel ways of doing the computation; so we should be on the lookout for that.

What is a quantum computer? Well, a quantum computer is a computer in which the memory elements are qubits. The qubits can be in basis states 0 or 1 like a regular bit, but they can also be in superpositions of 0 and 1, unlike a regular classical bit. Furthermore, many qubits might be entangled together; no classical computer can do that. The different bits could be in one of these strange, entangled quantum states.

What are the qubits? Well, it doesn't really matter whether the qubits are represented by photons or atoms or electrons. Whatever physical realization they have, they act as qubits. During a computation a quantum computer operates without any measurements of any kind, even inadvertent measurements—we don't even make measurements by accident. And because there are no measurements, the computer state, the state of the whole quantum computer, evolves according to Update Rule I, the rule that held when no measurements are made. Now, of course, at the end of the computation we'll need to go and do a measurement on the computer in order to read the output; there's a measurement at the end. But while the computer is running its computation, no measurements are made. It's all Update Rule I; no randomness involved, actually.

This presents us with a kind of a strange way to do a computation. The computer actually follows multiple paths, multiple computational paths, at the same time, analogous to the way that a photon could follow more than one path through an interferometer. And as the computer operates, no physical record is actually made of which of these computations is done. It does them all. And then at the end it combines the results of all these different computational paths and does a kind of interference experiment at the end. That opens some wild possibilities.

Now, quantum computing is still for the most part a theoretical subject; later on in this lecture I'll talk about some real experiments. And quantum computing is studied by a really interesting interdisciplinary group of physicists, mathematicians, computer scientists, even a few engineers. One of my colleagues is a professor of mechanical engineering at MIT; presumably he's a professor of quantum mechanical engineering.

The question that this miscellaneous group of scientists is asking is if a quantum computer existed, what could be done with it? Does quantum computing provide a shortcut for solving important problems? And the answer is yes. A quantum computer can solve some math problems much more efficiently than a classical computer. So we're going to describe three of the most important examples of that.

The first example I want to describe—and, in fact, the first example that really proved that quantum computers might be something very special—is the so-called "Deutsch-Jozsa problem," which was first analyzed in 1992. This was worked out by David Deutsch of Oxford University and Richard Jozsa of the University of Bristol, one of the authors of teleportation, and this is the first problem that showed that quantum computers can be far more powerful than ordinary computers. On the other hand, the problem's a very artificial one, so as I describe it you may have the reaction, "Why would you be interested in that?" The point is this was just the first gleam of the idea that quantum computers might be more powerful. So it's worth taking a minute to examine the details of the Deutsch-Jozsa problem.

One of the things that a computer often does is it evaluates functions. In other words, it takes some inputs and it computes a number. It's a very basic type of computation. It takes a set of numbers and it calculates the sum; it divides one number by another ... all evaluating functions. So what we're going to do is we're going to consider a kind of abstract version of that. The function we're going to call $f(n)$, and the input of the function is a number n, and the number is between 1 and some very large number M, the maximum value. It could be billions, between 1 and M, the number is somewhere in there. We feed that number to the function and it gives us an output, and for simplicity we're just going to imagine a function whose output is either 0 or 1. Now, that sounds pretty simple, but it might take a lot of calculation to figure out the value of the function from its input. It might take huge numbers of computations to work it out; it might be a really hard function to evaluate, but in the end we're going to say 0 or 1.

Now, what we're going to want to know is not something about this value of the function or that value of the function; we're going to want to know something about the overall properties of the function. That's kind of a tricky thing to get at, so in the Deutsch-Jozsa problem we imagine that we already know that the function is 1 of 2 types. The function is either a function that's constant, it always gives 0 or 1 as its output; or the function is a balanced function, it gives 0 or 1 equally often for its output. So we have a function, it's either constant or balanced. The question is how many times do we have to evaluate the function to tell for sure which type it is?

Imagine that we're doing this on a classical computer. We tell the computer: Start calculating the function. Evaluate $f(n)$ at 1 and $f(n)$ at 2 and so on. And for $f(1)$, we get 0. All right, that's a piece of information. For $f(2)$, well, if that's something besides 0, we know that it's a balanced function instead of a constant function. Well, let's suppose $f(2)$ is 0 as well. All right, maybe it's constant, I don't know. And for $f(3)$, 0; maybe it looks like a constant function. If they are always the same, we conclude that $f(n)$ is constant.

But how many calculations of $f(n)$ do we need to make to be sure? Because it might be that the function is 0 for the first half of the numbers and then 1 for the second half of the numbers. In that case we'd have to evaluate all the way up to the halfway point and then one more to be sure; and indeed, that's how many we have to evaluate to be sure. We have to evaluate $M/2$, M is our maximum number, $+ 1$ to be absolutely sure; and that might be a huge number. We might have to evaluate the function an enormous number of times. That's lots of work. It might take a really long time on our computer.

What Deutsch and Jozsa said is suppose we are calculating this function on a quantum computer. They proved that we can answer the question of whether the function is balanced or constant by evaluating the function, calculating the function, only once. You calculate the function using a superposition of all possible inputs. In this process you learn nothing about the individual values of the function—you don't know whether they're 0 or 1—but what you find out is a property that's a property of all the values taken together. It's a shortcut. The key point is that this quantum computer is more powerful not because it does the usual stuff in a faster way—it doesn't just calculate the function many, many times very quickly. It somehow calculates the function all at once for all kinds of inputs. It's powerful because it does new stuff, stuff that a classical computer could never do.

Now, something that came along a little bit later and is even more interesting than the Deutsch-Jozsa problem is the inverse phonebook problem, which was discovered by Lov Grover at Bell Labs in 1996. This is actually a problem that almost everyone has, in fact, run into. The phonebook is an alphabetical list of names, and then next to each name there's a phone number. And the fact that it's in a book doesn't really matter; you might have an electronic database. The whole point is that it's sorted by name. First there's the first name in the alphabet, then the second name, and so on; and the phone numbers aren't in any particular order, they're just associated with the names.

Now, suppose I have a piece of paper on which I've only written the phone number. Whose number is it? Well, the only way to really solve that, besides calling them, is to sit down with a phonebook and go through the phonebook one by one and compare my phone number with each entry in the book until I find it. How many entries do I have to check in the book, in the phonebook, in order to find out whose phone number it is?

Well, let's suppose we have a pretty thick phonebook. Let's suppose there are a million entries in the phonebook. Now, a classical computer, or me, would have to look up, on average, half of them before they ran across the right name to go with the number. That's 500,000 entries they have to consult on average, and the worst case is that the phone number happens to be the last one in the book, in which case I would have to consult 999,999 before I got to the name that was the name in the book. That could take a long time. Now, in point of fact, computers operate so fast that a million doesn't really take very long; but if the phonebook were actually a million times longer, or if you had to do this problem 100,000 times, it would become a challenge.

So here's what Grover said. Grover imagined that the phonebook data was actually on the quantum computer. The quantum computer could look up a phonebook entry in its own memory. And he showed that the quantum computer can find the name associated with the phone number by consulting the phonebook not half a million times, but only 1000 times; 1000 being the square root of a million. But the way it consults the phonebook is completely bizarre. It actually looks up a superposition of all of the phone numbers. It consults every name in the book, and it does this over and over again, and what happens is there's a kind of constructive interference that after only 1000 times pulls the name out of the phonebook.

This is amazing. Instead of having to consult it half a million times, just do it 1000 times. And this isn't really just about phonebooks; I phrased it that way because that's a problem we're all familiar with. No, the problem is really about searching for some unique target in a large set of possibilities. There's some target I want to find, I don't know where it is—how can I find it? It's looking for the needle in the haystack. And the point is that quantum computers can look everywhere in the haystack at once, and they can find the target; they can zero in on the target far more efficiently.

Finally, let's talk about the most exciting idea of all, the idea of quantum factoring. This was discovered by Peter Shor, who's now a professor at MIT, but at this time he was at Bell Labs; this was 1994. Shor considered the problem in which we're trying to find the factors which, when multiplied together, form a number. We're given a very large number, perhaps a number with hundreds of digits. And we know that this number is the product of 2 smaller numbers. Now, the 2 smaller numbers are themselves prime, they don't have any smaller factors. So we have a very large number which is the product of 2 smaller numbers that are prime. If our large number is 100 digits long, the 2 factors might each be 50 digits long. And so the problem is, given the large number, can we find the factors? This is the factoring problem. Can we find the 2 numbers which when multiplied together give us the original number?

On a classical computer this is a hard problem. How hard is it? Well, a 200-digit number was recently factored. It was a big achievement; it took hundreds of computers working together for over a year to find the 2 100-digit factors of the 200-digit number. And it's not that the problem just increases in difficulty slowly; it increases in difficulty very quickly with the size of the number. A 500-digit number is not just 2 and a half times as difficult as a 200-digit number; it's not even 2 and a half *million* times more difficult. A 500-digit number is so difficult that if you turned the entire observable universe into a computer and you ran it at top speed for billions of years, you would never find the factors of a 500-digit number that's a product of 2 large primes. No imaginable classical computer could do the job of factoring a 500-digit number.

What Peter Shor showed was that a quantum computer can factor numbers in a new super-efficient way; a way that's nothing like a classical computer would try it. Using the Shor method, a 500-digit number is actually only about 16 times more work to factor than a 200-digit number. In fact, a 500-digit number is only a million times harder than a 5-digit number. And a 5-digit number takes almost no time at all on a computer. So we can factor a 500-digit number, a number that would be too hard to factor with a classical computer of any imaginable size. What Shor showed was that factoring large integers is exponentially faster on a quantum computer.

Now why is everyone excited about this particular math problem? Well, it turns out that lots of modern cryptography is based on the difficulty of factoring numbers. Basically it works like this: Alice and Bob possess the factors; they use them for encryption. The eavesdropper Eve only knows the product of the factors; she can figure that out. Now, in principle, if she has that product of the factors, she could find the factors—there's only one set of factors that will work, and so she could read the message. So this scheme looks insecure. But in practice you use numbers that are so big that this is too hard, and Eve just has to give up. Secrecy is preserved. Why? Because although factoring large integers is possible, it's really, really hard, as a matter of computational practice.

However, if Eve can use a quantum computer, factoring is no longer that hard a problem. If a quantum computer could be created, a lot of secret data out there in the real world would no longer be secret. Of course, we can always fall back on quantum cryptography—even a quantum computer can't beat the no-cloning theorem. So quantum information theory not only proposes quantum cryptography, it also shows you why you might need it.

Now, a quantum computer would be powerful not because it is really small or fast, but because it can do its computations in a completely novel way; in a way that no classical computer could even contemplate. Can such a computer actually be built? It doesn't seem to contradict any of the laws of physics, but it also might be something that's really hard. Many scientists are working very hard indeed to build a real quantum computer, and the basic questions they have to answer are questions like these: What are the physical qubits? What physical systems are we going to use for our qubits? How do we control the computer operations very precisely to make the computation progress forward?

So here are some ideas that are being worked on: You might imagine you have some supercool atoms suspended in a vacuum in some laser beams and the operations are controlled by shooting laser beams at the atoms individually. That could act as a quantum computer. Or you might imagine that you had nuclear spins, the spins of atomic nuclei, aligned in a magnetic field controlled by radio waves; that's another possibility. You might imagine that you had superconducting electric circuits near absolute zero that could interact with each other. That's an idea. You might imagine that you had single electrons that you were able to move around inside the body of a semiconductor like silicon; that's another possibility.

With all these ideas, though, and with quite a lot of investment being made in trying to make them work, even the best efforts so far, as I speak, have only managed to have a few qubits working together for a few seconds to do a quantum computation. Still quite a bit short of what we'll need to crack secret codes.

Well, why is it so hard to build a quantum computer? This is kind of interesting. The builder of a quantum computer faces a fundamental dilemma. On the one hand, the computer must be extremely well isolated from the outside world, because otherwise stray molecules and photons and so on would make little inadvertent measurements of the computer's state. Whenever a measurement is made, even if it's not something we intended, that interrupts Update Rule I, the rule that preserves the superpositions in the computer—and that's where all the quantum magic is—and the computer has some sort of random error in it. So the computer has to be very well isolated from the outside world.

On the other hand, the different parts of the computer must interact really very rapidly with each other so that the computation gets done. After all, we're not just trying to store information in the computer, we're trying to manipulate it. We're trying to have this qubit and that qubit talk to each other. So the qubits can't talk to the outside world, but they have to talk to each other. The kinds of qubits that won't talk to the outside world also don't talk to each other, and the kinds of qubits that talk to each other are also happy to talk to the outside world. The 2 impulses are in direct conflict. We don't know how to satisfy both requirements at once.

Now, there is some good news. The good news is we don't have to be perfect. It's been discovered that there are techniques for quantum error correction. So our computer is going to be able to tolerate a little interference and still manage to keep the computation going in this wonderful quantum way. The bad news is even so, even with quantum error correction ideas, nobody knows how to resolve the fundamental dilemma of quantum computing.

There's an interesting historical precedent here from the middle of the 19th century. In those days, an English mathematician named Charles Babbage designed mechanical equivalents of modern computers. Instead of electronic circuits he had lots of tiny little gears and rods and wheels and cams. Babbage thought of a lot of the ideas of modern computers, but he thought of them in terms of little mechanical devices. Now, unfortunately, 19th-century machine tool technology was not quite up to his designs. And Babbage's efforts actually improved machine tool technology, improved our ability to make precise machines. But even so, he spent decades in vain trying to build his analytical engine. His ideas about computing were right, but they were not put into actual practice until the development of electronics in the 20th century. Mechanical computers really were never going to work very well; it wasn't until we had a different way of putting the ideas into practice that we were able to actually make the computers that Babbage foresaw.

Now, present-day attempts at quantum computing using atoms and traps, or nuclear spins, or superconducting loops, or electrons and semiconductors may be like Babbage's wheels. It may be that we have the right ideas but we have the wrong technologies. Who knows how long it will be before we have the right ones?

Okay, why should we be interested in quantum computing? Because we want to read financial secrets on the Internet? No. I think it's because our modern picture of the world is that the world is a huge information network. In some sense we think of the world as a kind of computer, the universe is a computer. The computer takes the present as input and it computes the future. So the universe does this by a kind of information processing, a natural information processing based on the laws of physics. I think we're interested in quantum computers because thinking about quantum computing tells us something about how nature's own computation, based on the laws of quantum physics, may work.

Now, the story of quantum information and quantum computing is far from finished. It's still a very young subject. There are new discoveries being made all the time and these discoveries disclose basic features of quantum mechanics that we did not know. I think we've learned more about the basic features of quantum mechanics in the last 10 years than we've learned in the previous 30. And so quantum information and quantum computing shed new light on the theory of quantum mechanics. These ideas sort of help us find ways to get our minds around the puzzles and paradoxes of the quantum world.

Next time we're going to begin the final Section of the course. We're going to turn to the deepest questions, to the philosophical questions, really; the same questions that haunted Einstein, Bohr, and the others right from the start. What is the meaning of quantum mechanics? What does it tell us about the nature of the physical world? How can the universe be like that? We're going to ask, what's the right way to interpret the abstract theory of quantum mechanics?

And it turns out there are several quite different schools of thought— different in their ideas about quantum probability, different in their ideas about measurement, different in their ideas about reality, different in their ideas about human experience, and so on. Every one of these schools of thought about the interpretation of quantum mechanics shares one thing in common: Our common-sense beliefs about the world must be greatly altered to accommodate the facts of quantum physics. So next time: the interpretation of quantum mechanics. I'll see you then.

Many Worlds or One?
Lecture 23

In the final 2 lectures of this course we will probe some philosophical issues about quantum mechanics. We'll ask: What does quantum mechanics mean? What does it tell us about the nature of reality? ... In this lecture we're going to examine three different ways that physicists have come to interpret the meaning of quantum mechanics.

Even though quantum mechanics is more than 80 years old (and some parts are more than 100), there is still a lot of debate about its interpretation. Physicists agree on how to use quantum mechanics. The question is what the theory is telling us about the nature of reality. Some issues are philosophical: Is the world really nondeterministic? Is a quantum state objective or subjective—something "out there" or "all in our heads"?

One key issue is the question of measurement. Measurement seems special. It forces us to use the probabilistic and instantaneous update rule II rather than the smooth and predictable update rule I. Yet any measurement apparatus is made of atoms. Why can we not treat it as just another quantum system?

There have been 3 main schools of interpretation: the Copenhagen interpretation, the hidden-variables interpretation, and the many-worlds interpretation. The Copenhagen interpretation is the standard approach. Championed by Bohr, this interpretation rests on the principle of complementarity. This interpretation says that the microscopic world does not really "exist" on its own, independent of an observer. You can sum up the idea here in this way: "No phenomenon is a phenomenon until it is an observed phenomenon." In this interpretation, measurement is special because it is the process by which quantum things are amplified into macroscopic reality.

The line between "microscopic" and "macroscopic" may be drawn in various places. We can analyze at least some of the workings of a measurement apparatus in a quantum-mechanical way. In the thought experiment of Schrödinger's cat, the cat is seemingly brought into a superposition state $a|\text{alive}\rangle + b|\text{dead}\rangle$. Eugene Wigner imagined his friend examining Schrödinger's cat. Does Wigner's friend now exist in a superposition state?

The Copenhagen interpretation has its drawbacks. It is not clear, for example, that orthodox approaches to quantum theory will be good enough for challenges like quantum gravity or quantum cosmology.

The hidden-variables interpretation is somewhat less popular. It was discussed most deeply by David Bohm, beginning in 1952. The work was based an earlier idea of de Broglie, who thought that both the quantum wave and the quantum particle exist together. The wave acts to "pilot" the particle through space. Bohm was able to create a theory that would appear exactly like quantum mechanics in any experiment, but the particles always had definite positions and velocities at every given moment, and they moved in a complicated but deterministic way.

No phenomenon is a phenomenon until it is an observed phenomenon.

What about Bell and entanglement? Bell's argument means that Bohm's hidden-variable theory must work in a nonlocal way. That is, distant parts of the universe can instantaneously affect each other. Bohm did not regard this as a flaw. He saw this as an expression of a large-scale cosmological order, something quite different from the "reductionist" ideas common to modern science. Relatively few quantum physicists subscribe to Bohm's ideas, though they continue to be discussed and developed.

The many-worlds interpretation was proposed by Hugh Everett III in 1957. The basic idea is that the measurement apparatus and observers are all quantum systems and that the whole universe always evolved according to update rule I. The quantum state thus evolves deterministically. The apparent randomness in quantum mechanics arises because we can only see part of the whole.

The many-worlds interpretation gives a strange account of measurement. Consider a simple universe containing an observer Joe and a spin-$\frac{1}{2}$ particle. The spin starts out in the state $a|\uparrow\rangle + b|\downarrow\rangle$, and Joe starts out in the state $|Joe_0\rangle$.

The initial state of the universe is

$$a|Joe_0, \uparrow\rangle + b|Joe_0, \downarrow\rangle.$$

Joe now measures z on the spin. This is an interaction (update rule I) that works like this on basis states:

$$|Joe_0, \uparrow\rangle \Rightarrow |Joe\ sees\ ``up,"\ \uparrow\rangle \text{ and } |Joe_0, \downarrow\rangle \Rightarrow |Joe\ sees\ ``down,"\ \downarrow\rangle.$$

The new state of the universe is

$$a|Joe\ sees\ ``up,"\ \uparrow\rangle + b|Joe\ sees\ ``down,"\ \downarrow\rangle.$$

In each branch of this superposition, Joe sees only 1 thing, and what Joe sees agrees with the state of the spin. But both branches are still present in the overall state of the universe. It is as if the world has split in 2, each branch invisible to the other. In the process of measurement, the observer becomes entangled with the observed.

The many-worlds interpretation is controversial but increasingly popular. One positive aspect of this interpretation is that it gets rid of any special measurement process and lets us apply quantum theory to the entire universe. This makes it attractive for physicists trying to develop a "theory of everything." However, it does have problems. One key one is that it asserts the existence of vast numbers of unobservable branches other than what we see, which seems to violate the logical principle of Occam's Razor. It involves another difficult puzzle as well: In our example, why does Joe see "up" with probability $|a|^2$ and "down" with probability $|b|^2$? Both branches are present, but why does he seem to experience them with this likelihood? The universe of the many-worlds interpretation contains all quantum possibilities in a vast, ever-more-complicated, stupendously entangled quantum superposition. ∎

Lecture 23: Many Worlds or One?

1. What do you find least satisfactory about each of the 3 main interpretations of quantum theory described in this lecture?

2. The principle of Occam's Razor has been invoked both to criticize the many-worlds interpretation (why imagine so many other worlds?) and to defend it (why imagine that the principle of superposition has any limits?). Which argument seems more sensible to you, and why?

3. Try to imagine how Bohr and Einstein might have responded to the many-worlds interpretation of quantum mechanics. Write a short fictional dialogue between them, discussing the idea.

Many Worlds or One?
Lecture 23—Transcript

Welcome to the 23rd lecture in our course on quantum mechanics. In the final 2 lectures of this course we will probe some philosophical issues about quantum mechanics. We'll ask: What does quantum mechanics mean? What does it tell us about the nature of reality?

Some physicists avoid such questions as a matter of principle. They say, I know how to use quantum mechanics, I can solve the mathematical problems, and I can make predictions about laboratory experiments, and that is good enough. This attitude is understandable. For many everyday purposes it makes sense to carry on with the practical business without worrying about deep philosophical puzzles. You don't have to resolve the nature of human existence before you get up in the morning.

Also, some physicists are wary about philosophy. They think philosophy is dangerous. They think that Einstein was led astray by his philosophical ideas, that he was prevented from accepting quantum mechanics because he was committed to determinism; because he believed "God does not play dice with the universe." These physicists would heartily agree with Bohr: "Einstein, stop telling God what to do." They would say that Einstein missed the boat. These physicists would say that the best thing to do is to just to set philosophy aside as much as possible and get to work on new physics.

With all due respect, I have to disagree. I think we have to wrestle with these questions. I think they're important. Part of the reason we are so fascinated with quantum mechanics is these questions.

I also disagree about Einstein. His philosophical concerns led him to draw attention to important issues, like entanglement. Even if he did not quite accept quantum mechanics, his questioning of the theory drove our understanding forward. His questioning forced us to sharpen our thinking, and that was a hugely valuable contribution. I think Bohr's general approach to things is right—that deep understanding comes from discussion, dialogue, argument—and disagreement can drive it forward. So we should not get hung up on philosophical issues, but we should not be afraid of them, either.

In this lecture we're going to examine three different ways that physicists have come to interpret the meaning of quantum mechanics. One way will be familiar, but the other 2 are quite different. And this is a remarkable fact. Even though quantum mechanics is 80 years old and counting—parts of it are more than 100 years old—there is still radical disagreement about its interpretation.

Physicists agree on how to use quantum mechanics, they agree how to do the mathematics, they agree how to apply it in experimental situations, but they disagree about what quantum mechanics tells us about the nature of reality. These are essentially philosophical questions. Is the world truly nondeterministic? What's the status of a quantum state? Is the quantum state of a system objective or subjective? Is it truly something out there, some actual property of a system, or is it all in our heads? Does it really just reflect our knowledge of the system? And here's a key question: What is measurement?

Measurement, after all, seems special. We use the instantaneous and random Update Rule II to tell what happens in a measurement, rather than the smooth, predictable Update Rule I. We have a whole special rule about measurement; and yet a measurement apparatus, like anything else, is made of atoms. Why don't we just treat the measurement apparatus as just another quantum system? What is it about a measurement apparatus that gives it its special "measurementness"?

Now, there are three main schools of interpretation of quantum mechanics, and they are: first, the Copenhagen interpretation; second, the hidden-variables interpretation; and third, the many-worlds interpretation. And we're going to discuss each of these in detail.

First, the Copenhagen interpretation—this is the standard approach; this is the one that we have used, the interpretation of quantum mechanics that has shaped our own discussion of the subject. It was formulated and championed by Niels Bohr, and it rested on the principle of quantum complementarity; that's what the Copenhagen interpretation is built on. In this interpretation, in some sense the microscopic world does not really exist on its own, not the way that large-scale objects and things exist. As John Wheeler said, "no phenomenon is a phenomenon until it is an observed phenomenon."

Wheeler actually liked to tell the following story about Bohr, who was his mentor. Bohr was trying to explain the quantum 2-slit experiment to his old philosophy professor, and the philosophy professor was having a little trouble understanding the details. He said, "Niels, when the electron is in the middle around the barrier with the 2 slits, where can it be said to be?" Bohr's reply was, "To be? To be? What does it mean, to be?" That's the Copenhagen interpretation.

In the Copenhagen interpretation, measurement is special, because it is how microscopic quantum "somethings" are amplified into macroscopic reality. Of course, that raises the question: What is the line between microscopic and macroscopic? And Bohr talked about this. Bohr said that line may be drawn in various places. He says that there's a whole chain of events, with the atom at one end and the physicist at the other, and the boundary between the microscopic and the macroscopic is somewhere in between. But exactly where that boundary is, he said, is actually not a crucial question. You can draw it various places and still get the same answers.

Now, we can analyze at least some of the workings of a measurement apparatus using quantum mechanics, by applying quantum mechanics to the measuring apparatus. But for the Copenhagen interpretation, it is vital that we draw the line between microscopic quantum and macroscopic classical somewhere.

There are some puzzles with this whole approach, and a famous one, I suppose, is the puzzle of Schrödinger's cat. This is a thought-experiment from a paper by Schrödinger from 1935. In this thought-experiment a cat is seemingly brought into a quantum superposition state, a superposition state where you have an amplitude times the alive state plus another amplitude times a dead state, $a|alive\rangle + b|dead\rangle$. That seemed like a very strange state of affairs for a cat.

Schrödinger himself did not take this too seriously; the paragraph in which the famous cat is introduced begins, "One can even construct quite ridiculous examples," and the Schrödinger cat was one of those examples. But others did take it seriously, and worried about the application of quantum mechanics to the macroscopic world. Eugene Wigner, the great Hungarian physicist, imagined his friend examining Schrödinger's cat; and he asked, is his friend now in a superposition state as well? A superposition state of seeing a live cat and seeing a dead cat?

All of these things suggest that there may be some problems with the Copenhagen interpretation. The Copenhagen interpretation relies on this distinction between the microscopic and the macroscopic, but it doesn't really tell us exactly how to tell the difference. It doesn't tell us where to draw the line; it doesn't establish the border. And that's a problematic thing, because all of the macroscopic apparatus, all of the pieces of equipment we use to do experiments in the quantum world are made of quantum pieces, atoms and molecules. How do we make sense of that? It's also the case that complementarity often seems like a way just to avoid tricky questions. Remember what Asher Peres said, "Unperformed experiments have no results." That seems like a great excuse, but does it really not make sense to ask what would have happened if we'd done something different?

Now, the Copenhagen interpretation does provide some fairly clear guidance for actually using quantum theory, which is why it has been the standard for interpreting quantum mechanics since the 1920s. But there's some question about whether that interpretation is good enough, is robust enough, for the challenges of extending quantum theory to a quantum theory of gravity; or quantum cosmology, which is applying quantum mechanics to the whole universe. These are things people want to think about, want to try to do. Is the Copenhagen view of quantum mechanics good enough for those problems?

Now we're going to turn to the second of our three great interpretations of quantum mechanics, and this one is the hidden-variables interpretation. If you go back to the origins of quantum mechanics, this was actually de Broglie's original way of thinking about quantum waves. He said that actually both particles and waves exist, that it's not like an electron can be a particle or a wave, it's actually both, they're both present. The wave travels through space and it guides the particle around; the wave is what's called "a pilot wave" for the particle. The particle's moving in some complicated way as steered by the wave. This general idea was actually put on solid footing by David Bohm in 1952. So let's talk about Bohm's theory.

Bohm's theory is a theory that appears exactly like quantum mechanics in any experiment, it makes exactly the same predictions as quantum mechanics, and that's why it counts as really a way of interpreting quantum mechanics. It's not really a different theory. But in Bohm's mathematics, particles always have definite positions and definite velocities at every moment. They move about in fiendishly complicated but completely deterministic ways, guided by a quantum field, a wave. So in the 2-slit experiment the quantum wave exhibits interference, and it's that quantum wave which steers the particle around in such a way that it winds up where the wave is strongest and stays away from places where the wave is zero.

Now, Bohm's theory was meant to prove that quantum mechanics was capable of supporting a deterministic interpretation. That quantum mechanics was compatible with physical determinism—because in the early 1950s, many people believed that it was not. But the result of his theory was that we have a new way of interpreting standard quantum mechanics. Standard quantum mechanics is just one way of calculating on average how Bohm's hidden variable mechanic works.

Now, you may be worried; you may say, what about entanglement? I mean, remember Bell's theorem. Bell's theorem says that you can't have any theory of hidden variables that function locally that agrees with quantum mechanics. And indeed, when you look at the details, Bohm's hidden variables must work in a non-local way, that distant parts of the universe in Bohm's theory can instantaneously affect each other at arbitrarily large distances.

Now, it seems a little strange, but in fact Bohm did not regard this as a flaw in his theory. Bohm thought that this was actually an expression of a large-scale, even cosmological, order in the universe. And this order is very different from the reductionist ideas that are common to modern science.

What do I mean by reductionist? Well, reductionism is the approach that, to understand something in the world, to understand x, what you do is you break x up into its parts and you understand the parts and how they interact with each other. So ultimately you try to explain everything in terms of the individual atoms and how they behave and interact. You understand everything by reducing it to a problem of the little tiny pieces. But if there were a large-scale cosmic order as Bohm suggests, then the more reductionist we were, the farther we would be from that cosmic order. So reductionism will never give us a complete picture of the world. Bohm says that standard quantum mechanics is about as far as we can go in understanding the world on the reductionist road, and that it is possible to get a deeper view of nature, but in order to get that deeper view it will require us to abandon our old ideas, including reductionism.

Now, Bohm's ideas have met only limited success. Relatively few quantum physicists have subscribed to this hidden-variables interpretation, but some of the ones that have include some of the giants. We saw that de Broglie was a subscriber to this view. Einstein probably would have agreed with this view. Arguably John Bell himself subscribed to this view of quantum mechanics. Bohm's ideas are subtle and provocative, and they continue to be developed and discussed to this day; so it's a real live interpretation of quantum mechanics.

Which brings us to our third and, in many ways, the strangest interpretation of quantum mechanics, the so-called "many-worlds interpretation." The many-worlds interpretation was proposed by Hugh Everett III in 1957. Like Feynman, Everett was another doctoral student of John Wheeler proposing something remarkable about quantum mechanics in his Ph.D. thesis.

Everett's basic idea is this: Why do we have 2 rules in quantum mechanics? Why do we have Update Rule I, which takes place when there's no measurement, and Update Rule II, which takes place when there is a measurement? He says that's not the way the world works. Everett says there is no Update Rule II. Everett wants to include measurement apparatus and even observers, you and me, all as quantum systems, all as parts of the universe. He says that the entire universe always evolves according to Update Rule I. And Update Rule I is a fixed rule; it's deterministic, in a sense, so the quantum mechanical state of the universe always changes in a deterministic way.

So if the quantum state always changes in a deterministic way, why do we see randomness? Why do we see probabilities, things happening one way or the other without apparent definite cause in quantum experiments? The reason is that we only see part of the universe, not the whole. Everett gives a very strange account of measurements. We're going to give an example of the Everett view and we're going to imagine a universe that's very simple, it contains just 2 things: It contains an observer, Joe, and it contains a spin-1/2 particle. That's the entire universe.

Now the spin starts out in a superposition state, $a|\uparrow\rangle + b|\downarrow\rangle$, a superposition with amplitudes a and b. And Joe starts out in some state, we'll call it $|\text{Joe}_0\rangle$. This is the state of Joe ready to make a measurement but not having made it yet. Joe is a quantum system; he gets a quantum state, too. So the initial state of the universe is one of these simple product states that we get by the composition rule; the initial state of the universe is $a|\text{Joe}_0,\uparrow\rangle + b|\text{Joe}_0,\downarrow\rangle$. That's the initial state of the universe.

So what happens? Well, now Joe proceeds to measure the z component of the spin of the particle. This would do the following: if the spin were initially spin up it would take you from the state $|\text{Joe}_0,\uparrow\rangle$ to the state $|\text{Joe sees "up," }\uparrow\rangle$—the state Joe sees "up" is shorthand for the state of Joe in which he has the psychological perception of the spin being $+1/2$ in the z direction. Similarly, if the spin were initially down, $|\text{Joe}_0,\downarrow\rangle$ would evolve to $|\text{Joe sees "down," }\downarrow\rangle$.

This is how the measurement process would work. But the measurement process is just a normal interaction of systems. There's nothing different about it, and so it follows Update Rule I—which respects and preserves superpositions, and so what happens is that the universe, which starts out in a superposition of spin state up and spin state down, now evolves into a new state: $a|\text{Joe sees "up," }\uparrow\rangle + b|\text{Joe sees "down," }\downarrow\rangle$. This is a definite deterministic evolution of the universe's state. Each term in that superposition, each branch of the superposition, has a situation in which Joe sees just one thing. Either Joe sees up or Joe sees down, and what Joe sees agrees with the state of the spin. In the branch of the superposition in which Joe sees spin up, the spin is up; and when Joe sees down, the spin is down.

And indeed if we had a more complicated universe, that had 2 observers—we had another observer, Willie—then Willie and Joe, when they measured the same component of spin, would see the same thing. They would agree with each other in each branch of the superpositions. But the branches are both still present in the overall state of the universe. They're still present in the overall state of the universe. It's as if the universe has split into 2; each branch is invisible to the other. So in the process of measurement, Joe becomes entangled with the thing that he observes, and it's that entanglement between Joe and the system that he observes that causes Joe so much conceptual trouble.

So how was Everett's radical idea received? Well, there were relatively few early adopters of the many-worlds interpretation; it was highly controversial. But over the years it's become increasingly popular among physicists. It's still a minority view, but another generation or so of physicists might see this change. It's a frequent plot device in science fiction writers who want to write about alternate worlds—for example, what if the Nazis had won World War II? You can write such a story, all you have to do is set your story in another branch of the cosmic quantum state, because in another branch of the cosmic quantum state, different quantum events happened and the Nazis won.

There are good points and bad points about the many-worlds interpretation. What are some of the good points? Well, one good point is that it gets rid of the special measurement process; we get rid of the curious Update Rule II. We can analyze measurement in the same way that we can analyze any physical interaction, on the same grounds with the same rules. It lets us apply quantum mechanics to the entire universe, and that makes it very attractive for those physicists who are working on developing a so-called "theory of everything." For example, physicists working on superstring theory and related ideas most often adopt some version of the many-worlds theory as their everyday interpretation of quantum mechanics because that allows them to apply their quantum theory to the whole universe; that's what they're after.

There are, on the other hand, some bad things about the many-worlds interpretation. One of the obvious bad things is that it asserts the existence of vast numbers of unobservable branches other than the things that we see. And this makes one think of Occam's razor. William of Occam was a 14th-century philosopher, and he said that a theory should not involve a lot of extra unnecessary stuff; that your theory should be economical. So it's a good question: Does the many-worlds interpretation, the many-worlds theory, violate this or does it exemplify it? Does it violate it in that it posits lots of unobservable worlds in which things happen that we don't see, but are still somehow part of the universe? Or does it exemplify Occam's razor by saying no, everything is simpler because we have a more unified set of principles. There aren't 2 ways for the state to change, there is just the one; everything always happens according to the same rules.

And there's another problem. After the measurement, the universe is in that state $a \big| \text{Joe sees "up," } \uparrow \big\rangle + b \big| \text{Joe sees "down," } \downarrow \big\rangle$. If that's the state of the universe, why is it that Joe subjectively sees the result "up" with the probability magnitude of a^2? Why does he see "down" with probability magnitude of b^2? Where did the probabilities come from? Both branches are present; why is it that Joe subjectively experiences them with these likelihoods? Where does the Born rule come from? That's one of the crucial elements of quantum mechanics; it's one of our basic rules. If all of the branches of the superposition are always all there, why is it that we subjectively see them with probabilities given by the Born rule? Now, there have been some very clever mathematical suggestions about this in recent years. In my view, none of these suggestions are 100% convincing yet. So I think that the observed probabilities that we see in quantum experiments are still a little puzzling in the many-worlds interpretation.

But with all these problems, the universe of the many-worlds interpretation is an astounding and dizzying thing to contemplate. It contains all of the quantum possibilities at once. It exists in a vast, ever more complicated, stupendously entangled quantum superposition. In fact, many people prefer to use the term "multiverse" for this quantum cosmos described by the many-worlds interpretation.

There are also a few other interpretations of quantum mechanics. Most of these appear to be variations on these basic three, the Copenhagen interpretation, the hidden-variables interpretation, or the many-worlds interpretation. These interpretations differ in some interesting ways. For example they differ in their regard to probabilities. It's only in the Copenhagen interpretation that probabilities are real, that there's real randomness in the world. In the hidden-variables interpretation the apparent randomness is simply due to our ignorance of hidden factors and the cosmic, universe-spanning order that governs the universe. In the many-worlds interpretation our perception of randomness comes from the fact that we only perceive part of the universe, only one branch of the superposition in our direct experience.

Now, that means that both the hidden-variables theory and the many-worlds theory, both the hidden-variables and many-worlds interpretations of quantum mechanics, are actually deterministic views of the world. Of course they mean something different by "the world" than the Copenhagen interpretation means; but each of these interpretations supposes that the world includes things that we don't see: in the hidden-variables interpretation tiny variables, hidden variables that are inaccessible to us; in the many-worlds interpretation all of these other worlds that contain the other possible results of measurement interactions.

All of the interpretations of quantum mechanics seem a little problematic. All of them are hard for us to imagine. All of them ask us to accept things about the world that seem bizarre. So what is it about quantum mechanics that makes it so hard to figure out? What is it about quantum mechanics that allows us to interpret it in so many different ways? There weren't rival schools of interpretation for Newtonian physics. What is it that makes quantum mechanics so different? What is that central mystery of quantum mechanics; the thing that makes it all so elusive? That's the question. That's the question we'll grapple with next time. I'll see you then.

The Great Smoky Dragon
Lecture 24

> The quantum realm is a wonderfully strange place. Indeed, we are not entirely sure just what kind of a place it is. There is significant disagreement about the meaning of quantum mechanics. ... In this final lecture, I would like to reflect on what it is that makes quantum mechanics so strange and so mysterious.

We return to our example of the photon in the Mach-Zehnder interferometer. In this example, interference challenges our intuition. Block either beam, and either detector might register the photon. Leave both beams open, and only 1 detector can possibly register it. Interference can occur when no measurement is made of which path the photon travels. This leads us to an astonishing point: When interference occurs, no physical record is made *anywhere in the universe* of the path of the photon. The photon on its journey is "informationally isolated" from the rest of the universe. Remember, "Quantum mechanics is what happens when no one is looking."

The "magic" of quantum mechanics is like a stage magician's trick box. With the box, we believe that we could peer inside and find out how the trick works. With the quantum mechanics box, the trick only works when the box is absolutely closed. We cannot find out how it works, even in principle.

Our description of the magic in the box is quantum mechanics, which is full of strange mathematical abstractions: states, amplitudes, etc. We can use quantum mechanics to perform amazing tricks, but the magic box remains no less mysterious.

Why is it hard to observe quantum interference of a baseball? Large objects are extremely difficult to isolate from the outside world. To observe baseball interference, we would have to remove all photons and gas molecules, then cool the baseball fantastically close to absolute zero. We would even have to worry about how the baseball's gravity is affecting nearby atoms! The point here is that macroscopic atoms are very strongly connected to the rest of the world. If we are very careful, we can observe interference for photons, electrons, atoms, etc. But we cannot cut a baseball away from the rest of the world and close the lid of the magic box.

Quantum mechanics is sometimes called the "Great Smoky Dragon." John Wheeler introduced a cartoon to illustrate the nature of quantum mechanics. The dragon's tail appears at the start of the experiment. The dragon's head bites one of the particle detectors at the end. In between, the dragon is shrouded in smoke, and we can never say exactly what its shape is.

The Great Smoky Dragon is a metaphor for the elusiveness of the quantum realm. It is found in every part of quantum mechanics, shrouded by the uncertainty principle and shielded by the principle of complementarity. It has a delicate touch; it can tickle a hair-trigger bomb without setting it off. A pair of identical particles is less like 2 dragons than a single dragon with 2 tails and 2 heads. Feynman's ribbon trick gives us a hint of how the dragon twists among particles with spin. In Feynman's view, the dragon gets from here to there by wriggling through everywhere in between. Virtual dragons stretch invisibly from particle to particle, carrying forces between them. Even when space appears empty, it fluctuates with the stirrings of the dragon. Quantum information reminds us of the Great Smoky Dragon, for it cannot be pinned down and copied. We can use the hiddenness of the dragon for our own purposes, sending secret messages that no eavesdropper can penetrate. Dragons carry signals in strange ways, even snaking backward in time; and with a quantum computer, we can quickly solve hard mathematical problems entirely inside the cloud of smoke.

> **The Great Smoky Dragon is a metaphor for the elusiveness of the quantum realm. It is found in every part of quantum mechanics, shrouded by the uncertainty principle and shielded by the principle of complementarity.**

Entanglement is the most dragonish aspect of quantum mechanics. If 2 particles are in an entangled state together, then neither of them can be entangled with any other particles in the universe. The relationship of entanglement is entirely "private." This fact is called the monogamy of quantum entanglement. (Abner Shimony called entanglement "passion at a distance.")

How should we regard the Great Smoky Dragon? It is a Copenhagen picture. The tail and head are where the dragon emerges into the macroscopic world; the smoky in-between is the indescribable quantum realm. (John Wheeler was a student of Niels Bohr.)

Other interpretations deal with the dragon in different ways. The hidden-variables interpretation asserts that the dragon has a definite shape. This shape is strange because parts of the world that seem far apart are actually close together on the dragon.

According to the many-worlds interpretation, the dragon has no tail and no head. Everything is inside the smoke, including us! When we think we see a tail or a head, we are only seeing a tiny part of the whole dragon, which encompasses every possible world.

None of this makes the Great Smoky Dragon less mysterious. Though its actions shape everything we see in the world, elusiveness is the quantum dragon's most essential feature. ■

Questions to Consider

1. In his writings on complementarity, Bohr laid great stress on "amplification"—the process by which a quantum event is magnified into a macroscopic measurement result. Based on the ideas in this lecture, explain how this takes the effect across the boundary between the quantum and classical realms.

2. Think about what you have learned about quantum mechanics from the previous lectures and pick out the phenomenon that you find most strange or striking. How does Wheeler's metaphor of the Great Smoky Dragon illuminate quantum physics in this example?

The Great Smoky Dragon
Lecture 24—Transcript

Welcome to the 24th and final lecture in our course on quantum mechanics. This course has been a journey into an extraordinary country, the realm of microscopic physics, the realm of quantum mechanics. We've seen how the 19th-century synthesis of classical physics was overturned in the first decades of the 20th century, and replaced by a new view of nature, quantum mechanics. We followed the struggles of the physicists of that time as they came to grips with the concepts of the new physics, and perhaps we've struggled a bit ourselves to master the abstract language of states and superpositions and amplitudes. We've explored some of the scenic byways of quantum mechanics, taking a look at the behavior of identical particles, at quantum entanglement, at virtual particles, and the physics of the quantum vacuum. We've looked at some more recent developments linking quantum theory to the idea of information. We've learned some of the basic rules governing quantum information, and we've talked about how quantum communication, and quantum computing, can accomplish tasks that would otherwise be impossible.

The quantum realm is a wonderfully strange place. Indeed, we are not entirely sure just what kind of a place it is. There is significant disagreement about the meaning of quantum mechanics. There are rival schools of interpretation, and we discussed three of them: the Copenhagen interpretation, the hidden-variables interpretation, and the many-worlds interpretation. So in this final lecture, I would like to reflect on what it is that makes quantum mechanics so strange and so mysterious.

A little of the answer, I think, is sheer unfamiliarity. The quantum realm is very far from our everyday experience. It's far away not in distance, but in size, so it's bound to be surprising; but there is more to it than that. I think that there is a thread running through all the bizarreness of quantum mechanics, a common theme that shows up again and again, sometimes in an obvious way, sometimes disguised. I think this is the very thing that gives quantum mechanics its enigmatic quality.

What is that theme? Well, let's return to the example of one photon in the Mach-Zehnder interferometer. This has been our prototype quantum experiment, our conceptual laboratory for exploring ideas.

It's where we return when we want to probe our perplexities. The interferometer is all about interference, and interference challenges our intuition. If we block either beam in the interferometer, then either detector might register the photon. If we leave both beams open, only one detector can possibly click, and this is because of constructive and destructive interference of quantum amplitudes, or of the quantum wave, if you prefer that language.

So when can interference between the 2 paths occur? The answer is: when there is no measurement. If we make a measurement of which path the photon takes, even with super nondestructive photon detectors, the interference effect goes away. What do I mean by a measurement? I mean the formation of any physical record, anywhere, of which path the photon takes. Measurement is not so much about conscious observers as about the rest of the universe.

And so, in the interference experiment, when interference is happening, that means that no physical record is being made anywhere in the universe of which path is being taken. No forensic examination of the interferometer or its surroundings could later establish what happened exactly, which way the photon went. That's an astonishing claim. The photon makes its journey through the interferometer under conditions of absolute secrecy.

It's all about information. The photon is informationally isolated during its trip. No information leaks into the rest of the universe. The magic of quantum interference between paths happens if, and only if, it is impossible in principle to determine what path is taken. This is just what we mean by the photon travels both paths through the interferometer.

This is the Copenhagen sort of language. So how would we describe this in hidden-variables language? Well, the quantum wave, says the hidden-variables interpretation, the quantum wave spreads throughout the interferometer, and any measurement apparatus will affect this wave. If I don't make a "which path" measurement, then we have wave interference at the second beam splitter. The quantum particle actually follows one path through the interferometer, guided by the wave. That's the interferometer experiment in hidden-variables language.

All right. How would I describe this experiment in many-worlds language? Well, when the photon enters the interferometer, the state of the whole universe branches in 2. But in a sense, this is a very tiny branching. It only involves one photon. It's still possible at this stage to bring the branches back together, which is exactly what happens at the second beam splitter. Interference in fact means bringing the branches of the universe back together. So, if we interact with the photon to determine its path, then the branching in the universe involves not just the photon, but lots and lots of other stuff: the apparatus of our measurement, our memories, the atoms and photons in the local environment, all are involved in that splitting. And so, in a sense, Humpty Dumpty has broken and all the king's horses and all the king's men cannot put the universe back together again. The branching in the superposition is now effectively permanent.

So the moral of this is that interesting and meaningful statements in one interpretation of quantum mechanics actually correspond to interesting and meaningful statements in the other interpretations, although mostly the meanings are quite different. From now on, I will mostly adopt Copenhagen language for talking about quantum mechanics. It's the most directly connected to our experience of the quantum world, so I find it easiest to talk that way.

Let's go back to the idea of informational isolation. Quantum interference only happens when the photon travels through the interferometer in secret. So if you want to put it into a slogan, you might say that quantum mechanics is what happens when no one is looking. I think it's a slogan suitable for a t-shirt.

Or put it another way: quantum mechanics is like a trick in a magic show. Imagine a stage magician has a trick box, and in it he puts a couple of eggs and he says "abracadabra," and he pulls out a bunny. We go, amazing, that's fantastic; we applaud. Now, before that trick, we believe that if we could peer inside the magician's box, we could find out how the trick works. We could find out that there was a secret compartment in the box, a trap door or something like that. If the box were opened, or its walls were somehow transparent, then we would be able to see how the trick is done. Now, the quantum magic box is different. The interference trick only works when the box is absolutely closed. If we open the box and look inside while doing the trick, the trick doesn't work. A closed box is a necessary part of the interference trick. Even in principle, therefore, we cannot find out how it's done. Of course, we can learn to do the trick, to predict what will happen, and that's exactly what quantum mechanics, the theory of physics, is for.

Quantum mechanics is full of strange mathematical abstractions. It's full of states and amplitudes and so forth. There are rules about superpositions, about probabilities, about how the state changes, rules about the composition of states. And we can learn to use quantum mechanics and learn to do some amazing tricks, and we've seen a few of those, but the magic in the box remains mysterious because that magic must remain hidden. The hiddenness is part of the magic. That's why quantum mechanics is so elusive. It only happens where we can't see what is happening.

We're really coming close to the heart of the whole business. One of the most magical things that we have considered is quantum entanglement. John Bell showed us that quantum mechanics is incompatible with our natural, common-sense, intuitive ideas about the world; that was Bell's theorem. We saw that quantum mechanics violates Bell's inequality, which must hold true in any world governed by local hidden variables, any world which is governed by tiny deterministic instructions that function locally. The relationship between 2 entangled particles simply cannot be explained by supposing that the particles act independently based on a prior agreement.

Now, what I want to tell you now is something else, another property of quantum entanglement that I haven't mentioned yet. And that is that entanglement is an exclusive relationship. Suppose you have particle number 1 entangled with particle number 2. If particle 1 is entangled with particle 2, that means that it is not entangled with particle number 3 or particle number 4 or particle number 5. There's actually—to do the math carefully—there's actually a tradeoff. The more entangled number 1 is with number 2, the less entangled it can be with number 3 or number 4 or number 5. And, if we have 2 spins in a total spin 0 state, an ebit, those 2 entangled spins are entangled to a maximum degree, and neither of them can be entangled with anything else in the universe. The relationship between them is absolutely unique.

The entanglement of quantum particles is not simple correlation. For example, my newspaper happens to be correlated with your newspaper. When we compare them we find they have exactly the same stories in them, exactly the same pictures, exactly the same ads. They're correlated to the maximum degree, but that does not mean that my newspaper therefore cannot be correlated just as much with other newspapers. There can be a great many newspapers that are all maximally correlated together. The relationship between your newspaper and mine is in no way unique.

Now, remember what the difference is between classical and quantum information. Quantum information cannot be copied, that was the quantum no-cloning theorem. Well, for entanglement, we have a kind of quantum information, we measured it actually in ebits, and no duplicate of particle number 1's relationship to particle number 2 can exist. This entanglement between 1 and 2 is a totally private relationship. The rest of the universe is excluded from sharing it. And this is actually a deep principle of quantum information theory. It's called the monogamy of entanglement.

Now I want to tell you something wonderful and actually quite new. Bell's theorem and the monogamy of entanglement are actually closely connected. It turns out that they are 2 sides of the same coin. So, to state it more carefully, 2 entangled particles can violate Bell's inequality only because their relationship is exclusive. Put it another way, relationships that can be shared with others, mere correlations like the correlations between 2 editions of the same newspaper, can always be explained by a common-sense sort of theory, a theory in which there are hidden variables in the world that function locally. So what Bell's theorem really tells us is this: Pairs of entangled particles have a relationship that is totally private, and this relationship cannot be shared with anything else in the entire universe. We on the outside cannot, in principle, see inside the relation between 2 entangled particles. This is the very thing that allows the particles to cooperate with each other in such a surprising fashion. I'm very fond of Abner Shimony's description of quantum entanglement. Not "action at a distance," but "passion at a distance," a very exclusive and private passion.

These things are possible in the microscopic quantum world. What about the macroscopic world, the world of our everyday experience? We can observe quantum interference in a photon or an electron; why is it hard to observe quantum interference in a baseball? After all, a baseball is made of atoms; a baseball is made out of quantum systems.

Now, the answer isn't simply because large objects are more massive. The answer is more subtle than that. The reason that we can't see interference effects in large objects like a baseball is that large objects are exceedingly difficult to isolate from the outside world. Remember, to see the interference in the photon experiment, we needed to make sure that the photon was informationally isolated from the outside world. What would it take to do the same thing for a baseball? What would it take to make sure that no record is made anywhere in the universe of which path the baseball follows?

Well, let's see. To begin with, we're going to have to remove all photons and gas molecules from the experiment, because as the baseball flies through space, if the gas molecule bounces off of it, that gas molecule will have recorded the presence of the baseball. And the same thing for photons: If a stray photon of light reflects off of the baseball, that's a measurement. That means later on, someone examining the photons in the room could tell where the baseball was. So we're going to have to eliminate the gas molecules and the atoms in the room.

We're also going to have cool the baseball very, very close, fantastically close, to absolute zero. Why? Because if the baseball has any appreciable temperature at all, it will itself emit photons, blackbody radiation, and those photons will carry an image of where the baseball is located. So we're going to have to cool the baseball really, really cold.

We're going to have to worry about all kinds of things, because we're even going to need to worry about how the gravitation of the baseball, fantastically small as that is, affects nearby atoms.

Why are we going to have to worry about all these tiny, tiny details? Because any information leakage, even information leakage into *one* atom of the environment, destroys the interference pattern, because that makes a record, a record that could in principle later be read to determine which way the baseball traveled. And because that is so very, very difficult, it's practically impossible to do an interference experiment with a baseball.

What's the fundamental point? The fundamental point is that macroscopic objects are very, very strongly connected to the rest of the world. If you will, they are the celebrities of the physical universe. Their every move is watched by the atoms and photons around them. Therefore, there's no possibility of interference, and their relationships are a matter of public record. And that means there's no possibility of entanglement between macroscopic objects, because entanglement is a purely private relationship.

Now, if we're careful, we can observe interference for photons, for electrons, atoms, and so on; but we cannot cut a baseball away from the rest of the world. We can't close the lid on the magic quantum box, so we can't do the trick. The hiddenness of quantum processes, their inaccessibility to our gaze, is not just an inconvenient fact: It's the central point in the whole thing.

John Wheeler introduced a beautiful metaphor for the nature of quantum mechanics. He said that quantum mechanics is the Great Smoky Dragon. The dragon's tail appears at the start of the experiment, the dragon's head bites one of the particle detectors at the end of the experiment, and in between, the dragon is shrouded in smoke. We can never say exactly where it is or what its shape might be.

The Great Smoky Dragon represents the basic elusiveness of the quantum realm. And Wheeler's Great Smoky Dragon lives in every part of quantum mechanics, in every part of the microscopic realm. The dragon is shrouded in the uncertainty principle, and it's shielded by the principle of complementarity. And it has a remarkably delicate touch, in fact. It can tickle a hair-trigger bomb without setting it off.

What about a pair of identical particles? Well, that's not exactly like 2 separate dragons. We can see here are a couple of tails, there are a couple of heads; but which tail goes with which head? In between, there's only smoke. So 2 identical particles behave more like a single dragon with 2 tails and 2 heads.

Nevertheless, Feynman's ribbon trick does give us a hint about how the dragon twists among the particles with spin, so we can say some things about the smoke. Now, in Feynman's view of quantum mechanics, the "sum-over-histories approach" as we call it, the dragon gets from here to there by wriggling through everywhere in between. The dragon is actually everywhere in the smoke. And this has a number of amazing consequences that we followed. For example, it seems that virtual dragons stretch invisibly, concealed altogether by the smoke between particle and particle throughout the universe, carrying forces between them. That's how the forces act between elementary particles. And even in places where space appears empty, it really isn't. It's like one of those old maps where the blank places have the inscription "here there be dragons." Even when space appears to be empty, the quantum vacuum is still alive with zero-point energy, with the stirrings of the quantum dragon.

And then there's quantum information. Quantum information reminds us once again of Wheeler's Great Smoky Dragon, for it cannot be pinned down, it cannot be copied. But the dragon of quantum information can be tamed. We can train the dragon to do our bidding. We can use the dragon to help send secret messages that no eavesdropper can penetrate, because no eavesdropper can penetrate the smoke of the Great Smoky Dragon. And we found that dragons carry their messages in strange ways, even snaking backward in time—although we can't quite catch them snaking backward in time, but it seems that they're doing that. And we also found out that we can educate the dragons considerably. In a quantum computer, the dragon can be persuaded to solve extremely hard math problems, and to do it very, very rapidly, completely inside that veil of smoke.

But entanglement, I think, is the most dragonish aspect of quantum mechanics. Entanglement is a relationship between quantum particles that is so exclusive, so private, that it cannot be shared with others. So it turns out that our Great Smoky Dragons are monogamous.

Now, the Great Smoky Dragon is really a Copenhagen picture of quantum mechanics, and that's really no surprise, because Niels Bohr was John Wheeler's mentor. And I guess it's also no surprise that I find the picture of the Great Smoky Dragon so compelling, because Wheeler was my own teacher, my own mentor in the ways of the dragon.

So here's a picture of me with the Great Smoky Dragon. This is actually a print in a Chinese restaurant near my home. I like this print especially because an actual quantum mechanics discovery was made right there. It was a problem in quantum information theory that we had been working on for years, and one day, at lunch, my friend and collaborator Mike Westmoreland found the last piece of the puzzle, about 2 yards away from this picture of the Great Smoky Dragon; so I find this picture doubly inspiring. They say that Chinese dragons are especially beneficent.

All right. In Copenhagen terms, the tail and head are the places where the dragon emerges into the macroscopic realm, the realm of classical physics, the world—the only world that we can unambiguously call real. And it's the smoky in-between where we have the indescribable quantum realm.

But of course, other interpretations of quantum mechanics are going to deal with the dragon in other ways. The hidden-variables interpretation says, yes, the dragon does have a definite shape. On the other hand, the shape of the dragon is exceedingly strange because parts of the world that seem far apart are actually close together on the dragon, influencing each other, because in the hidden-variables interpretation, distant parts of the universe have inseparable connections, inseparable influences. In the many-worlds interpretation, the dragon has no tail, the dragon has no head; everything is inside the smoke, including us. When we think we see a tail or a head, we are actually only seeing a tiny part of the whole dragon, which encompasses every possible quantum world.

Now, in my view, none of these make the quantum dragon any less mysterious, because the dragon's mystery is the one certain and inescapable aspect it has.

So, we have reached the end of the course, our journey into quantum mechanics. There is much that we have not explored. There is much still to learn. Indeed, I have to tell you, there is much still to be discovered about the quantum realm. I hope you found this journey as exciting, surprising, challenging, mind stretching, and wonderful as I have, and as I do.

Timeline

5th century B.C. .... Democritus proposes that all matter is composed of tiny, indivisible atoms.

4th century B.C. .... Aristotle develops a sophisticated theory of physics in which matter is continuous and infinitely divisible.

1678.. Christiaan Huygens writes his *Treatise on Light*, exploring the wave theory. (The book is eventually published in 1690.)

1687.. Isaac Newton publishes his *Principia Mathematica Naturalis Philosophiae* (*Mathematical Principles of Natural Philosophy*), establishing the basic laws of classical mechanics.

1704.. Isaac Newton publishes his *Opticks*, exploring the corpuscular theory of light.

1803.. John Dalton proposes the laws of chemical combination can be explained by assuming each element is made of its own type of atom; Thomas Young publishes the results of his 2-slit experiment, establishing the wave character of light and measuring its wavelength.

1862.. James Clerk Maxwell shows that light is an electromagnetic

wave, a traveling disturbance in
electric and magnetic fields.

1866.. Maxwell develops the "kinetic theory"
of gases, based on the idea that gases
are composed of huge numbers
of tiny molecules; a decade later,
Ludwig Boltzmann independently
duplicates Maxwell's work and
considerably extends the theory.

1887.. The photoelectric effect is
discovered by Heinrich Hertz.

1900.. William Thomson, Lord Kelvin,
delivers a lecture at the Royal
Institution noting "two dark clouds"
over the classical theory of heat
and radiation: the Michelson-
Morley experiment and blackbody
radiation; Max Planck introduces the
quantum hypothesis to explain the
properties of blackbody radiation.

1905.. Albert Einstein elaborates the
quantum hypothesis and explains
the photoelectric effect.

1907.. Einstein applies the quantum hypothesis
to the vibration of atoms in a solid,
explaining the anomalously low
heat capacity of some materials.

1911.. Ernest Rutherford shows that the atom
consists of a massive central nucleus
surrounded by orbiting electrons;
discovery of superconductivity.

1913... Niels Bohr publishes his quantum theory of atomic structure.

1922... Otto Stern and Walter Gerlach do the first experiment showing that atomic spins can only have discrete values.

1924... Louis de Broglie proposes, in his doctoral thesis, that wave-particle duality applies to matter as well as to light (a few years later, this was confirmed in diffraction experiments with electrons); Satyendra Bose develops the quantum statistical theory of photons, which Einstein later extends to other particles ("bosons"); Wolfgang Pauli proposes the exclusion principle for electrons in an atom.

1925... Werner Heisenberg develops his version of quantum mechanics, sometimes called "matrix mechanics."

1926... Erwin Schrödinger develops his version of quantum mechanics, called "wave mechanics," based on de Broglie's matter waves (this is later shown to be exactly equivalent to Heisenberg's matrix mechanics); Max Born proposes his rule for interpreting Schrödinger's waves as probability amplitudes; Enrico Fermi and Paul Dirac develop the quantum statistical theory of particles that obey the exclusion principle ("fermions").

1927..Heisenberg proposes the uncertainty
principle; Bohr proposes the principle
of complementarity, the basis for
the Copenhagen interpretation; the
Bohr-Einstein debate begins with
vigorous discussions at the Fifth Solvay
Conference on Physics in Belgium.

1930..The Bohr-Einstein debate ends its
first phase during further vigorous
discussions at the Sixth Solvay
Conference on Physics; after this
date, Einstein no longer argues that
quantum mechanics is inconsistent, but
he still believes it to be incomplete.

1935..Einstein, Boris Podolsky, and Nathan
Rosen draw attention to quantum
entanglement (a term coined by
Schrödinger in the same year) and
argue that quantum mechanics must
be incomplete; Bohr responds, but
the question remains unresolved.

1937..Discovery of superfluidity in He II.

1942..Richard Feynman, in his doctoral thesis,
proposes the "sum-over-histories"
approach to quantum mechanics.

1948...................................... Feynman applies the "sum-over-histories idea to quantum electrodynamics, introducing Feynman diagrams; Hendrik Casimir shows that 2 metal plates must attract one another due to their effect on the quantum vacuum; Claude Shannon develops (classical) information theory.

1952...................................... David Bohm proposes the hidden-variables interpretation of quantum mechanics.

1957...................................... Hugh Everett III proposes the many-worlds interpretation of quantum mechanics.

1960...................................... Invention of the laser.

1964...................................... John Bell proves that no local hidden-variable theory can account for quantum entanglement.

1978...................................... John Wheeler proposes his delayed-choice experiment.

1982...................................... The quantum no-cloning theorem is proved by William Wootters and Wojciech Zurek and independently by Dennis Dieks.

1984...................................... Charles Bennett and Gilles Brassard propose quantum key distribution, the beginning of quantum cryptography.

1992.. Bennett and Stephen Wiesner invent
dense coding, in which 1 ebit and
1 qubit can be used to transmit 2
classical bits of information; David
Deutsch and Richard Jozsa show that
a quantum computer could solve a
particular mathematical problem much
faster than any classical computer.

1993.. A collaboration of quantum physicists
(including Bennett, Brassard, Jozsa,
and Wootters) invents quantum
teleportation, in which 1 ebit and 2
classical bits can be used to transmit
a qubit; Avshalom Elitzur and
Lev Vaidman devise their bomb-
testing thought experiment.

1994.. Peter Shor shows that a quantum
computer could factor a large
integer much faster than any
classical computer.

1995.. First Bose-Einstein condensate
is created in the laboratory.

1996.. Lov Grover shows that a quantum
computer could solve the inverse
phonebook problem faster than
any classical computer.

1998.. The expansion of the cosmos is
discovered to be accelerating due to
an unknown "dark energy," possibly
related to quantum vacuum energy.

Glossary

absorption: A process in which a photon deposits its energy in matter and is destroyed.

amplitudes: The numerical coefficients in a superposition. If the amplitude is a, then the probability of finding that result in a measurement is $|a|^2$.

angular momentum: A measure of how much rotational motion is present in a system, analogous to momentum.

antiparticles: Particles that have the same mass but otherwise opposite properties to "ordinary" particles. Every type of particle has an antiparticle (although photons are their own antiparticles).

antisymmetric: The mathematical property of the quantum state of fermions, which pick up a negative sign when 2 identical particles are swapped.

atom: To Greek philosophers, a tiny and indivisible particle out of which all matter is made. In modern usage, atoms are the basic constituents of chemical elements, but they are in turn made up of smaller particles, including protons, neutrons, and electrons.

basis: A set of quantum states corresponding to the various possible outcomes of a measurement on a quantum system. Since there are many possible complementary measurements, there are many possible basis sets for that system.

beam splitter: *See* **half-silvered mirror**.

Bell's inequality: A mathematical relation that holds true in any local hidden variable theory but may be violated in quantum mechanics.

bit: The basic unit of classical information, defined as the information carried by a single binary digit (0 or 1).

blackbody radiation: The electromagnetic radiation emitted by a hot, absorbing object called a "blackbody." All blackbodies at a given temperature emit radiation with the same characteristics.

Bohr model: The atomic model proposed by Niels Bohr in 1913 in which electrons can only move in discrete orbits around the nucleus. When light is absorbed or emitted, the electron "jumps" from one orbit to another.

Born rule: The rule introduced by Max Born to interpret quantum waves. The intensity of the wave, which is the square of the absolute value of the amplitude, gives the probability of finding the particle.

Bose-Einstein condensate: A low-density cloud of atoms extremely close to absolute zero, so that all of the atoms are found in the same quantum state. Though this was predicted by Einstein in the 1920s, it was not created in the lab until 1995.

bosons: Identical quantum particles such as photons, helium atoms, etc., whose states do not change when the particles are swapped. Bosons have a tendency to be in the same state.

branch: In the many-worlds interpretation, one part of the superposition state of the whole universe—in effect, one "world."

Casimir effect: The weak attraction between metal plates, predicted by Hendrik Casimir in 1948 and later observed in the lab. The force is due to the plates' effect on the quantum vacuum.

ciphertext: In cryptography, the representation of the message that is actually transmitted. Generally, an eavesdropper only has access to the ciphertext and wishes to determine the plaintext. *See also* **key**.

classical information: The familiar type of information contained in text, audio, video, or data messages, measured in bits and described by Shannon's information theory.

classical mechanics: The theory of mechanics based on Newton's laws of motion.

classical physics: A general term that includes classical mechanics, thermodynamics, and electromagnetism. Classical physics prevailed before 1900.

code: Any way of representing information. Specifically, a code is an association of a particular message with a particular representation—representing "no" with "0," for example. In cryptography, a code may be used to conceal the meaning of the message.

coherent light: Light of a single wavelength and direction.

complementarity: The principle that different observations are incompatible. Thus we cannot design an experiment that measures both a particle's position and its momentum. Complementary quantities cannot both have exact values at the same time.

continuous: Having a whole connected range of values. The real numbers are continuous; between any 2 different real numbers there is an infinite range of intermediate values.

Cooper pairs: Bound pairs of electrons in a low-temperature metal. Although electrons themselves are fermions, Cooper pairs are bosons.

Copenhagen interpretation: The standard interpretation of quantum mechanics developed by Bohr and others, based on the principle of complementarity. In this interpretation, we cannot ascribe a definite meaning to quantum events until a measurement is made and the result is amplified to the macroscopic realm.

cosmic inflation: A brief period of extremely rapid expansion early in the history of the universe, likely driven by quantum vacuum energy.

cryptanalysis: The effort to "break" a secret code by mathematical analysis.

cryptography: The science of maintaining the privacy and integrity of information.

dark energy: A kind of unseen energy, nature unknown, that drives the accelerating expansion of the universe. One theory is that dark energy is the energy of the quantum vacuum.

de Broglie wave: A wave associated with a particle such as an electron, in accordance with the proposal of Louis de Broglie.

delayed-choice experiment: A thought experiment proposed by John Wheeler in which the decision between complementary measurements is made after the experiment is almost completed.

determinism: The belief that future events are completely determined by the present state of the universe—for example, by the exact positions and momenta of all the particles in the world. In this view, "randomness" is simply due to the practical inability to know the present and calculate the future in sufficient detail; in fact, nothing can be truly "random."

Deutsch-Jozsa problem: The problem of determining whether a binary function is "balanced" or "constant." Deutsch and Jozsa determined that a quantum computer can answer this question much faster than any ordinary computer.

diffraction: The spreading of waves that pass through a single opening in a barrier.

discrete: Having only disconnected values. The whole numbers are discrete because they are separated from each other; for example, there is no whole number between 2 and 3. (The opposite of continuous.)

distinguishable: Possible to tell apart, at least in principle, by some measurement. Quantum particles of different types (a proton and a neutron, say) are distinguishable. (The opposite of identical.)

eavesdropper: A person who tries to intercept private information without authorization.

ebit: The basic unit of quantum entanglement, defined as a pair of entangled qubits. As an example, 2 spins in a total spin 0 state form an ebit.

electromagnetic wave: A traveling disturbance in the electromagnetic field. Light is an electromagnetic wave; other examples with other wavelengths include radio waves, infrared radiation, ultraviolet radiation, X-rays, and gamma rays.

electromagnetism: The branch of physics that deals with the behavior of electric and magnetic fields.

electron: A low-mass, negatively charged particle that orbits the nucleus of an atom.

Elitzur-Vaidman bomb-testing problem: A thought experiment proposed by Avshalom Elitzur and Lev Vaidman in 1993, showing the surprising features of quantum interference.

entanglement: The correlation of 2 distinct quantum systems. Einstein drew attention to the strange features of entanglement, and Bell used those properties to prove that quantum mechanics is inconsistent with local hidden variable theories.

EPR argument: The argument made by Einstein, Podolsky, and Rosen in 1935 that the properties of quantum entanglement imply quantum mechanics must be an incomplete description of nature. The EPR argument is based on a "criterion of reality" that was later criticized by Bohr.

excited state: A state of a quantum system, such as an atom, that has a greater energy than the ground state.

exclusion principle: The physical principle, first discovered by Pauli for electrons, that no 2 identical fermions can be in exactly the same quantum state.

fermions: Identical quantum particles such as electrons, protons, etc., whose state acquires a negative sign when the particles are swapped. Fermions obey the exclusion principle, so that no 2 identical fermions can be in the same state.

Feynman diagram: A cartoonlike representation of a process in QED involving electrons and photons. (More general diagrams arise in more general particle theories.)

frequency: The number of wave cycles per second that pass a fixed point in space.

ground state: The state of lowest energy of a quantum system such as an atom. (The opposite of excited state.)

half-silvered mirror: A partially reflecting mirror, also known as a beam splitter. A light beam shining on a half-silvered mirror is divided into a reflected and transmitted beam, each of which has half of the original intensity.

heat capacity: The amount of heat energy necessary to increase the temperature of a material by 1°C. The anomalously low heat capacity of some solids was first explained by Einstein.

hidden variables: The conjectured unknown factors that might underlie quantum mechanics and predetermine the outcomes of measurements. Also, the assumption that such variables exist.

hidden-variables interpretation: The alternate interpretation of quantum mechanics proposed by David Bohm. Quantum mechanics is thought to be an incomplete description of nature. There are additional, hidden variables that make nature deterministic and that function in a highly nonlocal way.

identical: Impossible to tell apart by any conceivable measurement. Quantum particles of the same type (2 electrons, say) are identical. (The opposite of distinguishable.)

information theory: The mathematical science of communication developed by Claude Shannon in 1948. This theory, however, did not take quantum mechanics into account.

informationally isolated: Leaving no "footprints" behind to record what happened. A photon in an interferometer is informationally isolated, so that it is impossible to say which beam it followed. Quantum interference effects only appear in systems that are informationally isolated.

interference: The phenomenon in which 2 or more waves can reinforce each other (constructive interference) or cancel each other out (destructive interference).

interferometer: An optical apparatus in which 2 or more light beams are split, redirected, and combined by beam splitters, demonstrating interference effects.

inverse phonebook problem: Given only an alphabetical phonebook, the problem of finding a name associated with a given phone number. Lov Grover showed that this could be done more efficiently on a quantum computer.

ket: A mathematical object describing a quantum state. Symbolically, the ket is written this way: $\left| state \right\rangle$, where "*state*" is just a label designating the state.

key: In cryptography, the mathematical recipe for transforming plaintext into ciphertext and vice versa.

key distribution: In cryptography, the problem of distributing secret keys to users while keeping them secret from any eavesdropper. There is no perfect solution to this in classical cryptography.

kinetic energy: For a particle of mass m moving with velocity v, the kinetic energy is $K = \frac{1}{2}mv^2$.

laser: A device that uses stimulated emission to produce coherent light.

local hidden variable theory: A hypothetical type of theory studied by Bell. In this sort of theory, the quantum realm is assumed to be governed by hidden variables that act in a local way. Bell showed that such theories are incompatible with quantum entanglement.

locality: The assumption that what happens to a particle depends only on its own variables and its immediate circumstances, not what is happening to other particles far away.

Mach-Zehnder interferometer: A particular type of interferometer including just 2 beams. We use this as our basic thought experiment for understanding quantum mechanics.

macroscopic: A generic term for phenomena and objects at the large scale. Everything that we can directly perceive may be regarded as macroscopic.

many-worlds interpretation: The alternate interpretation of quantum mechanics proposed by Hugh Everett III. Macroscopic systems, including observers themselves, are considered to be part of the quantum system. Measurement creates entanglement between system and observer, and all measurement outcomes (all "worlds") are present in various branches of the state of the universe.

mechanics: The branch of physics that deals with force and motion.

microscopic: A generic term for phenomena and objects at the small scale. When we use this term in connection with quantum physics, we mean atomic-scale phenomena and objects (which are in fact too small to see under an ordinary microscope).

momentum: For a particle of mass m moving with velocity v, the momentum (usually denoted p) is $p = mv$.

Moore's law: An observation by Gordon Moore that computer power doubles about every 2 years. This has held true for 4 decades and counting.

neutron: A massive, uncharged particle found in the atomic nucleus.

one-time pad: A type of unbreakable secret code that only uses its key once. If an eavesdropper does not have the key, the message is perfectly secure. If the key is used more than once, however, an eavesdropper may be able to break the code.

optical pumping: In a laser, adding energy to a collection of atoms to produce a population inversion.

Pauli exclusion principle: *See* **exclusion principle**.

photoelectric effect: The emission of electrons from a polished metal surface that is exposed to light of a sufficiently high frequency. Einstein explained this effect using quantum ideas in 1905.

photon: A light quantum; the basic particle of light.

plaintext: In cryptography, the original message to be protected by a secret code. *See also* **key** and **ciphertext**.

Planck-de Broglie relations: Mathematical relations (involving Planck's constant h) between wave and particle properties. The particle energy E is connected to the wave frequency f by $E = hf$. The particle momentum p is connected to the wavelength λ by $p = h/\lambda$.

Planck's constant: A fundamental constant of nature, usually denoted h, with a value of 6.63×10^{-34} J·sec. The tiny value of h tells us that quantum effects are most important only at the microscopic scale and that macroscopic physics appears classical.

population inversion: A situation in a laser in which there are more excited atoms than atoms in the ground state.

positrons: The antiparticles of electrons, having the same mass but opposite electric charge. Positrons and electrons can be created or annihilated in pairs.

potential energy: A particle subject to a force has energy due to its position in space. For a simple pendulum, for instance, the potential energy is lowest at the low point of the pendulum and higher at either end of its swing. Kinetic plus potential energy will remain constant as the pendulum swings.

product state: A quantum state of a pair of particles in which each particle has its own definite quantum state. Such particles are completely independent. Not all states are product states, however. If the pair is not in a product state, it is said to have quantum entanglement.

proton: A massive, positively charged particle found in the atomic nucleus.

QED: Quantum electrodynamics, the highly precise theory of electron-photon interactions developed in the 1940s by Richard Feynman and others.

quantum cloning: A hypothetical process, impossible in the real world, by which an exact duplicate is made of the quantum state of a particle.

quantum computing: The use of quantum particles to process information.

quantum electrodynamics: *See* **QED**.

quantum factoring: A superefficient method of finding the factors of large numbers by using a quantum computer. Discovered by Peter Shor in 1994.

quantum hypothesis: Max Planck's radical idea, proposed in 1900, that a hot object only emits or absorbs light energy in discrete units, or quanta. The energy of 1 quantum of light is $E = hf$, where h is Planck's constant and f is the light frequency.

quantum information: The distinctive kind of information that is carried by quantum particles. Quantum information is measured in qubits.

quantum mechanics: The theory of mechanics developed between 1900 and 1930 that replaced classical mechanics based on Newton's laws.

quantum no-cloning theorem: The mathematical proof by Wootters, Zurek, and Dieks that it is impossible to perfectly duplicate the state of a quantum particle.

quantum physics: A general term for the physics of the microscopic world.

quantum theory: A more general term for quantum mechanics and related theories.

qubit: The basic unit of quantum information, defined as the information carried by a binary quantum system such as a spin-$\frac{1}{2}$ particle.

real photon: In quantum electrodynamics, a photon in a Feynman diagram that connects to the "outside world" and thus is subject to measurement. The opposite of virtual photon.

Schrödinger equation: The equation discovered by Erwin Schrödinger that controls how the quantum wave function behaves over time.

simple state: *See* **product state**.

snowflake principle: Heuristic principle that no 2 macroscopic objects are ever exactly the same in every detail.

spin: The internal angular momentum of a quantum particle, such as an electron. The spin of a particle can only have values of 0, $\frac{1}{2}$, 1, $\frac{3}{2}$, 2, etc. (in units of $h/2\pi$).

spin component: The total amount of spin angular momentum parallel to a particular axis in space. For a quantum spin-$\frac{1}{2}$ particle, any component of spin can only have the values $+\frac{1}{2}$ or $-\frac{1}{2}$ (in units of $h/2\pi$).

spin-statistics connection: The physical principle that particles with spin 0, 1, 2, and so on must be bosons, while those with spin $\frac{1}{2}$, $\frac{3}{2}$, and so on must be fermions.

spontaneous emission: A process in which matter emits a photon, even without the presence of other photons.

state: A physical situation for a quantum system, described by a ket.

Stern-Gerlach apparatus: A laboratory device in which a particle with spin is passed through an inhomogeneous magnetic field. This permits us to measure the particle's spin along any 1 axis we choose (but not along all axes at the same time).

stimulated emission: A process in which matter emits a photon with the same wavelength and direction as some already existing photons. The more photons are present, the more likely this process becomes.

sum-over-histories: An approach to quantum mechanics developed by Richard Feynman. An electron going from here to there takes all possible paths, each one contributing its own amplitude to the process. The total amplitude gives the total probability for the trip.

superconductivity: The phenomenon of zero electrical resistance in some materials at very low temperatures. Such materials are called superconductors. Superconductivity is due to the superfluid-like properties of Cooper pairs of electrons in the material.

superfluid: A liquid at extremely low temperatures that has many surprising properties, including zero viscosity.

superposition: A combination of basis states, written: $a|state\ 1\rangle + b|state\ 2\rangle + \cdots$.

superstring theory: A contemporary speculative theory of elementary particles and their interactions, developed within the general framework of quantum theory.

symmetric: The mathematical property of the quantum state of bosons, which is unchanged when 2 identical particles are swapped.

system: Any part of the quantum world that we wish to consider. A system may include 1 or more particles.

thermodynamics: The branch of physics that deals with heat and energy transformations.

thought experiment: A highly idealized experiment that is used to illustrate physical principles.

ultraviolet catastrophe: A prediction of classical physics that a blackbody should emit more and more intensely at higher and higher frequencies. This prediction is not correct.

uncertainty principle: The principle discovered by Heisenberg in 1927 that sets a fundamental trade-off between how precisely a particle's position and momentum may be defined. This is sometimes expressed by the relation $\Delta x \Delta p \geq h$. A variation of the principle gives a trade-off between uncertainties in energy and time.

vacuum: The physical situation in which no particles are present. In quantum theory, the vacuum actually contains considerable energy.

Van der Waals force: The "stickiness" between atoms and molecules that causes them to condense into liquids and solids at low temperatures.

vertex: A point in a Feynman diagram representing a photon interacting with an electron or a positron.

virtual photons: In QED, an internal photon in a Feynman diagram. Such photons can never be directly observed. The energy in a virtual photon is "borrowed," subject to the terms of the uncertainty principle.

wave: A periodic disturbance, such as sound. Waves may either be traveling (like a moving sound wave) or standing (like the vibrations of a wire with fixed ends).

wave function: The mathematical function, usually denoted Ψ, that describes how a quantum wave depends on space and time.

wavelength: The distance between adjacent crests in a wave.

wave-particle duality: The idea that light can show wave and particle characteristics in different experiments. Later, this idea was extended to matter as well.

zero-point energy: The energy present in any quantum system, even in its ground state, due to the uncertainty principle.

zero total spin state: A special state of a pair of spin-$\frac{1}{2}$ particles. If the same spin component is measured on the 2 particles, opposite results are always obtained. This state is useful for studying the properties of quantum entanglement.

Biographical Notes

Aristotle (384–322 B.C.): Greek philosopher and polymath; the most notable pupil of Plato. Aristotle had one of the widest-ranging intellects in human history. His works on logic, metaphysics, science, medicine, ethics, and law established systems of thought that remain influential to this day. Aristotle believed that matter comprises 5 basic elements (earth, air, fire, water, and a fifth element found in the heavens). However, he viewed these as continuous substances, not discrete atoms.

Babbage, Charles (1791–1871): English mathematician and engineer. Babbage, the son of a banker, studied mathematics at Cambridge. He spent his subsequent career trying to create mechanical calculating "engines" of increasing complexity. His designs followed principles closely resembling those of modern electronic computers, but the mechanical technology of 19th-century England was not advanced enough to realize his most ambitious designs. His Difference Engine, abandoned, was designed to compute the values of complex mathematical functions. His more complex Analytical Engine would have been a computer of a much more general and powerful sort. With different "programs" (encoded on punch cards), the Analytical Engine would have been capable of any sort of calculation at all. None of Babbage's engines were completed during his lifetime, but a working model of Difference Engine No. 2 (designed in 1849) was finally constructed in 2002.

Bardeen, John (1908–1991): American physicist and one of the few individuals in history to win two Nobel Prizes, one in 1956 and the other in 1972. The first was with W. Shockley and W. Brattain for the discovery of the transistor, which revolutionized electronics. The second was with Leon Cooper and John Robert Schrieffer for their "BCS" theory of superconductivity, a phenomenon that had been first observed as long ago as 1911. Bardeen spent the early part of his career at Bell Labs, then moved to the University of Illinois.

Bell, John (1928–1990): British physicist. Although he was trained and worked as a particle physicist, spending most of his career at the European particle physics lab CERN in Geneva, Bell found time to think deeply about the foundations of quantum theory. Inspired by the work of David Bohm on hidden variables, he did a careful reanalysis of the argument of Einstein, Podolsky, and Rosen. In 1964 he proved his remarkable theorem, stating that no mechanism of local hidden variables could ever reproduce the statistical correlations between entangled quantum systems. The exact conclusion to be drawn from this has been a subject of debate ever since; Bell's own view seems to have been that the concept of locality could not be maintained in quantum theory.

Bennett, Charles (b. 1943): American physicist and computer scientist. Bennett has been among the most profound thinkers about the physical nature of information and computation. In the 1970s, he showed that any computation can be done by a computer that operates in a thermodynamically reversible way—that is, with arbitrarily little "waste heat." With Gilles Brassard, he developed the BB84 scheme for quantum key distribution, essentially founding quantum cryptography. Later, in his office at IBM, he built the first working demonstration of the BB84 method. Bennett helped to discover quantum teleportation, dense coding, entanglement "distillation," and a host of other basic ideas in quantum information theory. Bennett is known for his creativity, his collegiality, his ability to communicate (one colleague admiringly called him a "troubadour") and his unfailing sense of humor. He has spent his career at IBM Research.

Bohm, David (1917–1992): American-born physicist who later became a British subject. After service on the Manhattan Project during World War II, Bohm was called upon to testify before the House Un-American Activities Committee. He declined, invoking the Fifth Amendment, leading to his suspension from the faculty of Princeton University. Bohm left the United States and eventually settled in England. Meanwhile, Bohm did important research on the basic concepts of quantum theory. He proved that a hidden-variables theory could in principle reproduce the observed phenomena of quantum mechanics. With Yakir Aharonov, Bohm demonstrated that a quantum particle can respond to a magnetic field even if the particle has zero probability of being found in the region of the field. This Aharonov-Bohm effect is one of the great insights of modern mathematical physics and has led to a deeper understanding of so-called gauge fields. In his writings, Bohm was unafraid to engage deep philosophical questions about the nature of the world and the human condition. Bohm's work on hidden variables in quantum theory, together with his classic discussion of the EPR argument, later inspired John Bell.

Bohr, Niels (1885–1962): Danish physicist and one of the fathers of quantum mechanics. After receiving his doctorate in Denmark, Bohr spent several years in England, where he worked for Ernest Rutherford. Bohr applied quantum ideas to atomic structure, explaining atomic spectra by the discrete orbits allowed for the electron in the atom. After returning to Denmark, he established the Institute for Theoretical Physics in Copenhagen. This became the center of work on the new quantum physics, and young physicists from all over Europe and America studied and worked there. While others such as Heisenberg and Schrödinger created the mathematical theory of quantum mechanics, Bohr carefully laid its conceptual foundations. His principle of complementarity, the foundation of the so-called Copenhagen interpretation of quantum mechanics, allowed physicists to use the strange new concepts without contradictions. His fierce but friendly debate with Einstein about the nature and meaning of quantum physics explored many of the puzzles of the quantum realm. He was awarded a Nobel Prize in 1922. In 1939, on the eve of World War II, Bohr and John Wheeler developed the liquid-drop model of the atomic nucleus, the basis for the theory of nuclear fission. Bohr spent the first part of the war in occupied Copenhagen, but then, forced to make a daring escape because of his Jewish ancestry, he participated in the U.S. Manhattan Project to develop the nuclear bomb. After the war, he returned to Denmark. Bohr's ideas and personality were tremendously influential among theoretical physicists. He was always ready to consider radical new thinking; to one colleague, he said, "Your theory is crazy, but it's not crazy enough to be true."

Boltzmann, Ludwig (1844–1906): Brilliant but troubled Austrian physicist, most notable for his work in connecting atomic theory to macroscopic physics. Boltzmann showed how very simple assumptions about the chaotic world of atoms and molecules lead to detailed predictions about the laws of gas behavior, together with many other phenomena. He was often involved in controversy and left the University of Vienna for some years due to a dispute with his fellow professor, Ernst Mach. Boltzmann suffered from bouts of severe depression, however, and a few years after his return to Vienna he committed suicide. On his tombstone in Vienna is inscribed his greatest discovery, a mathematical relation between the thermodynamic concept of entropy and the statistics of the microscopic world.

Born, Max (1882–1970): German physicist who later became a British subject and who contributed decisively to the development of quantum theory. Born assisted Heisenberg in developing the mathematics of his version of quantum mechanics. He also provided a key insight for the interpretation of the waves in de Broglie and Schrödinger's version: the Born rule, which states that the intensity of the wave at a point determines the probability of finding a particle there. Born taught for many years at the University of Göttingen, and among his students and postdoctoral assistants are numbered many of the most famous names in 20th-century physics. He received a Nobel Prize in 1954.

Bose, Satyendra (1894–1974): Indian physicist most notable for the discovery, in 1922, of the statistical laws governing one type of identical particle. Bose made his discovery in the middle of a lecture at the University of Dakha, in which he was attempting to demonstrate that classical statistical physics could not explain Planck's blackbody radiation law. During the lecture he made a "mistake" that unexpectedly led to the correct answer. Bose soon realized that he had stumbled on a new insight into the quantum world. Bose sent his paper to Einstein, who recognized it as an important contribution, saw to its publication, and worked to develop its ideas further. Bose became an important figure in the growth of science in India.

Brassard, Gilles (b. 1955): Canadian computer scientist at the University of Montreal. Brassard started out studying the mathematics of cryptography, but his collaboration with Charles Bennett on the BB84 protocol in quantum cryptography soon made him into a quantum physicist. He helped to discover quantum teleportation—indeed, it was invented at a workshop that he hosted at the University of Montreal. Brassard has also made fundamental contributions to entanglement "distillation" and the theory of quantum computing.

Casimir, Hendrik (1909–2000): Dutch physicist who contributed to both low-temperature physics and quantum electrodynamics. Casimir studied with the great Paul Ehrenfest, then worked with Bohr in Copenhagen and Pauli in Zurich. Although he was an industrial scientist, directing the Philips Research Laboratories in the Netherlands, he made numerous contributions to pure research. In 1948 he predicted the phenomenon that later bore his name (the Casimir effect), in which 2 metal plates are attracted to each other due to their modification of the quantum vacuum.

Cooper, Leon (b. 1930): American physicist who helped discover the mechanism of superconductivity and received a Nobel Prize in 1972. Cooper proposed that electrons in a superconductor join up in pairs, later called "Cooper pairs," that behave as bosons in a superfluid. This allows the material to conduct electricity without resistance. Cooper is a faculty member at Brown University, where he has most recently done research in theoretical neuroscience.

Dalton, John (1766–1844): English chemist and the father of modern atomic theory. After studying the known facts of chemical composition, Dalton proposed in 1803 that elements are made up of atoms of a uniform mass, that the atoms of different elements have different masses, and that these atoms combine in definite ways to create chemical compounds. The atoms themselves are neither created nor destroyed in a chemical process but simply change their combinations. This idea revolutionized chemistry and shed new light on the behavior of gases.

de Broglie, Louis (1892–1987): French physicist who, in one of the most influential doctoral dissertations in history, proposed that electrons and other quantum particles must have wave characteristics. De Broglie's work "closed the circle" of quantum ideas and in short order became the basis for the wave mechanics of Schrödinger. De Broglie, who was a member of the French nobility, received a Nobel Prize in 1929 and became one of the most eminent men in European science after World War II.

Democritus (c. 460–370 B.C.): Greek natural philosopher and one of the originators of "atomism," the idea that everything in the world is made of tiny, indivisible units. Democritus's theory is summarized in a famous quotation: "By convention there is sweet, by convention there is bitter, by convention hot and cold, by convention color; but in reality there are only atoms and the void."

Deutsch, David (b. 1953): Israeli-English physicist and one of the most creative and eccentric thinkers in contemporary quantum theory. Long a proponent of Everett's many-worlds interpretation of quantum mechanics, Deutsch became interested in the idea of a quantum computer. An intelligent quantum computer, he reasoned, could be a type of observer that was "aware" of the branching of the universe's quantum state. His development of the theory of quantum computing led to the discovery of the Deutsch-Jozsa problem, which in turn sparked widespread interest in the powers of quantum computers. Deutsch has also applied his combination of rigorous mathematics and powerful imagination to other topics, such as the quantum physics of time machines. Deutsch is affiliated with, but not a faculty member at, Oxford University. He is seldom seen outside of Oxford, but his ideas are closely followed by quantum physicists worldwide.

Dieks, Dennis (b. 20th century): Dutch philosopher of physics. Trained as a theoretical physicist, Dieks has spent his career studying the philosophical aspects of relativity and quantum physics. In 1982 he proved the quantum no-cloning theorem independently of William Wootters and Wojciech Zurek, using a different mathematical method. He is a member of the philosophy faculty at the University of Utrecht.

Dirac, Paul (1902–1984): English physicist who contributed deeply to the mathematical tools of quantum theory and received a Nobel Prize in 1933. As a graduate student at Cambridge University in the 1920s, Dirac seized upon the new theories of Heisenberg and Schrödinger, demonstrating their mathematical equivalence. The "ket" notation for quantum states used in our lectures was introduced by Dirac. In 1928 he proposed a new form of quantum theory compatible with Einstein's special theory of relativity, including a relativistic version of the Schrödinger equation later known as the Dirac equation. Consideration of this equation led Dirac to predict the existence of antiparticles. These were discovered only a few years later in studies of cosmic rays. Dirac laid the groundwork for the quantum theory of fields (including quantum electrodynamics) and was one of the first to analyze the statistical properties of identical particles—to mention only 2 of his remarkable contributions. For over 30 years he held Newton's old post as Lucasian Professor of Mathematics at Cambridge. Dirac's scientific work was guided by a passionate belief in the mathematical elegance of nature. He is buried in Florida, where he spent the last decade of his life, but his monument in Westminster Abbey is just a few steps from Newton's tomb.

Einstein, Albert (1879–1955): German physicist, later an American citizen, whose epoch-making contributions to physics during the early 20th century turned him into a public icon of a scientific genius. His fame was entirely deserved. In a series of brilliant papers in 1905, the young Einstein (then working as a patent clerk in Switzerland) made fundamental discoveries in statistical mechanics, established the special theory of relativity, and used Planck's quantum hypothesis to explain the photoelectric effect. More contributions followed, including his quantum explanation of the heat capacities of solids, many papers on the interaction of light with matter, and the statistical behavior of identical particles. Einstein's 1915 discovery of the general theory of relativity, which explains gravitation as the curvature of space and time, was as astonishing as it was profound. The confirmation of this theory came a few years later, just after World War I, when the deflection of starlight by the Sun's gravity was precisely measured. This was the event that catapulted Einstein to international celebrity. He received a Nobel Prize in 1921. Although Einstein was one of the pioneers of quantum theory, he later became its sharpest critic. His debates with Bohr at the 1927 and 1930 Solvay conferences were decisive turning points in the history of the subject. Einstein, a Jew, left Europe for America in 1932 and never returned. In 1935, Einstein, Podolsky, and Rosen argued that the phenomenon of quantum entanglement proved that quantum theory was an incomplete description of reality. (This argument, and Bohr's subtle reply, led John Bell to his remarkable work 3 decades later.) In later years, Einstein worked unsuccessfully to combine the known laws of physics into a "unified field theory." Einstein was never fully reconciled with quantum physics, never quite accepting that God "played dice with the Universe." In all of his scientific work, he was guided by the maxim, "The Lord God is subtle, but He is not malicious."

Everett, Hugh, III (1930–1982): American physicist. As a student of John Wheeler at Princeton in 1957, Everett developed the many-worlds interpretation of quantum mechanics. He saw this interpretation as a way to avoid the problems of the Copenhagen interpretation and give a solid framework for applying quantum theory to Einstein's general relativity (a problem still unsolved today). In the same Ph.D. thesis, Everett also pioneered the use of concepts from information theory in the analysis of quantum systems. Possibly discouraged by the cool reception his ideas received from most physicists, Everett switched fields and spent the rest of his career doing operations research for the U.S. defense establishment. His departure from physics research and his early death at age 51 deprived the world—this one, anyway—of a radical and creative thinker about the meaning of quantum theory.

Fermi, Enrico (1901–1954): Italian physicist, later an American citizen, who made brilliant contributions to both theoretical and experimental physics. In 1926, while still in Rome, Fermi helped to develop the statistical theory of identical particles such as electrons that obey the Pauli exclusion principle. Later he became even more famous for his remarkable experiments on neutron-induced nuclear transformation, for which he won the Nobel Prize in 1938 and in which he narrowly missed discovering nuclear fission. His groundbreaking theory of beta decay included Pauli's undiscovered "ghost" particle, which Fermi christened the "neutrino." After leaving fascist Italy and emigrating to the United States, Fermi worked on the Manhattan Project. His experimental reactor achieved the first sustained nuclear chain reaction in 1942.

Feynman, Richard (1918–1988): American physicist whose astounding scientific insight and quirky personality left an indelible stamp on 20th-century physics. As a graduate student of John Wheeler in 1942, Feynman developed his "sum-over-histories" approach to quantum mechanics. Like so many physicists, he worked on the Manhattan Project to develop the atomic bomb during World War II. Returning to theoretical pursuits after the war, he made decisive contributions to the development of quantum electrodynamics, introducing the remarkable Feynman diagrams to assist in calculations. He also made advances in the theory of superfluids and superconductors, in the theory of weak nuclear interactions, and in the quark model of nucleons, receiving a Nobel Prize in 1965. Feynman spent most of his career as a faculty member at Caltech, where he became a legend as a brilliant teacher. His 3-volume *Lectures on Physics* is standard equipment on any physicist's bookshelf. Feynman had the knack of seeing new possibilities in nature; both nanotechnology and quantum computing trace their origins in part to lectures given by Feynman. Many people first heard of Feynman during his work on the commission investigating the loss of the space shuttle *Challenger* in 1986; Feynman performed a dramatic demonstration using a clamp, a sample of material from the shuttle, and a glass of ice water that identified the root cause of the disaster. He was a remarkable raconteur, and his books of personal reminiscences gained a wide audience. It was said that Feynman's graduate students at Caltech learned 3 things from him: theoretical physics, safe-cracking (a talent Feynman had developed playing pranks on the security officers at Los Alamos during the war), and bongo drumming.

Grover, Lov (b. 1961): Indian-American computer scientist. Like Peter Shor, a fellow computer scientist at Bell Labs, Grover began moonlighting as a quantum physicist, studying the emerging field of quantum computing. In 1996 he discovered his quantum search algorithm, which would allow a quantum computer to "find a needle in a haystack" far more rapidly than any classical computer.

Heisenberg, Werner (1901–1976): German physicist and one of the creators of quantum mechanics. In 1924–1925, Heisenberg came to Copenhagen to work with Bohr on the new physics. There he discovered his own highly abstract version of quantum mechanics, which came to be called "matrix mechanics." Although the mathematics of the theory was very strange, it soon became clear that it gave a precise account of the strange behavior of the microscopic realm. The theory was at first seen as a competitor to Schrödinger's wave mechanics, until Paul Dirac showed that they were mathematically equivalent. Heisenberg also formulated the famous "uncertainty principle," which establishes limits on our ability to know about the microscopic world. Heisenberg later made fundamental contributions to quantum field theory, nuclear physics, and elementary particle physics. He received a Nobel Prize in 1932. During World War II, Heisenberg remained in Nazi Germany and directed part of the German nuclear program. This later led to considerable strain on his relationships with physicists from other countries, and his long friendship with Niels Bohr came to an end. After the war, Heisenberg wrote extensively about the philosophical ideas embedded in quantum theory.

Huygens, Christiaan (1629–1695): Dutch physicist and astronomer. As an astronomer, Huygens discovered Saturn's rings and its largest moon, Titan. As a mathematician, he contributed to the foundations of probability theory. As an inventor, he was responsible for several advances in the construction of accurate clocks. But it was as a physicist that he made his most notable contributions. Huygens was particularly interested in the nature of light, which he regarded as a wave phenomenon like sound. He introduced what is now called the "Huygens principle," which states that each point on a traveling wave front acts as a source for further waves. This principle allowed him to analyze the reflection and refraction of light based on his wave theory.

Jozsa, Richard (b. 20th century): British mathematician and physicist. After studying mathematical physics with the great Roger Penrose, Jozsa worked with David Deutsch on what came to be called the "Deutsch-Jozsa problem," the first-proposed mathematical problem that could be solved more efficiently by a quantum computer than by any classical one. He also helped to invent quantum teleportation. Jozsa is now a professor in the Department of Computer Science at the University of Bristol.

Maxwell, James Clerk (1831–1879): Scottish mathematician and physicist who made fundamental contributions to mechanics and electromagnetism. Maxwell applied Newtonian mechanics to the behavior of huge numbers of colliding molecules, deriving the statistical distribution of molecular speeds in a gas. He also derived many useful mathematical relations in the science of thermodynamics. By collecting together and analyzing the known laws of electromagnetism, Maxwell realized that the system was mathematically incomplete. When he supplied the missing pieces, he discovered that electromagnetic disturbances would travel through space in the form of polarized waves with a speed equal to that of light. He concluded that light is an electromagnetic wave, an idea that unified optics and electromagnetism, and his work indicated the possible existence of other related waves. The later discovery by H. Hertz of radio waves vindicated Maxwell's theory. Maxwell himself was a religious man, a guitar player, and the author of several amusing songs about physics and its study.

Newton, Isaac (1642–1727): English physicist and mathematician and without doubt the greatest scientific mind of his age. In his book *Mathematical Principles of Natural Philosophy* (1687), Newton established the science of mechanics based on universal laws of motion and gravitation. This work explained motions ranging from projectiles on Earth to the orbits of the planets, together with a host of other phenomena. Newton invented calculus, which he called "the method of fluxions," to deal with his new system of mechanics. Newtonian mechanics was the basis for physics for more than 2 centuries. Newton also made tremendous contributions to optics, including the invention of the reflecting telescope and the discovery that white light is a mixture of all colors. Newton's view, expounded in his book *Opticks* (1704), was that light was a stream of discrete corpuscles. In this he disagreed with the wave view of Huygens and others, but the matter was not settled experimentally for another century. In addition to his scientific pursuits, Newton commented on scripture, wrote about theology, and studied alchemy. Newton was a powerful and influential figure in the English science of his day and served as president of the Royal Society of London from 1701 until his death.

Pauli, Wolfgang (1900–1958): Austrian physicist, later an American citizen and a resident of Switzerland, and winner of a Nobel Prize in 1945; famous for his brilliant discoveries in theoretical physics and his sharp critique of shaky reasoning. Pauli developed his "exclusion principle" in 1924 to explain the structure of many-electron atoms. He was the first to use Heisenberg's quantum mechanics to explain atomic spectra, and he contributed a great deal to the theory of particle spin. He also proved the "spin-statistics" theorem, the connection between a particle's spin and its character as a boson or fermion. In 1929 he proposed that the mysteries of beta decay (one of the main types of radioactivity) could be explained by the existence of an almost-invisible "ghost particle," later called the neutrino by Fermi. (When the neutrino was finally discovered almost 30 years later, the discoverers sent a telegram congratulating Pauli. His reply: "Thanks for the message. Everything comes to him who knows how to wait.") Pauli was well known for his ready and caustic wit, and anecdotes about his various remarks are favorites among physicists. (Of one paper he said, "This isn't right. This isn't even wrong.")

Peres, Asher (1934–2005): Israeli physicist. After a perilous childhood during World War II hiding out in occupied France, Peres emigrated to Israel, where he studied theoretical physics at Technion under Nathan Rosen, one of the authors of the EPR paper. Peres went on to be a faculty member at Technion and to make many contributions to physics, especially to the foundations of quantum theory. He drew attention to the fundamental role that the concept of information plays in the theory and later was one of the inventors of quantum teleportation. He was once asked by a reporter, "Can you teleport only the body, or also the spirit?" He replied, "Only the spirit."

Planck, Max (1858–1947): German physicist and the originator of the quantum hypothesis; winner of a Nobel Prize in 1918. For most of his career, Planck was a professor at the University of Berlin. In the last years of the 19th century, he turned his attention to the problem of understanding the electromagnetic radiation emitted by hot bodies of all sorts. Since all black bodies, regardless of composition, emit radiation with the same characteristics, Planck recognized this as a problem of fundamental importance. His early work met with only partial success. Finally, in 1900 he adopted the quantum hypothesis as, in his words, "an act of despair." Though it involved a radical departure from previous ideas about energy, Planck's new theory accounted for blackbody radiation with great exactness. Planck observed the subsequent development of quantum theory with great interest. With a sad wisdom, he wrote, "A new scientific truth does not triumph by convincing its opponents and making them see the light, but rather because its opponents eventually die, and a new generation grows up that is familiar with it."

Rutherford, Ernest (1871–1937): New Zealand physicist and one of the great experimentalists in the history of science, he received a Nobel Prize in 1908. Though born in New Zealand, Rutherford spent most of his career in England. He identified the main kinds of radioactivity and discovered the law governing the rate of radioisotope decay. He supervised the scattering experiment of Hans Geiger and Ernest Marsden and correctly interpreted its results to construct the "solar system" model of the atom. Rutherford was the first researcher to produce an artificial transmutation of elements, using alpha particles to transform nitrogen into oxygen. Rutherford's students and assistants included many who won Nobel Prizes in their own right (including Niels Bohr). Rutherford had no false modesty about his remarkable accomplishments. When someone suggested that he had been lucky to ride "the crest of the wave" in discovering new physics, he answered, "Well, I made the wave, didn't I?" His untimely death in 1937 came when he was still at the height of his powers; just a few years earlier, his suggestion that the nucleus must contain a neutral particle had been confirmed by James Chadwick's discovery of the neutron.

Schrieffer, John Robert (b. 1931): American physicist who, as a graduate student at the University of Illinois, helped to formulate the theory of superconductivity; he received a Nobel Prize in 1972. Schrieffer figured out how to describe the flow of Cooper's electron pairs through a material. He holds posts as professor of physics at universities in both California and Florida.

Schrödinger, Erwin (1887–1961): Austrian physicist and one of the developers of quantum mechanics. Schrödinger's version, called "wave mechanics," was at first seen as a competitor to Heisenberg's wave mechanics, before Paul Dirac showed them to be mathematically equivalent. His basic equation, the Schrödinger equation, is one of the most fundamental relations of mathematical physics. Like so many of the physicists of Germany, Italy, and Austria, Schrödinger was obliged to leave in the early 1930s as the Nazis took power. He settled in Dublin, founding the Institute for Advanced Study at the university there and writing an influential book, *What is Life?*, about the physical nature of biological systems. This book inspired physicist Francis Crick to switch fields and become one of the discoverers of the structure of DNA. Schrödinger returned to Vienna for the last few years of his life. Schrödinger received a Nobel Prize in 1933, but in the popular mind he is most strongly linked to his 1935 thought experiment in which a cat enters a quantum superposition of being alive and dead. He wrote, "The [quantum state] of the entire system would express this by having in it the living and the dead cat (pardon the expression) mixed or smeared out in equal parts." (In his defense, one should note that this idea was introduced with the words, "One can even set up quite ridiculous cases.")

Shannon, Claude (1916–2001): American mathematician and engineer, founder of information theory. Shannon's many discoveries have been of incalculable importance in creating the "information age." His MIT master's thesis in 1937 laid the abstract groundwork for the digital computer. After World War II, he developed the mathematical theory of communication and soon applied it to everything from signal processing to human language to cryptography. He was a prolific inventor and game player, applying his genius to gambling, the stock market, and computer chess. Shannon did much of his work at Bell Labs, later joining the faculty at MIT.

Shor, Peter (b. 1959): American computer scientist who has made key discoveries in quantum computing and quantum information. As a computer scientist at Bell Labs, Shor became fascinated by the new idea of a quantum computer. In 1994 he discovered that a quantum computer algorithm could factor a large integer exponentially faster than any known procedure on a classical computer. Given the huge importance of the factoring problem in cryptography and number theory, this has provided much of the impetus for experimental work on quantum computers. Such computers are difficult to build, since their operation is very sensitive to environmental noise. Shor helped to find a possible answer, however: In 1995 he discovered the first method of "quantum error correction." Shor is now a professor of applied mathematics at MIT.

Wheeler, John (1911–2008): American physicist who made fundamental contributions to several areas of physics, from elementary particles to cosmology. Wheeler was deeply influenced by Niels Bohr, with whom he developed the theory of nuclear fission in 1939. An intensely patriotic man, he helped to develop both nuclear and thermonuclear weapons in the 1940s and 1950s. In the 1950s, Wheeler became interested in the implications of Einstein's general relativity. His work helped to revive the field of gravitational physics, and in 1967 he coined the term "black hole" to describe a completely collapsed star. Though he mentored Hugh Everett III in the creation of the many-worlds interpretation, Wheeler eventually rejected it and came to espouse a version of Bohr's Copenhagen interpretation. For Wheeler, the world itself comes into being through innumerable "elementary quantum phenomena." These elementary quantum phenomena are themselves not localized in space and time—as illustrated by his "delayed-choice experiment"—but form the real underlying structure of space, time, matter, and energy. The world is therefore essentially made of information—an idea Wheeler christened "it from bit." Wheeler was famous for his penetrating (if slightly oddball) questions and his striking way of expressing ideas in phrases and images. He spent most of his career at Princeton University, with a 10-year sojourn at the University of Texas. Wheeler was teacher and mentor to many physicists mentioned in this course, including Richard Feynman, Hugh Everett III, Wojciech Zurek, William Wootters, and your lecturer.

Wootters, William (b. 20th century): American physicist. While a graduate student at the University of Texas, Wootters, together with Wojciech Zurek, proved the quantum no-cloning theorem. Under the influence of John Wheeler, he became fascinated by the relation between quantum physics and information. He helped to discover quantum teleportation and protocols by which noisy entanglement may be "distilled," among many other contributions to quantum information theory. Wootters is a professor of physics at Williams College.

Young, Thomas (1773–1829): English physicist and polymath. Young was a physician who contributed to many areas of science, including the theory of elasticity. He is most famous for his decisive 2-slit experiment (performed in 1801) that demonstrated the wave nature of light and measured its wavelength. This experiment settled for a century the long-standing debate about whether light was made of continuous waves or discrete corpuscles. Young was also a linguist who made fundamental contributions to reading the Rosetta Stone, laying the groundwork for Champollion's later decipherment of Egyptian hieroglyphs.

Zurek, Wojciech (b. 1951): Polish physicist, now an American citizen, who has made contributions to statistical physics, quantum mechanics, black holes, and cosmology. Long interested in the relation between information and quantum physics, he proved (with William Wootters) the quantum no-cloning theorem and has long studied quantum decoherence. Decoherence is the process by which the environment of a system, by constantly "monitoring" it, destroys the coherence of quantum superpositions. Zurek is presently a researcher at Los Alamos National Laboratory.

Bibliography

Aczel, A. D. *Entanglement*. New York: Plume, 2001. Exactly as you would expect from the author and title, this is a well-written, interesting, popular book about quantum physics, focusing on quantum entanglement and its implications.

Albert, D. *Quantum Mechanics and Experience*. Cambridge, MA: Harvard University Press, 1992. I cannot decide whether David Albert is a physicist who does philosophy or a philosopher who does physics. In either case, here he has written an excellent introduction to the conceptual puzzles of quantum mechanics. Although some math is used, any graduate of our course should be able to follow along without trouble.

Bell, J. *Speakable and Unspeakable in Quantum Mechanics*. Cambridge: Cambridge University Press, 1987. A collection of John Bell's papers on the foundations of quantum mechanics.

Bohm, D. *Wholeness and the Implicate Order*. Boston: Routledge & Kegan Paul, 1980. A set of interconnected essays by David Bohm, explaining his "hidden variables" approach to quantum theory and embedding it in wider philosophical view of the cosmos.

Bruce, C. *Schrodinger's Rabbits*. Washington DC: Joseph Henry Press, 2004. This book is an account of quantum theory with particular focus on the many-worlds interpretation. Several chapters discuss the work and ideas of present-day researchers in the field.

Cropper, W. H. *The Quantum Physicists and an Introduction to Their Physics*. New York: Oxford University Press, 1970. Both an advanced quantum mechanics textbook and an historical account of the development of the theory—an unusual combination, and quite valuable for serious students who want to explore the real thinking of Einstein, Bohr, Heisenberg, and the rest.

Davies, P. C. W., and J. R. Brown. *The Ghost in the Atom.* Cambridge: Cambridge University Press, 1986. This is probably the finest accessible introduction to the various competing interpretations of quantum mechanics. Introduced by a 40-page introductory essay explaining the essential issues, the main part of the book is made up of transcripts of BBC interviews with 8 contemporary quantum physicists.

Feynman, R. *QED: The Strange Theory of Light and Matter.* Princeton: Princeton University Press, 1985. Feynman was at the same time a truly great physicist and a great explainer of physics. In this book he does the impossible, presenting the theory of quantum electrodynamics in a form that anyone can understand. An indispensible book for laypeople—and, for that matter, for quantum physicists.

Feynman, R. P., and S. Weinberg. *Elementary Particles and the Laws of Physics.* Cambridge: Cambridge University Press, 1987. This volume contains the two 1986 Dirac Memorial Lectures at Cambridge University, given by Feynman and Weinberg. Both lectures are challenging surveys of contemporary fundamental physics. Feynman's description of the ribbon demonstration (Lecture Fourteen) is on pages 56–59.

Ford, K. W. *The Quantum World.* Cambridge, MA: Harvard University Press, 2004. Ford, who used to be the director of the American Institute of Physics, has written an outstanding popular account of quantum theory and its impact on physics.

Gamow, G. *Mr. Tompkins in Paperback.* Cambridge: Cambridge University Press, 1965. Mr. Tompkins is a bank teller who is dating the daughter of a physics professor. As he listens to the professor, he falls asleep and has astonishing dreams of a town where the speed of light is 30 mph, a jungle where quantum tigers diffract among the trees, and many other astonishing locales. Gamow's tales are true classics.

———. *Thirty Years that Shook Physics.* Mineola, NY: Dover, 1966. A great account of the historical development of quantum physics from 1900 to 1930, illustrated with the author's inimitable cartoons. Gamow was involved in this story and knew all the principals very well, so this book is also filled with character sketches and funny stories. The last chapter is the script of a quantum physics spoof of *Faust* performed in 1932 by Bohr's students at his institute in Copenhagen.

Greenstein, G., and A. Zajonc. *The Quantum Challenge*. Sudbury, MA: Jones and Bartlett, 1997. This text aims to introduce undergraduate students to modern topics in the foundations of quantum mechanics. Though it occasionally descends into equations, these are for the most part quite skippable, and the reader will be rewarded with lots of information about contemporary quantum physics research.

Griffiths, D. J. *Introduction to Quantum Mechanics*. 2nd ed. Upper Saddle River, NJ: Pearson, 2005. A widely used quantum mechanics textbook aimed at senior-level undergraduates in physics—not for the general reader, in other words, but a good resource for the most serious students.

Herbert, N. *Quantum Reality*. Garden City, NY: Anchor Press, 1985. A lively, popular account of quantum physics, including the EPR argument and Bell's theorem, together with a good discussion of various interpretations.

Hey, T., and P. Walters. *The New Quantum Universe*. Cambridge: Cambridge University Press, 2003. A wide-ranging qualitative exploration of quantum physics, lavishly illustrated with magnificent diagrams and photographs.

Johnson, G. *A Shortcut Through Time*. New York: Alfred A. Knopf, 2003. A very readable introduction to quantum computers: how they work, what makes them so different, and what their ultimate importance might be.

Lloyd, S. *Programming the Universe*. New York: Alfred A. Knopf, 2006. Subtitled *A Quantum Computer Scientist Takes on the Cosmos*, this book tackles big ideas of quantum theory, information, thermodynamics, and cosmology, all seasoned with Lloyd's flair for vivid explanation and amusing anecdote.

McEvoy, J. P., and O. Zarate. *Introducing Quantum Theory*. Cambridge: Icon Books, 2007. This looks like a pocket-sized cartoon book. In fact, it is a superb and sometimes hilarious discussion of the development of quantum theory.

Mermin, N. D. *Quantum Computer Science: An Introduction*. Cambridge: Cambridge University Press, 2007. With the rise of quantum computing, Mermin faced the challenge of teaching quantum physics to computer scientists. The result is this excellent textbook. The math might be challenging for a beginner, but Mermin is careful to tell you everything you need to know. I am criticized—by name—on page 4 for the spelling of the term "qubit." (Mermin uses "Qbit.")

Pagels, H. *The Cosmic Code*. New York: Simon and Schuster, 1982. A popular account of quantum physics by Heinz Pagels, who was both a brilliant physicist and an excellent writer. I like the wide range of topics that he addresses.

Penrose, R. *The Emperor's New Mind*. Oxford: Oxford University Press, 1991. Computing, mathematics, relativity, quantum theory, cosmology— all are ingredients in this far-reaching book by one of the most brilliant mathematical physicists ever. It is included here because of chapter 6—a very fine introduction to quantum mechanics—and also because the book is one of my favorites. There are delights here for both the mathematician and the nonmathematician reader.

Polkinghorne, J. *The Quantum World*. New York: Longman, 1984. A very fine, brief introduction to the ideas of quantum physics, including entanglement. Though the text is not highly technical, the appendix fills in the math for those who are interested.

Rhodes, R. *The Making of the Atomic Bomb*. New York: Simon and Schuster, 1986. This massive, Pulitzer Prize–winning history does ultimately focus on the Bomb, of course, but the first 300 pages or so are among the best accounts of the development of 20th-century physics that I have ever read.

Styer, D. F. *The Strange World of Quantum Mechanics*. Cambridge: Cambridge University Press, 2000. A slender but rewarding book based on

Prof. Styer's fine course at Oberlin College. Spins, amplitudes, probability, entanglement, and more are given a very lucid and accessible treatment.

Tipler, P. *Elementary Modern Physics*. New York: Wirth, 1992. This is a physics textbook intended for first-year or second-year undergraduates and is mostly about quantum theory and its applications. I recommend this as a good textbook for the graduate of our course who is confident about math and ready for more of the details. The chapters are equipped with plenty of homework problems at various levels of difficulty.

Wheeler, J. A., and W. H. Zurek, eds. *Quantum Theory and Measurement*. Princeton: Princeton University Press, 1983. The best 1volume collection of important papers on the basic concepts of quantum mechanics. Bohr's own description of the Bohr-Einstein debate is here, with the original EPR paper, Bohr's response to EPR, John Bell's deeper analysis, Everett's many-worlds interpretation, original accounts of basic entanglement and delayed-choice experiments, and many other treasures. My copy is about to fall apart from use. (The level of some of the papers is pretty advanced and probably not for the general reader.)

Whitaker, A. *Einstein, Bohr and the Quantum Dilemma*. Cambridge: Cambridge University Press, 1996. This is a marvelous treatment of the development of quantum theory, the Bohr-Einstein debate, and beyond. Whitaker has a good sense for the conceptual issues at stake.

Wick. D. *The Infamous Boundary*. New York: Copernicus, 1995. An excellent book about the history, experiment, and theory involved in the great controversies of quantum mechanics. The book itself is descriptive and qualitative, but there is a mathematical appendix about quantum probability (by William Faris) that should please even the most technical reader.

Notes